NEW BREVET
PUBLICATIONS

STORIES FROM THE VILLAGE

by Harold P. Kurtz

Hardly a Silent Night
Ring the Bell and Count the People
The Missing Library Books
Plus four brand new Village stories

Edited by David Kurtz

New Brevet Publications
Minneapolis, MN
www.newbrevet.com

DEDICATIONS

Hardly a Silent Night
In memory of Duane R. Schroeder 1936-2004
The author's classmate and close Wartburg College friend

Ring the Bell and Count the People
To the author's grandchildren:
Emily Grace Kurtz
Joshua David Kurtz

The Missing Library Books
To the Brandon, Wisconsin, Public Library
In honor of its centennial 1913-2013

CONTENTS

* Stories marked with an asterisk are brand new and not part of the original publications.

Introduction

The Most Grievous Sin

My awareness of the stories from the Village goes back a long time, not nearly as long ago as the actual events which spawned the stories, for those happened to my father Harold in his youth in the 1940's and 1950's. However, he spoke about them often, so I knew about the Village, the mythical version of Brandon, Wisconsin, basically my whole life. The events began to crystalize in my father's mind as not just good memories (of which he wrote about in his book *Dear Phil* as he re-told them in letters to his brother), but as the basis for a series of excellent short stories, hanging together by the invisible thread of family, faith, and a bit of frivolity.

It happened that his memories and other somewhat fictionalized versions of them became the basis for an annual storytelling ritual around Christmas, often told after dinner was eaten Christmas Eve, before Midnight Services (at 11:00 p.m.), or sometimes after Christmas Day dinner (and possibly both times, I don't really recall). That particular venture I suppose one could call "Stories in the Suburbs" or something, for Harold had long since moved from the Village; the new suburban setting a milieu from the 1960s and onward.

Christmas in New Brighton (the Minnesota suburb where my parents brought us in 1977) begins, as all our neighbors and relations know, when my father gets that far-away look in his eye, on said Christmas Eve around the dinner table, after the ham or duck has been consumed but the aroma still wafts in the air next to the leaning tower of Advent Candles (which my mother has to dutifully straighten every five minutes or risk singeing her poinsettia tablecloth).

When young, I used to think this look meant he couldn't wait to open presents in the morning, but this was a displacement of my own muddled thinking. Myself too agitated to sit straight, dying to get more stuff, thinking about it over and over until I was so overstimulated I sometimes fell off my chair. This didn't stop until my mid-20's; even now my family remembers me as a terrible klutz around the holidays.

I understand now that a new tie and a book on secret gardening tips—though both well deployed—could never cause the same lack of concentration that Star Wars figures and a new baseball mitt did to me. No, my father got that far-off look in his eye, leaned back in his chair, wrapped his hands around one upraised knee to balance himself, and finally spoke over the ubiquitous pa-rum-pum-pum-pums coming from the stereo.

"Did I ever tell you about Christmas in Brandon?" he would say, and the storytelling would commence.

After a few years of this, when he asked us if he had ever told us about Brandon, "the Village", my brother and I both knew what to say to this: Nothing. Actually, once I had said "Yes," with that long, drawn-out bored-silly tone that only a 12-year-old can make (although I think I was 15 at the time), but a sharp scowl shot from my mother forced a quiet emendation. "I mean, 'No.'"

I don't know why my mother scowled at me for having said he'd told us all about his Christmases growing up. I mean, apart from the fact that he had indeed told us all about it, many times, I know of nothing that would have stopped him from telling it again (the mark of a true storyteller). Certainly no little "Yes" from me would have done the trick. That's why my brother and I stopped saying anything. We knew he wasn't listening, but our mother was. So, we figured, why take the chance on getting in trouble if there's no avoiding a story we've heard so often?

Off he would go, telling us about our grandparents, great-grandparents, aunt and uncle and himself. It was a simple, wonderful family ritual, that grew and solidified with the years.

Then, in 1987, when I was 17, I committed the Most Grievous Sin. That is, in my mother's eyes, because I don't think my father noticed. The Most Grievous Sin was: I fell asleep during the story.

Now, you've probably assumed that I was just a teenager bored with a parent and a story that's been told many times, but I swear it isn't true. What really irks me about having fallen asleep—apart from getting caught by my mother—was that it was a story I actually hadn't heard before.

Originally I didn't panic, because I felt sure of a reprise next Christmas, or at least the one following that. Spending the next Christmas with the extended family gathered in Door County, Wisconsin, he didn't tell it, but told one of the Golden Oldies. Same for the following year. When would it recur? What had I missed?

This is how the Most Grievous Sin on Christmas Eve came to pass and how I got caught.

I had gotten the ultimate job the previous summer: I was working in a toy store, one of those huge ones with aisles and aisles of merchandise. It was pure bliss ... for an 11-year-old, anyway. But a 17-year-old can find plenty of fun in it, too. I and my co-workers spent many a slow evening racing radio controlled cars around the store, ambushing each other with squirt guns, buying candy bars at employee discount rates, and generally having a really good time earning $3.45 an hour. You heard right, $3.45 an hour. I was rolling in the dough! I was so blinded by the good life that I failed to see the shadows on the horizon. For you see, for every summer in a toy store, there is a winter. And for every winter in a toy store, there is a Christmas war. It's not a "rush", it does not "get busy". My $3.45 an hour got bumped to $3.65 an hour starting the day after Thanksgiving. That's right: combat pay. My shift also went from 20 hours a week to 30, then 40.

That's when my decision to take college-level English courses in the fall semester of my high school senior year really turned out to be a bad one. See, for every college level English course, there is a massive load of theme papers. And for every massive load of theme papers, there is one 25-page Final paper due. And for every ... well, you've already guessed that the paper was due right before Christmas. You're right, too.

At the toy store I worked for—Children's Palace—we wore bright red vests during the Christmas season. Only it wasn't to be festive. It was a target. My boss Mr. Halverson, a jovial man in the autumn who wore a deeper and deeper scowl as temperatures dropped, put it very succinctly to me. "Listen, Kurtz," he said, without that far-away dreamy look of my father, "80% of our sales comes during the month between Thanksgiving and Christmas. We're huge and people have a hard time finding what they want."

"We have signs up all over, Mr. Halverson," I said. I shouldn't have.

"Maybe our customers can't read! I don't know, I don't care. But your job is, shall we say, customer service. You wear this vest, they see you—"

"And they come charging in at me, is that it?" I finished for him.

"Exactly."

"Have you ever been to Spain, Mr. Halverson?"

"No. Why?"

For hours on end, while a single, hour-long soundtrack of formerly beloved Christmas favorites played continuously over the sound system, I stood and pointed, answered phone calls and pointed, got boxes from top shelves and pointed. I forget why I pointed so often, since I actually had to lead people to what they desired. While my arm got tired, the store just kept getting busier. The boss helped out by hiring a couple of new people, but as they were new, when they were asked a question, all they were able to do was walk on over to me and ask me where the "Astronaut Barbies" were.

I nearly cracked when Mr. Halvorson told me that the store was extending its normal hours. Instead of closing at 10:00 p.m., we would be closing at midnight, until Christmas Eve when we'd be blissfully done at 6:00 p.m. But for the only future I could contemplate, we'd stay open until 12:00 a.m. Who would work that late, though?

"Uh, I have a question, boss."

"Kurtz, your shift goes to midnight. Now what's your question?"

"Um, never mind."

I'm sure you think that I got off work at midnight, was home 15 minutes after that, changed into pajamas, brushed my teeth and went straight to bed, so I could be bright-eyed and bushy-tailed at 6:00 a.m. when the alarm went off for school. Well, if you think I've got a tail that can get bushy, then you may be right about all that other stuff, too.

In my universe, a toy store during the Christmas season gets destroyed. Before going home, we had to get it ready for tomorrow's shoppers. We called it "assessing battle damage". The customer service team became "medics". I had to stay strong, for the younger ones couldn't stand the sight of "blood". They needed leadership.

"There's a hole in the 'Clue' shelf, sir! It's deep!"

"Quick, man! Fill it with 'Hungry Hungry Hippos'! Fill it with 'Hungry Hungry Hippos'!"

"That's the fortieth time I've heard *Jolly Old Saint Nicholas* today, I just know it! If a guy walks in here wearing a red outfit and a fake beard, I'm gonna lose it!"

"Keep it together, man! Keep it together!"

Before we could turn the lights out and lock up, it was quarter to one. Since this was Minnesota, it had also snowed during the preceding eight hours since I had driven there fifteen minutes after getting home from school. Another fifteen minutes were invariably spent cleaning and scraping the car and warming it up. Once, being in such a hurry during a stormy afternoon, I had failed to turn off my lights after parking and heading into the trenches. A faithful lieutenant retrieved jumper cables from her home, though, and saved me, at a cost of only an extra 57 minutes of precious, sweet, lovely slumber.

And I still had that Final Paper to write! It was on ... it was on ... I can't even remember now. All I can remember was that my classmates and I were convinced that Jesus was going to return about half an hour after we turned in our papers—too late to not have to do the work, too soon to see what grade we'd get.

But somehow the paper did get done. I know it did, because without it I wouldn't have passed that class. (Because it was a requirement for passing!)

There was light at the end of the tunnel, even as we started earning a precious minute or two more of sunlight per day. Only a few more days— these all 12 hour shifts now that school was out—until that most terrible of wonderful holidays, Christmas, came and relieved us. I thought I could easily get a Section 8 discharge, based on how insane I was going. I thought I deserved a Purple Heart, too.

Still, the hordes came on. The ranks started thinning a bit, though. The veteran corps had been dispersed in earlier engagements. These were reserves, or new recruits, all with a scared look on their faces, green, their first time in battle. They looked as bad as the stock remaining on our shattered shelves.

And yet they came.

"Customer Service, Line One, please. Customer Service, Line One."

The page was for me to pick up and answer another stupid question. I anticipated a feint around "Nintendo", in order to catch me off guard with asking me to search through a pile of "Cabbage Patch" dolls to find one with green eyes or red hair, or—shudder—both.

"May I help you?"

"Yeah, uh, how late are you guys open?"

"We're open until midnight, sir."

"You are? That's great! Thanks!" And he hung up the phone.

"Easiest one I had all day," I muttered and, just for the heck of it, reached out and pulled the string on the sample "Talking Pee-Wee Herman" doll. Then I remembered my wits and ran away from it.

Half an hour later, my boss walked by and told me to start straightening up. I looked at my watch. It was only 5:30 p.m.

"Why?" I asked him.

"Because it's Christmas Eve, Kurtz! We close up at 6:00 p.m. on Christmas Eve. I told you that last week."

He walked away shaking his head. I stood there, jaw agape, picturing a desperate, procrastinating father, driving up to a dark, silent Children's Palace at 10:00 or 11:00 that evening, stepping out of his car, shaking a fist at the closed store and calling curses down on whoever had told him the store was open until midnight.

"I forgot," I mumbled, shell-shocked. "I totally forgot!"

Now, everyone can get a little forgetful around the holidays. It's busy, there's a million things to do. It's perfectly reasonable for someone to forget something their boss said about a different closing time.

Except I hadn't forgotten that. I knew we closed at 6:00 p.m. on Christmas Eve. I had been longing for Christmas Eve for just that reason. No, I had forgotten what day it was. Up until 5:30 p.m. that day, I was convinced it was the 23rd of December.

I stumbled through the clean-up. At 6:00 p.m., I thought I heard a deep bell chime, a solemn announcement of an armistice of sorts. Christmas was almost here! It was the angel proclaiming the Good News! Children's Palace is now closed! We can all go home early!

And then a full meal, and then that far-away look in my father's eyes. My own eyes were so heavy, my entire body so exhausted, stretched beyond its endurance levels, that I almost missed the look. When I caught it, I rejoiced, and thought: I'll just close my eyes and listen along. I'll face Dad and away from Mom. I know the parts where I have to nod along, no one will ever know. I'll just ... close them, just ... rest them.

"Did I ever tell you about Christmas in Brandon?" Dad said. Then he launched into an unfamiliar story, something about the Dobrecht Family and singing Christmas carols. I was confused by it. I knew I should open my eyes and pay attention because this was one I didn't know! I didn't know where to nod along so as not to get caught by my mother. I should open my eyes and just enjoy the story. He was saying something about ... Christmas in the Village ... and trying to picture it, all my mind's eye had was the blackness of deep sleep and I totally lost track of the story.

Sometime after that is when I fell out of my chair and screamed, "We're open till midnight!" as I hit the carpet.

"That's when I told Mother that we had become a famous singing family," my dad said, wrapping up his story, oblivious to me. "She was not amused."

Never were truer words spoken, however, since my own mother had most definitely noticed me. The scowl I received as I clambered back onto my chair told me that I had committed the Most Grievous Sin, and I should be kinder to my father.

But that was the end of his story. I had missed it. I cheered myself by recognizing that I had at least gotten half an hour's sleep, but it paled in comparison to how I felt. Luckily, my parents were good sports. My mother realized soon how tired I was, and knew I had been working so much, so she excused me from helping with the dishes, told me to take a nap until we had to leave for Midnight Services (around 10:30 p.m. or so). This she regretted immediately because my brother then complained about the unfairness of the situation, so he too got excused from dishes (though I don't think he took a nap).

And my father? Well, though he usually helped out quite a bit in the kitchen, it was different on Christmas Eve, when he still had that far-away look in his eye, thinking of Christmas in the Village, his hometown of Brandon, Wisconsin.

I can't picture what he's picturing. I get a dark cloud that makes me sleepy. Or at least I used to. He wrote down the story that I had missed that year, entitled "It Was Hardly a Silent Night", and gave me a copy of it. Then each year he wrote down another story, and another. He wrote them all and called the book *Hardly a Silent Night* and sent it out into the world in 2004, so then I could see a little bit of what he sees. These stories were of his Village, of a bygone time, of preachers and preachers' kids, of small-town Wisconsin (like so many small towns of the Midwest and everywhere), when the War had been won and a new world was just beginning.

We know from this vantage point what ills remained in that new world, still a fallen world, of course. That part's easy. Anyone can remind us of that. We need storytellers to remind us of the good things, the easily-forgotten things, of family and faith and yes, frivolity, too.

Hardly a Silent Night was well-received, and a small clamor came for more stories. As Harold's memory, imagination, and penchant for his years in the Village burned ever brighter, never dimmer, more stories were read around the dinner table and became *Ring the Bell and Count the People* in 2008. A final installment in 2012 was *The Missing Library Books*. Now, for the first time, they are compiled together, along with four new stories, never before published (though one was read to the family after Christmas dinner).

Every now and then I take out my inscribed copy of *Hardly a Silent Night*, or one of the others, and read about the Village, Brandon, Wisconsin. It always makes me think of Christmas in New Brighton.

Now it's your turn to sit back and enjoy, to become immersed in the Village or to think of your own, or that of your parents' or even grandparents'. There are many classics here in which to indulge, including: "Why the Preachers Never Finished Their Card Game"; "I Get Stuck With Cousin Brenda"; "Helene Learns to Eat a Cream Puff"; "What Was in Mr. Schiffler's Barn"; "Mr. West Coast Makes a Bet" and many, many more. Some stories should never die, but should keep being retold.

(By the way, like the stories from the Village, the Christmas story of "The Most Grievous Sin" is based on fact, but was slightly fictionalized. As Harold always says: "Never let a few facts ruin a good story.")

David Kurtz
Coon Rapids, MN
August 2020

HARDLY A SILENT NIGHT

CHRISTMAS IN A SMALL TOWN PARSONAGE

Chapter 1

Looking Back at Christmas

"I am so looking forward to Easter," Mother sighed as she sat down at the supper table.

"Easter!" my sister said. "Can we color eggs?"

"For heaven's sake—it's only January 2," I told her.

Dad cut in. "Let's pray."

We folded our hands, bowed our heads, and repeated, "Come, Lord Jesus, be our guest and let this food to us be blessed. Amen."

Dad picked up the platter of meatloaf and handed it to Mother, "And why are you so anxious for Easter?"

"Oh, it isn't that I'm that anxious for Easter. I am just so glad to be done with Christmas."

"I suppose that means we won't color eggs tonight," my sister said. I looked at her and shook my head.

"I can see your point," said Dad, helping himself to the riced potatoes. We were having one of my favorite meals: meatloaf with riced potatoes and hot tomato juice to go over the potatoes and homemade applesauce. We filled our plates and began eating.

"What do you mean you're glad that Christmas is over?" I asked. "I thought this was the best Christmas we ever had. Why, the Christmas of 1947 will go down in the annals of the Kurtz family history."

"I didn't know we had any annals," my sister said. "When did we get them? No one ever tells me anything."

"Everyone has annals. It means, like, recorded history," I told her.

"But we don't have a recorder," she answered.

"Never mind," said Mother. "He's just trying to show off his knowledge. Ever since he got into Mr. Franklin's class, he's been learning all sorts of new words."

"You know why?" my brother cut in. "It's because Mr. Franklin makes students copy pages of the dictionary when they're caught talking. That's how come he's learning all the new words."

I glared at him across the table. Mother never let my brother sit next to me at meal times. Otherwise we would spend the time fighting and never eat anything.

"That's enough," Mother said.

"Is that really how you're learning all those new words?" my sister asked me.

"Well, only partly," I said. "I just like learning new words. Uncle Carl told me that writers have to learn a lot of words if they're going to become successful. Anyway, I still think this was the best Christmas we ever had."

"Well," said Dad, as he helped himself to another slice of meatloaf, "why do you say that?"

"It was great having Cousin Esther here. And when the firemen came and the preachers had to hide—now that was exciting. Don't forget the decorating contest prize. And how Mother made us go caroling, and look what happened then. And the Christmas Eve service was about the best ever for the family. Why even having Grandpa Kurtz here wasn't all that bad."

"Now, now," said Mother. "You shouldn't say anything bad about your grandfather."

"I wasn't saying anything bad," I protested. "I meant it wasn't as bad as it usually is when he's here."

Dad just shook his head. Grandpa was his father, but he knew that it was tough on the family when Grandpa came to visit.

Before we go any further, I suppose I better tell you a few things about Grandpa. No, I better tell about our family and then tell you about why Grandpa was visiting us. I might as well tell all that happened at Christmas time and why Mother was glad it was over and why I thought it was the best Christmas ever.

First, let me tell you about our family. There were five of us in our family. Dad was a preacher. About the time World War II began, we had left Milwaukee and moved to our present home—a Village of 700 people in eastern Wisconsin.

Leaving the city and moving to the Village was quite a change. I liked it. We had a big house here which meant I had a room of my own, so I didn't have to share a bedroom with my brother. There was a big barn in back of the parsonage, left over from the days when the pastor kept a horse (and probably a cow, too). We had a big yard, and we could walk anywhere in the Village which had been a good thing during World War II when gasoline and tires were rationed. Of course, it meant that we didn't get to ride the street cars and go downtown in Milwaukee to see Santa and the parade and stuff like that.

Anyway, I was going to tell you about Grandpa. Grandpa didn't have a home. Grandma had died in 1938 and a few years later Grandpa decided to retire. This presented a problem since he was a pastor and had lived all his life in parsonages owned by the congregations. When it came time to retire, he had no place to live. He had no money to buy a home of his own. None of his nine children had big enough houses that he could go and live with one of them. Besides, with his personality it was highly unlikely that any of the nine would have been able to contend with him on a permanent basis.

The retirement dilemma was solved when Grandpa suggested he could rotate among them, staying six to eight weeks at each home. His children thought this was a good idea since each family could house him for that length of time without totally jeopardizing marriages. His children were scattered around the country, so that meant Grandpa could have a change of scenery.

Grandpa's arrival was not something we awaited with any major degree of anticipation. For one thing, it meant that Phil had to give up his bedroom and move in with me. This irritated Phil and it irritated me as well, so we were never too happy when we heard that Grandpa was coming for a visit. Grandpa would spend a goodly portion of the day sitting in Phil's room, smoking his pipe, and smelling up the whole house with tobacco smoke. That irritated everyone else in the family.

Grandpa usually visited during the summer which meant he could have the windows open when he smoked, or he could smoke as he took walks around the Village.

Grandpa hadn't planned to be with us that Christmas. Usually in winter he would stay with Aunt Ida who lived in Texas. But Aunt Ida just had a new baby and felt that she couldn't take Grandpa and a new baby at the same time, so Grandpa decided he would go to Aunt Helen's. Meanwhile, Aunt Helen, Uncle Walter and Cousin Esther had decided they would come to visit us at Christmas, so Grandpa announced that he may as well come and be with us over Christmas. It was lucky we had a big house, I thought when I heard the news. So that was how come Grandpa came to spend the Christmas season with us.

Grandpa had been born in Berlin, and he always seemed like a cold-hearted Prussian to me. He was a tall, heavy-set man with a big mustache and just a hint of a German accent. (For someone who had spoken nothing but German for the first 20 years of his life, Grandpa had exceptionally good

English. At his father's suggestion, he had spent a year taking graduate work in English where he had shed most of his accent.) But though Grandpa often seemed gruff, he loved his grandchildren and I always felt he would do most anything for them.

Mother was none too pleased about Grandpa's visit at any time, but Christmas was even worse. My grandfather did not like either of his daughters-in-law too well. There seemed to be several theories about this. One theory was that he didn't feel that they could compare with his daughters. Another was that both daughters-in-law were Norwegians who somehow didn't measure up to his Germanic standards.

But Mother, perhaps recalling that portion of the marriage vows which talked about "for better or for worse," was firm. Philip had to give up his room and I had to put up with Philip. And that was that, and she would hear no more complaints.

So Grandpa came. It was always bad enough having him around. Poor Phil didn't have his room to himself. Grandpa would sit in it, smoking his pipe. Phil would complain about not having his room. I would complain about having Phil in my room. Helene would complain because Grandpa would sit and talk to Dad, and therefore Dad wouldn't be able to read to Helene.

Having him there at Christmas time was worse—we couldn't complain about it. You don't complain at Christmas time. If you complained about things, Billy the Brownie would find out and then the Magic Book wouldn't open and you would be in trouble because all of your friends would know about it.

Chapter 2

Billy the Brownie Checks Our Behavior

There was no question in my mind that Billy the Brownie kept an eye on things. I had not believed in Santa Claus for quite a while. But Billy the Brownie—that was different. I had the feeling that he did go around checking on how we were behaving.

Ever since the time I had gotten in trouble with Mother, and that night the Magic Book didn't open ... well, it was hard for me not to believe that Billy the Brownie wasn't keeping an eye on us.

But I better explain about Billie the Brownie and the Magic Book.

At the start of the Christmas season, oh, about the middle of November, WTMJ Radio in Milwaukee would begin broadcasting the *Billy the Brownie Show*. Every afternoon at five, the program, sponsored by Schuster's Department Store in Milwaukee, would be on the radio. Billy was Santa's main helper. As far as I could determine, he stayed around eastern Wisconsin all year and kept track of things for Santa.

Even though I would tell my friends that the *Billy the Brownie Show* was kids' stuff, I always made it home in time to listen to the show. Of course, I told Mother that I was just keeping Helene company.

Helene and I would sit in front of the big Coronado radio console and look at the pointer on the yellow dial set at 620. Promptly at 5:00 p.m., the chorus would sing *Jingle Bells*, and then Larry the announcer (I often wondered why Larry didn't have a last name; he was just "Larry") would welcome all of us to the show. Before Thanksgiving there would be a static-filled shortwave radio report from the North Pole, with Santa telling Larry and Billy when he and the rest of the Brownies would pack the sleigh and start the trip to Milwaukee.

After the North Pole report, Larry and Billy would tell listeners to begin writing their letters to Santa—letters they would begin reading once Santa arrived in Milwaukee. Obviously there was no need to read the letters if Santa wasn't around to hear them.

Then came the best part of the program: THE STORY. Larry would intone the litany of the Magic Story Book: "Now, boys and girls, face the radio and say, 'I have been good.'"

Now this was the moment of truth for us. I kinda knew that maybe no one besides Mother was really listening to our statements that we had been good, but a person couldn't lie either. There were days when I had been less than good, and I couldn't stand in front of the radio and proclaim that "I have been good." Now that's what the instructions were: "Face the radio and say, 'I have been good.'" It wasn't: "Face the radio and say, 'I've been fairly good' or, 'I haven't been the greatest, but at least let me explain.'"

No, it was a black and white issue. You had been good or you hadn't been good.

My goal was to have an unblemished deportment record for about an hour before the program began. That usually wasn't too difficult, and there would not be any episodes fresh in Mother's mind.

As we heard Larry's injunction, my mind would always go back to an earlier year when indeed I had not been good, and I could not face the radio to say "I have been good," and that night THE MAGIC BOOK STAYED CLOSED.

And it was all my fault. I just knew it. No one had to point it out; although Mother was standing in the door to the living room, nodding her head when the Magic Book stayed closed that night.

"Now maybe you'll remember," Mother warned.

Remember! How could I ever forget it? Even to this day I was afraid that I would be discovered. I had checked outside our windows to see if I could discover Brownie tracks. I wasn't sure exactly what Brownie tracks would look like, but I would recognize them if I saw them. I never did discover any tracks from a peeping Billy the Brownie. I also knew that the night the book stayed closed it was altogether possible that Billy had been there.

Of course, the Village was a small place, and Billy had all of eastern Wisconsin to cover, so he probably only ever got there once every few years. But one couldn't take chances since he could be back at any time.

A week or so before Thanksgiving, the shortwave radio broadcast reported that Santa was preparing to leave the North Pole. We hoped he left in plenty of time so he could arrive in Milwaukee on the Friday after Thanksgiving. Friday evening was the big Santa Claus parade down Wisconsin Avenue in Milwaukee.

Every year I would tell Helene about the time I had actually gone to see the Schuster's Department Store Santa Claus parade.

We were still living in Milwaukee then. I must have been four or five years old. My Uncle Carl took my brother and me to the parade. Uncle Carl was Mother's unmarried brother. He taught school in Milwaukee and lived with us. Usually on holidays he would go back to his hometown and visit his parents. That year he stayed in Milwaukee.

I can still remember him saying to Mother, "How would it be if I took the boys to the Schuster's parade?"

Mother immediately began detailing reasons why we shouldn't go.

"You know how Phil always gets earaches in winter," she began.

"Oh, Minnie," Carl told his sister, "he can wear his winter cap over his ears and he'll be fine."

"But it will probably be cold, and I don't want them getting pneumonia," Mother continued. Mother feared pneumonia more than her Norwegian ancestors feared the Black Plague.

"They can bundle up," Carl answered. "They won't get pneumonia."

"I worry about crowds. It would be so easy to get lost," Mother went on.

"I guarantee they won't get lost," my uncle assured his sister.

I can't recall the whole list of objections Mother raised. There was something about kidnappers, people you couldn't trust, pickpockets, and if it had been a year later after World War II had started, she probably would have added German Storm Troopers and Japanese secret agents.

Finally Mother was either convinced or was just worn down.

"Well," she finally agreed, "I guess it will be OK. But they will have to dress warmly."

Now Milwaukee at Thanksgiving time isn't all that cold. Downtown Milwaukee is close to Lake Michigan, and, while it could get uncomfortable and windy, the temperature even at night rarely got much below freezing.

Mother felt that we were actually traveling to the North Pole to see Santa, not just going to Wisconsin Avenue. She started with the basics.

"You boys put on your long underwear," she ordered. There would be no arguing tonight. Do as Mother said or stay home. We understood that.

That was followed by a flannel shirt and corduroy pants, then a sweater. She was ready to get out the snow pants when Dad intervened.

"Minnie," he said quietly, "I think they'll be warm enough without them."

"I don't want them getting pneumonia," she countered to Dad.

Behind Mother's back, Phil and I grimaced at Dad. Dad smiled at us and assured Mother that we would be OK.

We did end up with our winter coats, heavy caps pulled down over our ears, and a scarf covering most of my face.

I could move, but just barely, and every time I breathed, my glasses fogged up.

I'll never see Santa, I thought.

"Let's go," said Uncle Carl. We waved goodbye to Mother and Dad and went out to get into Uncle Carl's Hudson. We drove down the street until we were out of sight of our house. Uncle Carl stopped the car.

"Let's take some of this off," he told us. I removed the scarf, opened the top of my coat, and pulled the cap off my ears.

"Now I can breathe and see," I said. Much relieved, we drove through the north side of Milwaukee, passing factories along the way.

"See that," Uncle Carl said, pointing to stacks of metal cylinders alongside one of the factories. "Those are bomb shells. Just wait—it won't be long until we'll be at war."

Bombs, I thought, war. That was pretty serious stuff.

"Won't those bombs explode there?" I asked.

"No, they're just the shells. They'll need to be filled with gunpowder and explosives. They do that somewhere else. These are empty," Uncle Carl explained.

We soon were near Wisconsin Avenue, Milwaukee's main street. Uncle Carl found a parking place, and we got out of the car.

"It's a couple of blocks to walk, but this should be a good spot to watch the parade," he told us as we trudged down the sidewalk.

Wisconsin Avenue was an impressive sight to us kids. All of the light posts had Christmas decorations, and at every block strands of lights and Christmas greens were strung across the street.

We found a place to stand, and Uncle Carl began pointing out the sights.

"Over there is the Hotel Schroeder. It's the biggest hotel in Wisconsin."

We were impressed at the tall hotel, decorated with Christmas lights.

"Where's Schuster's Department Store?" I wanted to know. After all, that was where Santa would be and where Billy the Brownie worked.

"You can't see it from here," Uncle Carl said. "It's eight or ten blocks east of here, closer to Lake Michigan."

"Is it near Gimbels?" I asked. I had been to Gimbels Department Store last year. Gimbels was Schuster's big department store competitor. It was also a competitor for the Christmas radio audience as well. Gimbels didn't have Billy the Brownie, Larry, or Santa Claus. Gimbels had two magic elephants named Gimby and Elly.

On the radio the two elephants did all sorts of magical feats. They flew, they danced, they worked in Santa's workshop, and they played with kids. There wasn't much those two elephants couldn't do. They were on the radio at the same time as Billy the Brownie, so we didn't listen to them at home. However, my friend Dicky always listened to them. His aunt worked at Gimbels, so the family thought they should show their loyalty by listening to Gimby and Elly. When I played at Dicky's house, we would listen to Gimby and Elly.

Gimbels didn't have a Christmas parade. They did have a Gimby and Elly show in the Gimbels auditorium. The year before we went to the parade, Dickey's aunt got tickets for the show and took Dicky and me.

I was excited about going. Since it was held inside, Mother didn't make me put on every article of winter clothing she could find. It would be great to see those magic elephants.

"Think we'll see them fly?" I asked Dicky.

Dicky's aunt smiled. "I don't think they fly. They just do tricks," she told us.

Dicky's aunt was right. They did not fly. They did some tricks, if walking on a plank could be called a trick. Mother had warned me that I better be polite, so I didn't say anything except to thank Dicky's aunt when we got home.

"But it was really dumb," I told Mother. "Billy the Brownie is a lot better."

So Phil, Uncle Carl, and I stood on the sidewalk and waited. Pretty soon we heard music and a band came marching past us.

"It's a good thing it isn't too cold. Otherwise, their band instruments might freeze," Uncle Carl commented.

A marching unit of the Milwaukee Police Department came by, followed by a float.

"Look, there are some of the Brownies," I said. "I wonder which one is Billy."

"I don't think any of them are. I bet he has his own special float," Phil said.

Another band came by, then some horse riders and more floats.

I stood there watching. All of a sudden I blinked and looked again. What in the world was that?

A float came down the street with a live cow on it. A man in a suit was seated on a stool, milking the cow and squirting the milk at people in the crowd.

"Who is that?" I asked. Uncle Carl was laughing as were most of the people watching the parade.

"That man," said Uncle Carl, "is Julius Heil, the governor of the state of Wisconsin."

We looked again—the governor, I thought. That's almost like the President or something.

"Why is he milking the cow here?" I asked. It certainly wasn't any Christmas story I had ever heard.

"Governor Heil does everything he can to let people know Wisconsin is a big dairy state. He even got the legislature to put 'America's Dairyland' on every car license plate."

"Watch out," Phil yelled.

The governor was all set to squirt milk at us. I quickly ducked behind Uncle Carl and no one got hit.

"Well, I think that's kind of silly," I said.

"So do a lot of people," Uncle Carl agreed.

More bands and more floats came by.

Then from down the street we began hearing high pitched squeals.

"Santa, Santa," we heard.

"Santa's coming," Uncle Carl announced. I barely noticed a smirk on Phil's face as I moved up to the curb.

A big float came slowly down Wisconsin Avenue. It seemed to fill the entire street.

There, perched on a large platform, was a big red and green sleigh. There were reindeer in the front—at least they looked like reindeer. Seated in the driver's seat was Santa himself. His amplified "Ho, Ho, Ho," filled the air. And in back of the sleigh was a huge book, opened just like it was on the radio.

Standing beside him on the platform was ... it had to be ... Billy the Brownie. He looked just like he sounded on the radio.

"Where's Larry?" I asked. There wasn't anyone else on the platform or in the sleigh.

"I bet he's driving the float," Uncle Carl said. I tried to see the driver, but he was hidden by red and green streamers.

Oh well, I did get to see Santa and Billy.

"Boy, that was neat," I said to Uncle Carl as we walked to the car. "That was about the best parade ever. Thanks for taking us."

"Just don't tell your mother that I let you take off all those winter clothes. She would have a fit if she knew it."

Phil and I promised that we wouldn't tell.

That was the story I told Helene.

"You mean, you actually saw Santa and the Christmas parade?" Helene asked.

"Yes," I nodded, "it was about the biggest event in my life."

"I sure wish we still lived in Milwaukee, and I could go see the parade," Helene said.

"I sure wish you could too," I answered.

Little did I know that soon there would be no more Billy the Brownie program on radio because something called television would do away with radio programs, and that the Christmas parade too would be a thing of the past.

Chapter 3

Mother and the Decorating Contest

The Thursday Club felt the Village needed to get more into the spirit of Christmas, so members voted to sponsor an outdoor decorating contest. Awards of $25, $15, and $5 were established.

I don't know if Mother was the one who came up with the idea for the contest or not. Knowing Mother, she probably thought of it and then got another member to propose it.

The Thursday Club along with the Music Club were the two general women's clubs in the Village. The Village was filled with organizations for women. All six Village churches had women's clubs. There were two lodges which had auxiliaries—the Eastern Star for the Masons and the Rebekahs, the women's auxiliary of the defunct Odd Fellows. The Odd Fellows had evidently been a flourishing organization in the Village in years past. There still remained a large, two-story Odd Fellows Hall which had once been the center of Village activity: the high school teams had played their basketball games there, concerts and plays were performed, and the old timers still talked about the time when "Fighting Bob" La Follette packed the hall with his fiery campaign speech. Both the lodge and the hall had fallen on tough times. The last Odd Fellow had died several years before we moved to town, and the hall was now used as a warehouse by the local canning company. However, the auxiliary remained active.

There was also the Legion Auxiliary and the WCTU—The Women's Christian Temperance Union, devoted to promoting not the temperate use of alcoholic beverages but the prohibition of them. (It was not a large organization in a community where beer-drinking Germans were the dominant group.)

The Music Club had the higher status of the two general women's clubs. It met in the evening, and membership was by invitation. Members actually listened to music: a recording, perhaps the radio broadcast of a concert, and on occasion a recital by a visiting artist.

The Thursday Club was open to any woman who applied. It met on the third Thursday of each month in members' homes. I asked Mother one time how come it was the Thursday Club and not the Monday or Tuesday or Friday Club.

"Well," Mother explained, "it's the Thursday Club because it meets on Thursday and the reason that it meets on Thursday is that on Monday everybody washes clothes. On Tuesday they do the ironing. On Wednesday most of the church groups meet, and Friday is usually busy with school things, so that leaves Thursday as the day for the meeting."

The Thursday Club was a general interest group. During World War II it had sold war bonds, wrapped bandages, and sponsored the Village Honor Roll—a large wooden billboard in the Village park which listed all the area residents who were serving in World War II.

After the War ended, members had to find new ways of helping the Village, so the idea of a Christmas decorating contest was a welcome thought after four years of the War.

Mother was all excited when she came home from the Thursday Club meeting in October.

"Henry," she said to Dad as we gathered at the supper table, "you always have such good ideas. We must decorate our house and enter the contest."

"But we do decorate our house," I protested. After all, I had the job of going around each evening and plugging in the electric candles and wreaths. The downstairs windows all had electric candles with white bulbs. The upstairs windows had wreaths with red bulbs. "I sure think we do enough now."

"Yes," responded Mother. "The wreaths and candles are very nice, but they won't win any prizes. We have to do something original."

"What do you mean 'original'?" asked Helene.

"Well," replied Mother, pausing a bit, "something nice. You know, something that the members would appreciate."

Ah, yes, I thought, the "members". The "members" referred to the parishioners of Emanuel Lutheran Church where Dad was the pastor. Mother constantly worried about the "members".

"Now, don't leave the milk bottle sitting on the table while we're eating," Mother would admonish us. "What if the members would come in and see it. They would think we didn't have any manners."

I had visions of our house surrounded in the evening by members of the congregation. Over there by the kitchen windows would be Old Man

Schroeder, the president of the congregation. "Hey, look, Clara," I could hear him saying to his wife, who was crouching beside him. "Mrs. Kurtz left the milk bottle on the table. Boy, she sure doesn't have any manners."

And peering through the windows at the side of the house would be August Bachman, a member of the church board. He scanned the table. "Yup," he told Frieda, his wife. "They did it again. Left the catsup bottle sitting right there in the middle of the table."

"Honestly," Frieda would reply. "Doesn't that beat all. Just think of that catsup bottle sitting there."

Somehow I felt that even the nosiest of our parishioners had better things to do than go around peering in the parsonage windows to see what was on the kitchen table. Besides, most of them were busy milking cows at that time of the night anyway.

But we always had to take into account what the members might be thinking.

"Now, Henry," said Mother, turning to Dad, "I bet you could come up with something really clever."

Dad said he would think about it. That seemed to satisfy Mother, and we finished supper talking about other matters.

A couple of nights later Mother brought up the subject again.

"I think it would be a good idea for us to begin working on the Christmas decorations. You know how busy things get around here at Christmas time. Besides, with Grandpa Kurtz coming, things will be more hectic."

"What's Grandpa going to be hectic about?" Helene asked.

"Oh, he's not going to be hectic. It will just make things ... well, busier," Mother said.

"I've never seen Grandpa hectic," Helene said thoughtfully. "Maybe I can ask him to be hectic when he's here."

"You'll do nothing of the kind, and I don't want you to say a word about it," Mother said emphatically.

She got back to the subject of the decorating contest.

"We need to begin planning for the contest. It will make the house look nice, and it will help the Village be more Christmasy. Henry, what have you come up with?" asked Mother.

"I've given it some thought," Dad said slowly. "I haven't decided what we might do."

I felt sorry for Dad. He was very creative. He could compose music, write poetry, do sculpturing, and Mother thought he could even be a painter. Last Christmas she had bought him a set of oil paints. So far they had sat unused, much to Mother's disappointment.

"Now, Henry, you ought to sit down some time and try painting. I know how creative you are. I bet you could really do some nice work." She had been urging him on for some time, all to no avail.

You can't push Dad, I thought. Mother always tried, but Dad would always do things his way when he felt like doing them. Oh, he was conscientious about his work. Sermons were well prepared. He always took care of sick calls and teaching and choir directing and all the other things the pastor had to do in a small parish. I meant the stuff Mother tried to get him to do.

"Let me think about it some more," Dad pleaded.

I knew another thing which was bothering Dad. He didn't want to do anything involving building something. For all his artistic ability, Dad was about the least handy guy I knew. Dad's grandfather had been a carpenter, and Dad had inherited most of his tools. They were slightly old fashioned, but of good quality.

Dad seemed to have trouble with most of them. I remember one time he was doing a fairly simple task—pounding a nail into the wall to hang a picture. I was standing there holding the picture. He held the nail between his thumb and finger, raised the hammer, and promptly struck his thumb a heavy blow. Now ordinary humans would have responded with an expletive or two. Dad carefully pondered his thumb for a moment, shook away the pain, and then burst out with a faint, "Oh, darn."

Mother kept bringing up the subject almost every night at supper.

"You know," she would say, "I heard at the Thursday Club meeting that there aren't too many people entering. I think we would stand a real good chance of winning if we did something."

Dad would nod and change the subject.

We kids didn't know for sure if decorating would be a good idea. The way things worked in our family was usually Mother got the idea, and the rest of us would have to do the work to carry it out. Like the time she thought it would be nice if we all helped Mrs. Lamer, our elderly next-door neighbor, get her house ready for winter. Mother's part in the neighborliness consisted of drinking tea with Mrs. Lamer while we kids raked leaves, picked up rotting apples from the old apple tree, and put up the storm windows.

At supper that night, Mother's comment was, "It certainly gives you a nice, warm feeling when you do something nice for people."

I heard Phil mutter under his breath, "Yeah, your nice warm feeling came from drinking tea."

We figured if there was going to be a decorating contest entry from our house, it would be 99 percent work from us kids and one percent final touches from Mother.

During the next couple of weeks Dad was non-responsive when Mother would bring up the topic.

"If we're going to do something, we should really get going on it," Mother would say.

Dad would respond by mentioning he had been to Fond du Lac that day and had visited Mrs. Rechlein in the hospital and had seen the new baby. We kids immediately started asking details, and the subject of decorating would get lost.

October changed into November. Mother kept bringing up the subject of the decorating contest, and Dad kept changing the subject.

One morning at breakfast in late November, Dad told us that the next day Mother was going to be gone all day.

"Where in the world is she going?" I asked. Mother never went away without Dad, except maybe to Grandma and Grandpa's once in a while.

"The conference is having an evangelism workshop for church women at Ripon, and Mrs. Mueller is going to take a carload of women to it," Dad answered. The conference was the group of Lutheran churches from the area communities which would sponsor various programs for women, men, and young people.

"And," he reminded us (as though we needed reminding), "school is getting out at noon because of the teachers' workshop."

Dad then told us that we should come right home from school and not to say anything to Mother about our plans. Since Mother frequently didn't get up for breakfast, we could talk without her hearing the discussion.

"Hey, want to come to my house and work on stamps?" my friend Norman asked as we left class the next day.

"Nope, can't do it. Got to get home right away. Dad said so," I told him. Quoting your dad as the authority meant that the issue was closed. You could argue with mothers, but not with dads.

Phil, Helene, and I arrived home a few minutes apart. Helene usually got a ride. The grandfather of her friend from across the street would generally give them a ride home in his pickup truck.

Phil walked home with a couple of his friends, and I came a couple of minutes later. I always stopped at the post office to pick up our mail and bring it home. I loved opening our postal box, zipping through the combination and reaching in and pulling things out. We got a lot of mail: Dad's church stuff, magazines, and envelopes from stamp companies for me.

I would check to see if there might be a red slip to show that we had a parcel to be picked up at the window. There was none today, and I put everything inside *The Lutheran Standard* magazine and brought it home.

"OK," Dad greeted us, "there's some soup on the stove. Let's have lunch and then we have to get busy."

Over lunch Dad explained that we were going to surprise Mother by getting the house all decorated while she was away.

"You mean, put up the candles and wreaths?" I asked.

"No, we'll do that some other time. Today we need to get our outside decorations up."

"What is that going to be?" Phil asked.

"Well, stack your dishes in the sink and I'll show you. Come on."

After putting the dishes in the sink, we followed him out the door and over to the church where we went down to the basement and into the furnace room.

"What do you think?" Dad asked.

There it was—a great, big multi-colored rendition of the Christmas carol *Silent Night*, complete with all the notes and two verses of the song.

"Where did you get that?" we all asked, almost in unison.

Phil looked more closely.

"Did you paint it?" he asked.

"Yes," replied Dad, smiling with as much pride as he ever showed. "I finally put Mother's gift to a good use."

"It's wonderful," Helene said. "But who will see it here in the furnace room?"

Dad chuckled. "I just did the painting here. We're going to put it up on the front of the house, and that's why we need to get busy."

Dad explained the plan. We would hang it from the upstairs windows at the front of the house. Then we would decorate it by placing evergreen branches around the border.

"Mother has been after me to prune the big evergreens, so I did it yesterday and have the branches all ready," he said.

We all helped carry the large piece of plywood out of the furnace room and up the stairs.

"When did you do this?" I asked.

"Oh, I told Mother I was working on some things at church, so I would do it when no one was around."

"Where did you get the plywood?" Phil asked. "Wasn't that expensive?"

"No, it was left over when we did the remodeling of the church. It has just been sitting around, so I decided to use it."

As we carried it, we saw he had painted the board white and then used his oil paints to draw in the music and words.

Dad got the hand drill from the basement, the one he had inherited from his Grandfather. Phil drilled holes in the upper corners.

"OK, Phil, you take this piece of rope, and Harold, you take the other and go upstairs, open the window and lower the ropes down," Dad told us.

We did this. Dad took the ropes and put one through each of the holes and knotted them in place.

"Just stay there," Dad said. He went into the house and came to the window where I was holding the rope.

"OK," he told Phil. "Now, let's pull it into place. Helene, you tell us when it's in the center of the house."

We slowly pulled it into place and Helene importantly stood back watching us.

"OK," she called. "That's about right."

Dad tied the rope to the corner of the radiator and then went into the other bedroom and did the same thing.

We all went outside to check our work.

"Looks good, doesn't it?" Dad asked.

We agreed.

"Phil, go get the ladder and I'll go upstairs to see if I can figure out how to tie the ropes in place."

Helene and I went in back of the house and began carrying the pine branches to the front while Phil brought the ladder. After he had put the ladder in place, he went down to the basement, got the hammer and some small nails.

Dad had finally gotten the ropes tied. He shut the windows and came down.

"We'll have to stuff some towels or something around the windows," he told us.

He and Phil started putting up the pine branches. Helene and I handed the branches to them. Soon the *Silent Night* painting was surrounded with green branches.

I glanced across the street and saw Mrs. Homestock watching intently from her living room window.

Phil took down the ladder, and we stood back to admire our work. Afternoon was turning into evening.

"This will be OK in the daylight," I said, "but no one will see it at night."

"I got an idea," Phil said, dashing away. He came back carrying a light and a reflector.

"What's that?" I asked.

"It was up in the church attic," Phil said. "I think they used it for a Christmas program or something."

We rigged it up. Phil got an extension cord which we ran through a basement window. Phil went into the house and plugged the cord in.

Just as the light went on, Mrs. Mueller drove up with Mother in the car.

Mother got out of the car and just stood there.

"Well, what do you think?" Dad asked.

"Well, Henry," she said. "I told you that you could paint if you just put your mind to it."

We were all pleased when we received the $25.00 prize for first place. And all the members commented to Mother how nice it looked and she certainly had a good idea.

Mother just smiled.

Chapter 4

I Get Stuck with Cousin Brenda

"It's my turn to blow out the candles," my sister said.

"But didn't you do it last night?" Dad asked.

"Yes, but that was because I got gypped out of doing it the night before when I was over at Joan's house for supper, and it was my turn, but Harold did it, so I get two turns in a row to make up for it," she explained.

Blowing out the candles on the Advent wreath after evening devotions probably wasn't that big of a deal. But once a long time ago, Phil had told us that the one who blew out the most candles on the Advent Wreath would get the most presents for Christmas. Of course, we didn't tell Mother or Dad that because Dad would get all upset that we were forgetting the real meaning of Christmas, and Mother would give us a lecture about how it was more blessed to give than to receive and we should be thankful for any presents we would get, and we shouldn't be selfish about such things.

But we thought Phil was probably right about it since he was the oldest and had been around the longest. We figured he knew.

"But we never did it that way before," I protested. It probably really didn't matter, but there was a serious principle involved here, so I thought I better enter some sort of a protest.

"Now if you kids are going to fight over this, I'll just blow the candles out," Mother interjected. "Hurry up now. We need to talk about your cousins' presents."

Before anyone could say another word, Helene blew out the candles. I was going to protest, but before I could open my mouth, Mother began talking.

"Now do you all know what you are going to get your cousins for the name drawing?" Mother asked. "Time is getting short."

There were 24 cousins on the Kurtz side of the family, and they were scattered all over the country. The aunts (Dad's seven sisters) had decided that the cousins should draw names. (The two sisters-in-law would have probably agreed had they been consulted, but as was the usual case, they were not included in the discussion.) The aunts felt it would be a good way for us to get to know our cousins better, and it would help us learn the meaning of Christmas as well since, they figured, it would make us think of someone besides ourselves. Although Mother was an aunt, the seven sisters pretty much ran things in the family. Actually, the three oldest aunts were the ones in charge.

The aunts drew up the rules. After all, Mother told us privately, the aunts didn't want to make it too much fun for us. We had to learn some good old-fashioned Germanic duty as well. (Because World War II was just completed, there was not a lot of bragging about how great Germans were, but the implication was there, my Norwegian mother pointed out.)

So the rules were explained:

1. The gift could not cost more than $2.00. (Besides, the aunts pointed out, there was also the cost of postage.)

2. Except for the younger ones, the cousins had to select the gifts and buy them by themselves. It was felt that this would help us each learn how important it was to give. (There were a lot of preachers in our family, so most family activities had some sort of a minor morality play attached to them.)

3. Parents would have the responsibility to see that the presents got mailed on time.

We didn't see most of our cousins very often. In fact, there were some we didn't even know. But we knew all about them because of the Circle Letter. For years our family had kept in touch with one another by a rotating letter. While it was called the "Circle Letter", it was really a collection of letters. The way it worked was that when our family got the Circle Letter, we would take out the letter Dad had written during the letter's last visit, and he would write a new one. Then, after reading all the other letters, our family would mail it off to the next family on the list.

There were a number of unwritten rules associated with the Circle Letter. For one thing, it couldn't be kept too long. If someone kept it longer than a week, there better be a good reason such as having a broken wrist or being in the hospital with the birth of a new baby. Otherwise, the next time the letters would come around, there would be subtle and sometimes not too subtle comments that "we need to be conscientious and see that the letter keeps on time."

Most of the family members were conscientious, and the Circle Letter would make its route in about nine weeks. The one family member who was periodically excluded was Uncle Ernie. He was Dad's only brother, and Uncle Ernie was a procrastinator. He really meant to write a letter to go in the Circle Letter and when he did write, the letter was always interesting and amusing as contrasted with the letters from the aunts who tended to write about what was happening in the congregations where their husbands were pastors. But Uncle Ernie would get distracted, and the letter would sit at his house until my Aunt Martha, who also lived in Omaha where Uncle Ernie lived, would either call him up and tell him to send the letter right away, or, as it happened on occasion, she would drive over to his house and demand that he hand over the letter. After that, Uncle Ernie would be excluded from the Circle Letter for a time until he was given another chance. The first two or three cycles would be fine, and then when it came to Uncle Ernie's house, he would be busy getting ready for a big choir concert (he was the choir director in his congregation), and the letter would sit unanswered until Aunt Martha had to swoop into action.

Another rule was that one should always put on enough postage. I recall one aunt complaining she had to pay three cents postage due when the letter got to her house.

The Circle Letter kept us informed about all the families. As a result, we knew all about our cousins even though we did not know some of them very well.

But back to the name drawing. In due course we received the names of the three cousins for whom we were to purchase gifts. Phil got his cousin Edward. This was no problem. Edward (I can't recall that he was ever called Ed or Eddie; he was always Edward) was slightly younger than Phil but about in the same age grouping. Phil had a dozen ideas even without consulting the Sears Roebuck Christmas catalog. A baseball glove, a book on *Experiments for the Young Chemist* (Edward was big in science), a football or maybe a tie or shirt. (Edward was starting to get to the age where he liked getting dressed up.) All were good gift ideas and were within the price range agreed upon.

Helene got Lois. Lois was a year younger than Helene, and they were good friends, so that would be an easy enough gift for her. Besides, Helene was young enough so if she needed help, it would be acceptable for a parent to help her.

Me? I got my cousin Brenda. This was bad news for me. For one thing, she was a girl. What did I know about girls? For another thing, she was younger than I was, but not so young that she could get baby toys. Worse yet, I didn't know her. Her mother was Dad's youngest sister who was married to a farmer in southern Nebraska. (He was one of the few males in the family who was not a preacher.) I had only seen her parents once that I could remember, and I had never ever seen Brenda. They never came to family gatherings, and we had never visited them.

"They never go more than two hours from home," I recall one of the uncles saying to Dad. "They always need to get back to milk the cows."

Cousin Brenda, I thought. Who is Cousin Brenda?

"Do I know Brenda?" I asked Mother.

"I don't think you've seen her, but we must have a picture of her around somewhere."

Mother started going through the old metal fruit cake box where she kept all the family pictures. She said this was just a temporary place because she planned to get them all organized and put in an album when she got the time.

"Here's a picture. See, that's her standing next to Grandpa."

Mother handed me a small snapshot. I looked at it. There were girls standing on both sides of Grandpa.

"Is she the one with the curls or the long, straight hair?" I asked.

"Yes, that's Brenda. The one with the curly hair is your cousin Marie."

So now I knew who she was, but that didn't solve my problem.

"What could I get her?" I asked Mother.

Mother pointed out that it was really my responsibility to come up with an idea; although, if I got desperate, she would help.

"I am desperate," I told her.

"You haven't even given it any thought. You're just mad because you didn't get a cousin you wanted."

She was right, of course, but why did I have to get Brenda? I hadn't the faintest idea what to get her. I might as well be buying a gift for an orphan in New Guinea.

I started looking through the Sears Roebuck Christmas catalog. There were lots of things, but most were too expensive. A doll? I wouldn't buy anybody a doll! Dolls were dumb and I wouldn't buy dumb gifts.

"I wonder if she plays baseball? Probably not."

"How old is Brenda, anyway?" I asked Mother.

"Let's see," Mother began figuring. "Now she was born after Lois, and Lois is a year younger than Shirley. But wait a minute, Brenda is actually younger than Dorothy, and Dorothy is younger than Lois. So if Dorothy is two years younger than her sister Lois, that would make her three years younger than Shirley. Now let's see, that would have to make Brenda ... no, that can't be right because Martin was born after Lois, and I know Brenda is younger than Martin, so that must mean ..."

Mother stopped. She would never admit she didn't know. "Tell you what. Let me check in my birthday book and see if I have Brenda's birthday in it."

"Never mind," I said, "it really doesn't matter."

On the way home from school the next day, I stopped and looked in the window of Miller's Drug Store. Christmas gifts filled the window. It was better than looking at the Sears Roebuck catalog. Here you could actually see the things; although you couldn't touch them because Mrs. Miller would get mad at you and yell if you came in and started to pick something up from the display. If you could convince her you were a serious customer, she would bring the item out for you to examine.

As I stood there looking and weighing the possibilities, I suddenly got an idea. I knew just the thing. It was such a great idea that I wasn't going to tell Mother or Dad or Phil or even Helene about it, and there wasn't much I wouldn't tell Helene.

I would buy it and wrap it by myself and not tell anyone. We were supposed to be independent about this, and I would be independent.

There was a problem. Miller's didn't have it in stock. I couldn't order it from Sears Roebuck without telling Mother and Dad. I had to figure out a way to go to Fond du Lac to buy it when Mother and Dad weren't around. Fond du Lac was the nearest city for serious shopping. It was a city of 25,000, a metropolis compared with the 700 people who lived in the Village.

How could I get to Fond du Lac without Mother and Dad knowing what I was going to buy? Then I remembered. I had my annual examination with the eye doctor coming up. I had worn glasses since I was three years old, and Mother and Dad were always concerned that my eyes weren't getting worse.

"Isn't it about time for my eye check-up?" I asked Mother.

"Yes, we've got it scheduled when Dad preaches at the old folks' home."

The old folks' home was the Lutheran Home for the Aged in Fond du Lac. The Lutheran preachers from the area took turns holding services there. The services were held on Monday, so the preachers could use their sermons from the preceding Sunday.

"Are you going too?" I asked.

"No," she answered, "I've got to stay home and get the laundry done."

Good, I thought. I'll just ask Dad to let me stay downtown while he goes to the home, and I can do my shopping. He won't mind if I go shopping by myself. I will just tell him I had to get my gift for the cousin's exchange, and he will say, "Fine," and not give it another thought.

Mother, on the other hand, would never let me be by myself in the city. Why, she would hardly let us kids go downtown on Saturday night in the Village.

"I don't want you kids down there getting into trouble," she would explain when we asked why we couldn't go downtown on Saturday nights like all the other kids.

"What kind of trouble could we possibly get into?" Phil would demand to know.

Mother was adamant. We would not be lured into the temptation of the bright lights and sinful ways of the one-block long business district of the Village. If she wouldn't let me go downtown in the Village on Saturday night by myself, there was no way she would let me shop alone in the big city of Fond du Lac. But Dad wouldn't mind.

Things went as scheduled. I got excused from school for the day. Dad and I drove the 20 miles to Fond du Lac. On the way, I told him that I had a Christmas gift to buy and, after my eye exam, could he drop me off downtown?

"That will be fine," Dad agreed. "That way you won't have to sit around the old folks' home."

The eye exam went fine. I was in no danger of immediate blindness. Dad dropped me off in front of Hills Department Store and said he would meet me there in an hour and a half. He left for the home.

It took me a while to find what I was looking for. I was a bit embarrassed to ask a clerk for help, so I had to wander around a while until I finally found it. The clerk was helpful, and I made my purchase. She even wrapped it for me. I looked around the store a bit and then went out in front to meet Dad.

For once things went well. Mother only asked about the eye exam and didn't even ask if I had gone to the old folks' home with Dad.

I didn't tell my family what I got Brenda for the cousin gift exchange. Dad mailed it along with the other exchange gifts. Dad didn't pay any attention to it, but Mother persistently questioned me on what I had given Brenda. Some of this was just plain curiosity on Mother's part; the other concern she had was that I might have done something which would embarrass her, and the aunts would talk among themselves about how she was raising her children.

But I could be as persistent as Mother. No, I wouldn't tell her.

"After all, you decided that this would be a good way for us to learn to be independent, so I was," I replied to Mother.

Even when I got a thank you from Cousin Brenda, it didn't tell Mother anything.

"Thank you for the Christmas present," the letter read. "I like it very much. I hope you had a good Christmas. We did. Brenda."

It was February when the Circle Letter arrived at our house. Since Mother was reading the letters aloud she started to read the letter from Aunt Mildred. "And for the life of me, I can't figure out how Harold thought to buy Brenda a children's Toni permanent wave set. Brenda thought it was wonderful. Her hair is so straight and her dad wouldn't think of letting her go to the beauty shop. She thought this was absolutely wonderful. The only problem is that she doesn't know who her cousin Harold is."

Chapter 5

Was It Really a Miracle?

Helene was sobbing as she came into the house after school.

"What in the world is wrong?" I heard Mother ask. "Did you hurt yourself?"

"No," she answered between tears, "but on the way home from school, Billy Vandenhoefel started teasing me by saying that Daddy wasn't much of a preacher."

"He said what?" Mother asked.

"Yes, he said if Daddy didn't believe the cross at the Smitstern house was a miracle, he must not be much of a preacher."

Oh, I thought, the cross on the wall. It was big news in the Village. Several weeks ago, a cross suddenly appeared on the wall above the bed where Old Man Smitstern had died.

The cross was first reported by his son, Cletus Smitstern, a week or so after his father's death.

"Suddenly, one evening, there it was," Cletus told people from the Village who visited the home and confirmed the report. There indeed was a cross on the wall at the head of the bed where Mr. Smitstern had died.

Some people weren't surprised that a cross would appear where he had died. Mr. Smitstern had been a pious old gentleman who attended church services twice every Sunday. They were more surprised that Cletus was the one who reported the sighting of the cross.

"Yup," people in the Village would say, "Old Man Smitstern goes to church two times every Sunday and Cletus goes two times every year."

The news about the cross spread quickly through the area, and soon every evening there was a steady procession of people to the home.

The number of visitors steadily increased. The daily newspaper in the county seat published a story about the mysterious cross. More people came.

Then the *Milwaukee Journal*, the biggest newspaper in the state, ran a story about it. The reporter called several clergy in the Village, including Dad. One of the pastors said he thought the cross probably was a miracle—how else could you explain it?

Dad was more cautious, saying something to the effect that he was certain that there was a logical explanation for the cross and that people's faith would be better served by regular attendance at church.

Some people in town took exception to his comments. They felt that Dad was casting aspersions on Mr. Smitstern. Besides, they pointed out, Dad had never even visited the Smitstern house to see the cross. Billy's parents were some of these critics.

The controversy continued. The other preachers in the Village thought the cross was a miracle. Dad remained skeptical.

One morning as Dad was at the post office picking up the mail, he met Mr. Franklin, my teacher.

"Well, Reverend, it sounds as though there are some people in town who aren't too happy with your views on the cross," he said to Dad.

"So I've heard. I'm sorry people feel that way. I certainly don't like to have people angry with me, especially at Christmas time. But, I have to be honest with my beliefs," Dad answered.

"I agree with you, Reverend. As you know, I'm Catholic, and we place a lot of stock in miracles. But there is something fishy about this cross. I've known Cletus for a long time. He's not above creating a phony miracle, especially if there's something in it for him."

"Is that right?" Dad responded.

"Absolutely. Tell you what—I'm going to talk with the science teacher at the high school and do a little research. Maybe we can figure this out. I'll let you know."

A couple of days later during our science class at school, Mr. Franklin brought up the subject.

"I know you all have heard about the cross at the Smitstern house. How many of you have seen it?"

A couple of hands went up.

"I thought it might be an interesting science project for our class to see if we can figure out the cross. Let's visit and see for ourselves. Ask your parents if it's OK for you to go. For those who want to visit, let's plan on going on Wednesday night. We'll meet at the school and walk over to the house."

Wednesday night most of the class met at the school.

"Now," Mr. Franklin said, "remember, this is a science project. I want everyone to be especially observant, and tomorrow we'll discuss what we saw this evening. I want you to be polite, not say anything and not touch anything. Everyone understand?"

We all nodded and followed Mr. Franklin as we walked the few short blocks to the Smitstern home. The house was located on a dead-end street, near the railroad tracks. There were six or seven cars parked on the street near the house. A handwritten sign on the door invited people to come in. We followed Mr. Franklin through the door and into the front hall. A man in his mid-20's motioned us into the living room.

"That's Cletus," my friend Norman whispered to me as we went into an old-fashioned parlor. There was floral paper on the walls. A big console radio stood against the wall by an arm chair. The next room looked as though it had once been a dining room, but now there was a small bed in a corner with a group of people standing near it.

"This is the room where my father died," Cletus explained to the visitors, "right on that bed."

We went into the room and, sure enough, there was a lighted cross reflected on the wall. A piece of clothes line was strung in front of the bed, so people could not get close.

The cross looked to be about two feet high and was made up of what appeared to be cross beams of light. A small table with a gooseneck lamp on it stood near the middle of the bed with the light turned toward the wall at the end of the bed. A mirror hung on that wall.

As we stood there observing the scene, people continued to arrive while others left. We all intently surveyed the scene, making mental notes for our discussion the next day.

After about ten minutes, Mr. Franklin motioned us to leave. We said "thank you" to Cletus as we went out the door.

"Did you see Cletus scowl at Mr. Franklin?" I whispered to Norman as we walked away from the house.

"Yeah," Norman replied, "he didn't seem real happy to see him."

We walked back to Main Street. Mr. Franklin stopped and said, "When you get home, write down what you remember and bring your notes to class tomorrow. We'll discuss it first thing in the morning when everything is fresh in our minds."

We all said good night and walked to our homes.

At school the next morning, right after the Pledge of Allegiance, Mr. Franklin said, "We normally have reading the first thing in the morning, but I thought we would have reading this afternoon and have science this morning, so we can talk about our visit last night."

That was one of the many things we liked about Mr. Franklin. He always seemed to know when we were really ready to concentrate on a particular lesson.

"OK, I know some of you were not able to take part in our little visit last night. Wayne, why don't you give us a report on what you saw. When you're done, we'll see what others want to add."

Wayne began by describing how we went to the house and what we saw. As he finished, Mr. Franklin said, "Good report, Wayne. Who wants to add anything?"

I raised my hand and Mr. Franklin pointed to me.

"One thing I noticed was the funny way the lamp was facing and where it was sitting. If you have a lamp in a bedroom, it's usually by the head of the bed where a person would use it for reading. This was sitting on a night stand, kinda halfway down near the foot of the bed."

"Let's make a drawing of the room," suggested Mr. Franklin. "Who wants to do this on the blackboard?"

Ann quickly raised her hand. She didn't volunteer much in discussion, but when it came to art, she was always quick to raise her hand.

"OK, Ann. Make a diagram of the room," Mr. Franklin suggested.

Ann drew an outline of the room and turned to the class for further instructions.

"Now, where was the bed?" the teacher asked.

"It was in the upper right corner," several of us called out.

Ann carefully sketched in the location of the bed.

"What else was there in the room?" was the next question.

"The night stand," I offered.

Ann stood with the piece of chalk in her hand, waiting for direction.

"It was about halfway between the foot and the head of the bed," I told her.

She drew a square where I had indicted.

"Add the lamp," someone suggested.

Ann paused, thinking about how to draw a lamp.

"It was a goose-neck lamp, with the light pointed toward the wall," I instructed.

We all studied the diagram.

"What else do you remember?" Mr. Franklin asked.

We sat there thinking.

"I believe there was a window on one side of the room," someone remembered

"Here?" asked Ann.

"That's about right," came the response.

We continued to sit quietly, some of us reading over the notes we had made after we got home.

"Wait a minute," I exclaimed, "there was the mirror."

"That's right," others in the class responded, "on the wall at the foot of the bed."

Ann drew an oval.

"No," we corrected her. "It was oblong—kind of narrow."

She erased the oval and drew a rectangle.

"Anything else?" the teacher asked.

A few additional suggestions were added.

We sat and studied the room layout.

"Before we talk about the room, was there anything else in the house anyone saw?" Mr. Franklin asked.

We sat silently, trying to remember.

"Wait," I exclaimed, "there was something else. There was like an offering plate with money in it."

Mr. Franklin chuckled. (He told me later that he wasn't surprised that a preacher's kid would notice an offering plate.)

"I saw it, too," Donna added. "I counted at least five one dollar bills plus a five and a bunch of change."

"Well," Mr. Franklin said, looking at the clock. "We've gone way over our science time."

"Can't we talk about this some more?" we all called out.

"Tell you what," Mr. Franklin responded. "Let's leave the diagram on the board. I want to talk with Mr. Wilson, the high school science teacher, and see what he thinks about it. Then we'll work on it tomorrow. Now let's get out our math books."

The next day we again started with science. Mr. Franklin began by saying, "We need to discuss a couple of things. There are people who think the cross is a miracle and, if it is, then there is no way to explain it. Others think there is an explanation for it, and it will be just a matter of time before someone explains the cross. My guess is that most people don't quite know what to believe. It could very well be that this is a miracle. But then again, maybe it's something which we can help figure out. If some of you believe this is a miracle, I don't want to try to change your mind. If indeed it is a miracle, then it will stand up to our little investigation. If we can figure it out, fine. If not, we will have had a good learning experience. If someone is concerned, let me know, and we'll work things out.

"Now," he continued, "let's see if there is a logical, scientific explanation for the cross. Who has any ideas?"

"Does anyone remember if the cross was a light or could it have been painted on the wall?" Galen asked.

"It looked like a light, not a painting," most of us agreed.

The class sat quietly, staring at the diagram on the blackboard.

"It must be something with the mirror," John ventured. "There's a mirror, a light, and a wall. It can't be anything else."

Several of us nodded in agreement.

"Any other possibilities?" asked Mr. Franklin.

"Could the light have come down from the ceiling?" Lois wondered.

We thought about this for a while.

"I don't remember seeing anything on the ceiling," I answered.

Several others agreed. The ceiling did not seem to be a possibility. We continued to sit and stare at the blackboard.

"You know," Arlyn said, breaking the silence, "it's easy to reflect light off a mirror. I remember in Boy Scouts we learned how to send signals with a mirror using the sun."

More nodding from those of us who were in Scouts.

"So," he continued, "it must be a reflection from the mirror."

"That's what Mr. Wilson seemed to think when I talked with him," Mr. Franklin said. "I brought a few mirrors and a lamp from home. Let's see what we can figure out. A couple of you guys pull down the window shades."

The class gathered around Mr. Franklin's desk where he set up a small lamp, similar to the one we had seen at the Smitstern home. He had three small mirrors with him. He switched off the classroom lights and we stood in the dimly lighted classroom.

He turned on the lamp.

"OK, Arlyn, see what you can do."

Arlyn picked up a hand mirror and walked over to the side of the desk. The light from the lamp faced him. He picked up the mirror and held it so it reflected the light on the wall of the classroom. He moved it up and down and back and forth. There was a reflection of light on the wall, but no pattern.

"John, try a different mirror," Mr. Franklin directed.

John picked up a small, square mirror and held it in front of the lamp. The pattern was different, but the results were the same—no cross.

Dayle tried the remaining mirror with the same result.

"Let's try all the mirrors together," Richard suggested.

This was done. The result? Three patterns, but no cross.

We stood around the desk, contemplating the situation.

"Any other ideas?" the teacher asked.

"Well," said Alice, "maybe it is a miracle."

Several classmates nodded in agreement.

"That's always a possibility," Mr. Franklin agreed. "Well, we haven't figured it out so far. We have spent quite a bit of time on this, but we do have to get back to our regular science lessons. Let's continue to think about this and, at the start of science, if you have new ideas, tell us."

Mr. Franklin switched off the lamp and turned on the classroom lights. We pulled up the shades and went back to our desks.

"Let's get out our math books and turn to chapter eight," Mr. Franklin directed.

Nothing happened for the next few days. Cars made a nightly procession to the Smitstern home. People continued to debate whether this was a miracle or an explainable phenomenon.

In our science class, several ideas were discussed, but nothing could be determined. During supper, Phil reported that the physics class at the high school was working on the matter but had not been able to figure it out either.

At home one afternoon I went to put away my coat in the front hall closet. The late afternoon December sun was streaming through the front windows, hitting the mirror on the front of the closet door. As I swung the door to close it, the sunlight reflected on the side wall. As the door swung closed, I got a brief glimpse of what looked like a bar of light on the side wall. I gradually opened the door, keeping out of the way of the sunlight and watching the reflection on the wall. The mirror did reflect a definite straight line of light. As I stood staring at the reflection, the sun went behind a cloud, and no more reflection appeared. I waited for the sun to reappear, but the sun was setting in the short December day.

The next day in science class, I reported what I had observed.

"What kind of mirror is it?" my classmates asked.

"Ah, just a mirror," I answered, "it's about the size of a door."

"Is there anything special about it?" Mr. Franklin wanted to know. "Is it perfectly flat?"

I thought about this for a moment.

"Gee, I don't know. It's, well, it's just a mirror on the door. It's been there all the time we've lived in the house. I never paid much attention to it."

"Take a good hard look at it tonight to see if there is anything special about the mirror. See if you can get a reflection again and report back to us tomorrow," Mr. Franklin suggested.

I said I would.

When I got home from school that afternoon, I closely examined the front hall mirror. It was a cloudy day so there was no reflection. Turning on the hall light didn't do any good. I did notice one thing about the mirror—it had sort of an edging on all four sides. I saw that these edges were slanted away from the main section of the mirror. I studied it for a little bit until Mother called me to help her set the table for supper.

The next day at school, I reported on the mirror.

"It was something like this," I said as I went to the blackboard and tried to draw the mirror.

Mr. Franklin nodded.

"It's called a bevel. Better quality mirrors are made that way. That may be a clue. I think I have a small beveled mirror at home. I'll bring it tomorrow, and we'll try some experiments," he said.

At supper that night, Phil said the high school physics class had given up on trying to figure out the cross. I decided that I wouldn't say anything about what our science class was doing. Phil would probably start teasing me about it.

The next day, Mr. Franklin brought in an oblong mirror about 12 by 18 inches. He also brought back the gooseneck lamp. We all gathered around his desk.

"Here's what is meant by a beveled mirror," he explained, pointing out the slanted portion of the glass on each side of the mirror. "We need to be careful with this. I took it from my mother's bedroom, and she would be pretty mad if we broke it."

The class solemnly nodded. We didn't want Mr. Franklin to get in trouble with his mother.

We set the lamp up on the desk, pulled down the shades and turned off the overhead lights. Mr. Franklin turned on the lamp and held the mirror off to one side so the reflection shown on the wall. There was just a reflection of light on the wall.

"How did you position the door to get the reflection?" Mr. Franklin asked me.

"I'm not certain," I answered, "but I kinda swung it back and forth."

Mr. Franklin held the mirror at an angle and slowly rotated it sideways. A fuzzy outline of light began to show.

"Put the mirror further away from the light," someone suggested.

Mr. Franklin pulled the mirror back several feet. The reflection got a bit more distinct. He backed up further. Now there were bars of light going crossways and up and down.

"Look," several classmates said, "you're starting to get something there."

Mr. Franklin pulled the mirror back a little further and rotated it back and forth.

"There! Stop!" I almost shouted. "See, there's a cross."

Sure enough—there on the wall was a white, lighted cross. It wasn't quite as perfect as the one we had seen at the house, but nonetheless it was a cross.

We continued to move the mirror back and forth and gradually got a more focused image.

"Well," said Mr. Franklin after we had opened the shades and turned the lights back on, "I believe we figured out the mystery of the cross. However, we still don't have a scientific explanation for it. I'm going to talk to Mr. Wilson and see if he can get some more information for us. Meanwhile, why don't we keep quiet about this until we can better explain it."

We nodded in agreement.

The following day Mr. Franklin reported he had talked with Mr. Wilson. "Mr. Wilson has a friend who teaches at the University. Mr. Wilson said he would write to him to see if he can explain things."

About a week later Mr. Franklin brought in a letter. He held it up. It looked very official with the big University of Wisconsin letterhead.

"Here's what Mr. Wilson's friend wrote," Mr. Franklin said. He began to read: "There's a very simple explanation for this phenomenon. It's one of the basic laws of reflective light physics. By doing some fairly simple experimenting with a light and a beveled mirror, it is possible to create a cross similar to the one you described. Based on the description you provided, my students and I were able to project all different sizes of crosses on the walls of my laboratory. I do have to admit, I had never previously come across this particular application of the laws of physics. It was a good learning experience for me as well. Please feel free to use this letter if there is anyone who doubts that the cross is something other than a visible manifestation of a basic element of physics."

The class broke into applause.

"That means we were right," I said. "We figured it out, and the professor at the University of Wisconsin agreed with us."

"And explained the science of it," Mr. Franklin added. "Ann, go to the blackboard and let's see if we can do a drawing of how this actually works."

With coaching from Mr. Franklin and the class, Ann came up with a pretty good drawing, showing how the light from the lamp reflected on the mirror and then projected on the wall.

She made a copy of the drawing on a sheet of paper. Mr. Franklin took it and the professor's letter to Mr. Henley, the editor of the Village newspaper.

"I'll have an engraving made of the drawing, and I'll run the story on the front page next week," he told Mr. Franklin. "I'll give your class the credit for figuring it out."

The following Thursday when the paper appeared, everyone in the Village was talking about it.

On Friday, Helene was smiling when she came into the house.

"Well, Billy Vandenhoefel apologized," she told Mother. "He guessed that maybe the cross was not a miracle after all."

Not everyone in the Village accepted the explanation. The following week there were a couple of letters to the editor from people who believed the cross was a truly a miracle. "Scientists can explain all they want, but they'll never convince me that this was not a miracle," one lady wrote.

Our class was very proud of its work. We discussed it again in science class.

"There are some things I don't understand," I said, during the discussion. "First, how did Cletus know how to do this? Second, why did he do it?"

"Well," Mr. Franklin answered, "I don't know for certain, but I have a couple of ideas. I found out that when Cletus served in the Armed Forces, he was in the Signal Corps. He probably learned a lot about mirrors and how they reflect. And why did he do it? Well, you noticed the collection plate. He was probably taking in $15 or $20 a night."

"And that's a lot more than he made working at the shoe factory in Waupun," Allen added.

The next time Mr. Franklin saw Dad at the post office he said, "You know, Reverend, I knew that the cross wasn't a miracle. I figured if there was going to be a miracle, it would be in a good Catholic home."

Dad chuckled. "You're probably right, Mr. Franklin, you're probably right."

Chapter 6

When Santa Visited the Country School

I was excited, so excited I could hardly wait for supper to tell the rest of the family the news. We always saved important news for the supper table.

I barely had the "Amen" of our table prayer out of my mouth before I said, "Guess what!" and without waiting for anyone to make a guess, I continued, "Mr. Franklin asked if I wanted to go to the Grant School Christmas program. He's going to take a carload of kids from our class."

Children who lived in the countryside attended one-room schools. They received their first eight years of education in these schools and then would come to the Village for their high school education. By and large these schools probably provided as good of an education as did our school in the Village. Both the rural schools and the Village grade school were taught by graduates of county normal schools. Wisconsin had the nation's largest system of county normal schools (which in their later years of life during the 1960s successfully lobbied the state legislature to get their names changed to county teachers' colleges). There were more than two dozen of these institutions which offered a two-year program to prepare the graduates to teach in one-room schools and state graded schools such as ours in the Village. The more sophisticated school systems in the surrounding cities required bachelor degrees for their teachers. The county normals offered an inexpensive education for local students, the overwhelming number of whom were women. The general rule was that a woman would teach a few years, get married, and drop out of the job market. The few men and the career women (usually referred to as old maid teachers) would attend summer sessions at one of the area four-year teachers' colleges and gradually complete their degrees.

Those of us who attended elementary school in the Village felt smugly superior to the students from the country who went to one-room schools. After all, we had all sorts of advantages: we had kindergarten, we only had two grades per room rather than having all eight grades in one room, we had the high school gymnasium available to us, and we had indoor plumbing. The one-room rural schools had outhouses.

There was only one time during the year when we felt the students in the one-room schools had an advantage over us. That was at Christmas. The Village school did recognize Christmas. The high school band and chorus put on a Christmas concert. Each of the grade school rooms had a Christmas tree, decorated with ornaments made during art class. But we had nothing to compare with the Christmas programs of the one-room schools. In fact, there was nothing quite comparable to the one-room school Christmas program.

The typical school had perhaps fifteen to twenty students spread over all eight grades. There would always be some unevenness. There might be five in one grade, six in another and only one in each of the other grades. In some schools two or three families might constitute the entire student body.

Christmas programs were a tradition in the schools. Their content would be a cross between the secular and the religious. The religious aspect would depend both upon the religious persuasion of the teacher and the dominant faith of the families in the district. For example, if there were a Catholic teacher and a heavy representation of Irish-Catholic families, the program would have a major focus on the role of the Virgin Mary. With a Protestant constituency, there would be more carols and even a reading of Luke 2. Since most of the schools had a blend of Catholic and Protestant students, the program tended to be somewhat pan-religious with enough religion to assure the local taxpayers that Christ was being kept in Christmas, but not enough to compete with the churches. Since our family lived in town, we didn't attend the programs; although we always heard about them from our friends in the congregation.

Of course, having an invitation from Mr. Franklin was something special. Mr. Franklin was different from the other teachers at our school. He actually lived in town. He had attended the Village schools, graduated from the normal college in the next county, and had come back to teach in the Village school. It was more than he just lived here. He actually seemed to enjoy kids. He would coach the grade school basketball team. He helped with the Boy Scout troop and he would often pile a bunch of us kids into his old Buick to attend an out of town basketball game or to go to a concert in a neighboring community.

Mr. Franklin lived with his mother who was recently widowed. The girls in our class said he had a girlfriend who taught in Waupun, a city of some 5,000 people near our Village. Girls always seemed to know that sort of thing.

"How do you know that?" we boys would demand when they made some comment about Mr. Franklin and his girlfriend.

"You boys just don't know anything," they would taunt back to us. "Maybe if you paid attention to things instead of playing basketball all the time, you'd know these things too." They would usually then make faces at us and run away to continue talking among themselves.

Mr. Franklin's mother, also a graduate of a county normal, was the teacher at Grant School. That's the reason Mr. Franklin was going to the Christmas program.

Grant School was located about three miles east of the Village. It was built of Milwaukee brick, a light, cream-colored brick, used in the construction of most brick buildings in eastern Wisconsin. It had a small belfry which housed the school bell. A set of swings, a slide and a teeter-totter were on one side of the school and a field, large enough for a softball diamond, was on the other side. At back of the school were two outhouses: one for boys and one for girls.

The December evening was clear and crisp as we left town and drove out to the school. I was glad it wasn't too cold because Mr. Franklin's old Buick didn't have a very good heater.

"Mother is really having a tough time this year," said Mr. Franklin as he drove out of the Village.

"How come?" I asked. "I thought the kids really liked her."

"Most of the kids do," Mr. Franklin answered, "but the Johnston kids are really causing problems."

"What kind of problems?" asked Alice.

"Well, maybe it isn't right to blame the kids, not when you consider their parents."

Mr. Franklin explained that the Johnstons had recently moved into the district.

"They're renting the old Kempthorne place," Mr. Franklin said. "I'm not certain what Mr. Johnston does for a living. He isn't farming. All I know is that he doesn't pay any attention to what his kids do in school. As a result, he and his wife never will do anything about their kids' behavior, and so they are a constant problem to Mother.

"The kids won't pay attention and they cause problems for the other kids as well. I sure would like to help Mother with those kids."

We drove on, down the state highway and then turned off on County Road B. In Wisconsin, the state highways have numbers and the county highways have letters. When county roads intersect, there would be a sign saying "Junction with AB" or whatever the letters would be.

We always liked going this route because County Road B intersected with County Road O, and the sign said "Junction with BO". To us, this was great humor.

We soon arrived at the school. There were cars all over, extending back along the highway

"I'll drop you kids off. You go in to get a place to see the program. I've seen it before, so if I don't get a place, that's no problem," he told us as he stopped in front of the school.

Coats were piled high in the entryway. We dumped ours on top of the stack.

"I hope we can find them again," I said to Norman.

We edged our way into the school room. The student desks had been pushed aside, and the teacher's desk had been moved off the raised platform. A curtain had been hung to make a small stage.

Parents, grandparents, younger and older siblings, and residents of the district crowded the room. The black, cast-iron stove was roasting those standing close by. With the crowd there tonight, no one would get cold, no matter how far they were from the stove.

The school had 25 students. That evening there must have been a hundred or more people jammed in. We found a place in the corner and stood patiently, waiting for the program to begin. The room was so crowded it was hard to tell who was there.

The students milled around the front as Mrs. Franklin gave last-minute instructions. She saw us when we came in and waved. The room got even more crowded as the last people entered.

It was soon time to start. An eighth grade girl sat down at the piano. The chairman of the school board rose and, as the audience quieted, welcomed everyone and introduced the teacher and the students, not that anyone really needed introducing. After all, Mrs. Franklin had been teaching at Grant School for the past ten years, and everyone knew her, just as everyone knew all of the students. Since this was Mr. Goetsch's first year as board chairman, he felt that as the leader of the three-man (women didn't have much of a role in school governance in rural districts) governing body, he deserved a little of the limelight.

The eighth grade pianist, one of the Van Roekel girls, struck some introductory chords, and the entire student body joined in singing *Jingle Bells*.

After the round of applause died down, the first grade class—both students—moved to the center of the stage and said their pieces. The VanderGalen girl recited a couplet about getting ready for Christmas. Enunciation was flawless, and there was never a pause as the recitation went without a missed word. The Boetcher boy was a different story. He had a piece of perhaps six lines and the recitation required an equal number of promptings from Mrs. Franklin. An embarrassed Mrs. Boetcher was heard whispering to her neighbor, "He could say it perfectly at home."

So the program continued. There were more pieces and readings including the familiar: "'Twas the Night Before Christmas" and "Yes, Virginia, There Is a Santa Claus". There were several musical selections sung by the student body, and the final number was a play by the older students—those in fifth through eighth grades.

There probably was a title, and there probably was a plot, but the eighth grade boy doing the narration (the older Gieseking boy) had a speech impediment, and most of what he said was lost on the crowd.

The play ended with loud applause, and the student body paraded to the front as the Van Roekel girl struck up *Santa Claus Is Coming to Town*. As they started the second verse, the sound of jingling bells was heard, the door of the school burst open, and in came Santa Claus.

"Santa, Santa," the young children in the audience squealed, jumping up and down with excitement. Santa coming to Grant School—what an occasion!

The older and wiser children checked the audience to see whose father was missing. They knew it must be a father, but it was carefully kept secret who would play Santa each year.

The younger children paid no attention. This was Santa and that was all that mattered.

"Have you been good boys and girls?" asked Santa in a deep, bass voice.

"Yes, yes," the children responded. The older boys smirked knowingly.

Santa turned to the smirking boys.

"No need for you to say, 'I have been good.' I heard all about how you locked Timmy Rohrschneider in the outhouse last week," Santa said, looking at the boys who began to look worried.

The boys paled. Who was Santa this year? How did he know about that? And what if there really was a Santa Claus?

"We're sorry. We won't ever do that again, will we?" Clarence Hookstra quickly responded, turning to his companions. They all nodded and looked down. They didn't see the amused looks on the faces of the audience.

"And what's this I hear about you not doing your reading lessons?" he said, turning to the Johnston children. He looked directly at Sheldon, the youngest of the three, who was in second grade. "What would happen if Santa couldn't read? You know, I get all the letters from children. Now suppose I couldn't read them? Would any of you get Christmas presents from me?"

Sheldon looked horror-stricken.

"I'll work at my reading. Honest," he said, looking up at Santa.

"I wonder who that Santa is," Norman whispered to me. "He sure must have talked with Mrs. Franklin."

Mrs. Franklin, I thought ... I wonder if ...

Santa was talking with the other two Johnston children.

"Now then, I hope you two will work at your reading like your brother. And you better work at your writing too. After all, if you can't write, how can you send letters to Santa? And you better watch how you behave too."

The two nodded earnestly.

"Remember," Santa warned, "I only come around at Christmas time, but Billy the Brownie can come around any time."

"Now," he turned to the three Johnston boys, "I want you all to work hard at your reading and your writing. And you better watch how you behave. Will you do that?"

The three boys nodded.

"Good, and remember, someone will be watching," Santa admonished them. "Now let's see if I have some presents here."

He walked over to the Christmas tree where a pile of presents was spread.

"I think I'll need some help here. The Brownies are still working in my workshop tonight, so I don't have any helpers with me. How about if you two would help me?" He pointed to the two first graders who jumped excitedly to help.

"I'll read off the names," Santa told them, "and you can deliver the presents."

Santa began reading the names, starting with the first graders and then going grade by grade to the eighth grade.

"Now," said Santa, "you all have a Merry Christmas. And I want you all to study hard and listen to what Mrs. Franklin tells you at school. Remember, Billy the Brownie will be watching, so if you don't work hard in school and behave, next Christmas you may be disappointed."

"Merry Christmas, everyone," he called as he strolled out the door into the night.

"Merry Christmas, Santa," the students and the remainder of the crowd called after him as the door closed.

"Well," said Mrs. Franklin, "wasn't it wonderful to have Santa come?"

The parents applauded loudly while those students who had been called by name looked sheepish as they weakly struck their hands together.

"And for a final number," Mrs. Franklin said, "let's all join in singing *Jolly Old Saint Nicholas.*"

As the Van Roekel girl began playing, many in the audience were chuckling. After all, the Saint Nicholas who had come that night had not been all that jolly.

As the singing began, it suddenly came to me. I leaned over and whispered to Norm.

"I know who Santa Claus was."

Norm thought for a moment and then whispered back, "Mr. Franklin?"

I nodded.

The song ended and everyone began talking. There was Mr. Franklin in the middle of the group, talking with the parents and smiling at his mother's students.

"Great program," he told the children.

"You did a super job on the piano," he told the Van Roekel girl. "We'll look forward to having you in the high school band next year."

Mothers were bringing out cake and cookies, and we lined up for the refreshments.

"How did you like the one-room school Christmas program?" asked Mr. Franklin as he joined us for cake.

"It was great," we all said.

"We especially liked Santa Claus," I said, smiling with the rest of our group.

Mr. Franklin put his finger to his lips.

"Don't say anything," he whispered.

"Your secret is safe," I assured him.

Chapter 7

Christmas Eve Chaos

It was our normal Christmas Eve—total chaos. Mother was running around, getting everything organized for the Christmas pageant. Helene was roaming around the house, rehearsing her recitation for the pageant. Dad was in his study with the door closed, working on his German sermon for Christmas Day. Ah yes, I thought, there's nothing quite like Christmas Eve day in the Kurtz family.

I thought back to yesterday morning. I was upstairs in my room, lying on the bed reading. I could clearly hear Mother as she made Helene practice her Christmas piece.

"Say it one more time. I want you to speak up so the congregation can hear you way at the back of the church."

Helene began belting out her piece. One thing about my sister, if someone told her to speak up, she did. Most of the time, people were telling her to be quiet.

"And the Angel of the Lord said, 'Fear not ...'."

I resumed my reading.

Thank goodness I'm past that time, I thought. Speaking your piece at the children's program was about the worst thing that took place at Christmas. In fact, it was the only bad thing about Christmas. I remember the arguments I had with Mother.

"How come my piece is 16 lines long and the Boelter kid has only four lines," I complained.

"Well, for heaven's sake, you're a lot smarter than Albert Boelter. He'll be lucky if he can get through four lines," Mother replied.

What Mother didn't explain was that this was the time for Mother to show off, not herself, but that her children being preacher's kids were obviously well-versed in church matters and that included speaking extra-long pieces at the children's Christmas program.

Ah yes, the Christmas program. Emanuel Lutheran had two services on Christmas Eve. The children's pageant was at 7:00 p.m. and there was an 11:00 p.m. candlelight service which Mother always called the Midnight Service. "Well, it gets out at midnight, doesn't it?" she explained.

In ordinary years, Christmas Eve was never peaceful at our house. This year, with Grandpa there and Cousin Esther and her parents coming, it was especially chaotic. Mother was all flustered trying to make last-minute arrangements.

"Now, let's see," she said, standing in the hall. I had noticed that whenever Mother was worried about something, she would stand and talk to herself. "Grandpa is sleeping in Phil's room. We'll give Walter and Helen our room. We can sleep in the spare room. Helene and Esther can share a room. Phil is in Harold's room. I guess it will all work out." Having reassured herself, she returned to the kitchen, only to be interrupted by the ringing of the doorbell.

It was one of the members with a gift for the family.

"It's one of our farm raised geese," the member said. "I hope you folks like goose."

He handed Mother the large, frozen bird.

"Oh yes," Mother responded. "Roast goose will be a real treat."

No matter what members proffered, Mother would always assure them that what they brought was a prize and a family favorite.

Presents continued to arrive throughout the day. Most of them were gifts of meat, and we kids were kept busy carrying them to the locker plant. In the days before people had home freezers, most small towns had a business called (for reasons I never knew) a locker plant. The locker plant had lockers (actually sliding drawers) in a large walk-in freezer. People would rent these lockers and store their frozen meat, vegetables, and fruits in them. On a hot summer day it was a real treat to go get something from our locker. You would walk in and cool down immediately.

When the food was already frozen it was a simple matter to put it in the locker. We would simply unlock the drawer and fit the frozen goose in among all of the vegetables from Dad's garden. If the meat was unfrozen, we would take it to Mr. Brueggemann, the locker plant owner. He would write our name and locker number on the package and then place it in sharp freeze where it would be frozen at a sub-zero temperature. Later he would place it in our locker.

The parsonage family was well remembered at Christmas time.

"Helps make up for the low salary they pay you," I remember Mother saying to Dad.

Farm families usually remembered the pastor's family with meat they had raised on their farms—beef roasts, chicken, duck, goose, pork chops—all sorts of things. We never had much money, but we did eat well.

Families who lived in town would usually bring baked goods—*stollen*, ginger bread or Christmas cookies. There would often be small presents for us kids. These would go under the tree.

Evening was approaching as I made my last trip to the locker plant. Snow had fallen the day before and the whole Village was white. The Christmas lights on Main Street sparkled through their covering of snow. The big pine trees next to the parsonage glistened with a pristine coating.

When I got home I scurried around the house, turning on all the Christmas lights. The upstairs windows had wreaths with red bulbs. The downstairs windows had electric candles with white bulbs. Our living room Christmas tree twinkled with multicolored bulbs and the floodlights shone on Dad's *Silent Night* decoration outside. As I finished up, Mother said, "Let's go out and look at the house."

She put on her coat, and we went outside to admire the house.

"It really looks like Christmas now. I think the members will really be impressed," Mother decided.

Although the house had been decorated for several weeks, most of the members had not seen the house at night.

We ate supper quickly. Most families had a traditional Christmas Eve meal, but not the parsonage family. It was soup, sandwiches, and hurry up—it's time to get ready for the Christmas pageant.

By 6:30 cars were pulling up to the church. The children's program had the largest attendance of the year. It was the only service when people came early to get a parking place and a good seat.

"It's a good thing we live next to the church," I commented to Phil as we walked from the parsonage. "That way we don't have to worry about finding a parking place."

"That's about the only advantage," Phil answered.

Phil and I weren't in the Christmas pageant. Phil was helping Willard Monk, the Sunday School superintendent, with the lighting. When we entered the church, Phil went up to the balcony to check with Willard. I went to the church basement. I didn't really have an assignment. I was too old for the pageant and too young to teach Sunday School.

"Just be there to help," Mother told me.

So I was there to help.

"Here," said Mother, "get the shepherds fixed up."

The Hofmeister twins (I never could tell them apart), Warren Feldenmeier, and LeRoy Stroessenreuter were the shepherds. There really wasn't much for me to do. The boys were wearing their bathrobes as shepherd robes and their teacher had fashioned headpieces out of bath towels.

"My bathrobe is a Christmas present," LeRoy told me. "Ma gave it to me early because she knew I was going to be a shepherd. I think it's a pretty dumb present. I don't need a bathrobe. I only take a bath on Saturday night anyway."

"It's a nice robe, LeRoy," I told him. "You make a great shepherd."

"Yeah, LeRoy," Warren said. "Who knows? Maybe you can start taking baths twice a week."

I shook my head at Warren.

I heard the organ blower motor begin to hum. Upstairs I knew that Martha Buehler had slid onto the organ bench, and in a few moments the prelude would begin.

"OK, children," the voice of Willard Monk, the Sunday School superintendent, cut through the chatter. "Let's get ready to go in. Children, follow your teachers. We'll start with the preschool. They'll sit in the front pew. The others fill in behind them."

We moved up the stairs to the entry way. Dad always referred to it as the narthex, but everyone else called it the entry. Latecomers were standing in the narthex waiting until the Sunday School entered. Then the ushers could put up folding chairs in the aisle.

The organ prelude ended, and Ornie Mueller, the janitor, began ringing the bell. I silently counted. It was 40 rings. That would be enough to tire Ornie since pulling the rope to get the big bell swinging was no easy task.

"Everyone ready?" Willard asked as the bell ringing ended. "As soon as the organ begins, let's process in."

The organ struck up *Come Hither, Ye Faithful*. Most others sang it as *Oh, Come, All Ye Faithful*, but our version of the Lutheran hymnal had a translation not found in other books.

The procession began, except that processing in was not exactly what happened. It was more pouring than processing. The 60 or so Sunday School members and their teachers were packed tightly in the front pews. I squeezed in with the shepherds.

Dad stood up and welcomed the congregation. It was the only service of the year where Dad dressed informally, that is, if wearing a black suit and a clerical collar was informal. At every other service he wore a clergy robe.

The program began. The preschool sang *Away in a Manger*. Then the pieces began.

One by one the first, second, and third grade students went to the front near the altar and spoke their lines. In most instances, it was classic speed speaking—say it as fast as you can to get it over with before your forgot the lines. Helene was the exception. She moved calmly up the first step and intoned her piece, speaking loudly and slowly:

"Fear not ..." she boomed out.

I could see Dad and noticed he was smiling. I was certain Mother was also pleased; although she was out of my line of vision. Probably she was keeping a sober face so it didn't look like she was gloating. It was OK to be proud of your children, but you should never let it show, I had often observed.

The recitations were finished, and the church lights dimmed—well, Ornie Miller turned off the lights in the front half of the church. The low lights from the altar provided soft illumination as the Holy Family moved into position.

The words of Luke 2 were read. The angels appeared to the shepherds. The shepherds hastened to Bethlehem. The Wise Men came bearing their gifts.

The lights were turned on and the Sunday School joined the congregation in singing *Joy to the World*.

The ushers came down the aisle with the offering plates as Martha played the organ, and her daughter joined in with violin music.

I looked to the back of the church. The ushers had finished collecting the offering and were now getting ready to distribute the bags.

The bags! The highlight of the Christmas pageant for the Sunday School students! Handing out bags of treats was a great Lutheran tradition. I wondered if Martin Luther started it. (Among Lutherans, it was commonly believed that Martin Luther started all the good Christmas traditions like decorated Christmas trees, Christmas carols—practically everything.)

The more sophisticated congregations bought red net stockings already filled with candy and nuts. Not Emanuel. Herbert Schmuhl, the owner of one of the Village's grocery stores and a member of the congregation, brought in the bags and contents. Earlier in the day the Sunday School teachers had gathered in the church basement and filled them. This year I got to help. We lined up the brown paper bags on tables.

"How many should we fill?" Nora Klosterbuhr, one of the teachers, asked Willard.

"Well, we have about 60 children in the program. We should also have bags for the little ones who aren't in Sunday School yet. I think it's nice to have bags for any visitors too," he answered.

"Don't forget Jessie Rhee," one of the teachers called out.

Oh, yes, Jessie Rhee. Did every town have a person like Jessie Rhee? I wondered. I guess now he would be called autistic. Then he was regarded as something of the Village idiot. Jessie lived with his mother in a small house near the school. He was somewhat retarded, but had great recall of events, often reciting word for word a sermon or a speech he had heard somewhere.

Jessie worked as a handyman around town, mowing lawns, raking leaves, and doing various odd jobs. He was not a member of any of the Village's half dozen congregations, but he would attend any evening service a church would conduct. He always came to the Christmas pageant and sat in the back row of the balcony. After the service, he would make his way down to the front and ask whoever was there if he could get a bag "to take home to my mother." The request was always granted.

"Yes, we'll have a bag for Jessie," Willard responded.

To fill the brown paper bags, there was a supply of oranges, two big containers of peanuts (still in the shell), and sacks of candy, including brightly colored hard Christmas candy, chocolate covered creams, and candy canes.

We began an assembly line of placing items in the bags. This was my first year to help. I got the job of putting an orange in each bag. (The teachers figured that there was no need to tempt me by having me put the candy in the bags.) The bags were filled, the tops turned down, and then they were placed in bushel baskets ready for the ushers to distribute that evening.

Before the ushers began distributing the bags, they waited for another of Emanuel Lutheran Christmas Eve traditions—Dad's annual Christmas Eve message. No Babe in the manger, no shepherds in the fields keeping watch over their flock, no angels singing from on high, no Wise Men.

No, his annual Christmas Eve message was much more practical. As Dad rose and walked to the front, I could practically say his message word for word with him.

"Before the ushers bring you your Christmas bags, I want to ask each of you to wait until you get home to eat any of the contents. I especially don't want you to eat any peanuts in church and get shells all over the floor. We have our candlelight service later this evening and our hard-working janitor won't have time to sweep the floor before the service. So please cooperate and wait until you get home to enjoy your treats from the Sunday School. Now the ushers will please distribute the bags."

As the bags were handed out, each child quickly opened the bag to check and see if there was anything different this year. One or two of the older boys surreptitiously popped a piece of candy into his mouth and a few of the bolder ones picked up peanuts, but a stern look from the Sunday School teacher quickly dissuaded them from cracking the shells.

After the ushers finished with the bags, there came the real highlight of Christmas, at least as far as the parsonage family was concerned. The president of the congregation rose and came to the front of the church. "I would like pastor to come up," he said.

Dad joined him in front of the congregation. For the past few years, Roland Berwald had been president. Roland's brother was a minister, and Roland could have been one as well. He enjoyed being in front of the congregation and would always have a verse or two of Scripture to quote as he thanked Dad for his work in leading the congregation. He would then hand Dad an envelope containing a check. The council members had taken up a collection from the congregation for the pastor's Christmas gift.

But this year there was a new president. Roland had stepped down and Charlie Rhindflesch had succeeded him. Charlie was a retired farmer whose usual attire was a flannel shirt with suspenders holding up his trousers. "They probably didn't make belts big enough to go around his stomach," Phil told me. Since this was Christmas, he wore a tie with his flannel shirt.

"Well, Reverend," Charlie began. "It's been a good year for the church, and we appreciate all you do here. Here's a gift from the congregation."

I watched as Dad smiled, took the envelope, warmly shook Charlie's hand and said, "Thank you very much, Charlie," and turning to the congregation he continued, "And thank all of you as well. My family and I thank you for this gift. We appreciate all the ways you have remembered us during this Christmas season. So many of you have been so thoughtful and generous. Thank you, too, for coming this evening. Remember, there is a beautiful candlelight service starting at 11:00 p.m. tonight. Tomorrow morning at 8:00 a.m. there will be a service in German. Let us close with prayer."

The prayer was said, the organ struck up *Joy to the World*, and most of the Sunday School kids were down the aisle before the ushers could get the folding chairs picked up.

Into the basement they swarmed. In addition to their bags of treats, the younger children received presents from their teachers. Some got pencils imprinted with John 3:16. Others got a bronze bookmark with a picture of Jesus the Good Shepherd at the top. The lucky ones got plastic crosses which glowed in the dark. I remember I got one when I was in third grade. You would take the cross, hold it against a light bulb, and then sit in a dark closet and see it shine. That wasn't the real idea behind it. You were supposed to hang it on your bedroom wall and then it would glow in the dark after you turned the light out and went to bed.

"It is supposed to remind you that Jesus is always present," Mother told me when she found me in the closet one time.

"That's no fun," I told Mother. "You can hardly see it that way."

The gifts were distributed to the children. Most of the teachers received small presents from their students. The church basement quickly cleared as families went home to open their Christmas presents.

Practically everyone in the congregation opened their presents on Christmas Eve.

Everyone but us.

"How come we have to wait until Christmas morning?" my sister demanded every year since she learned how to talk. "Why can't we open them on Christmas Eve like everyone else?"

The answers varied. When we were little we were told that we had to wait until morning because Santa Claus came at night. Then there were other answers such as, "There will be more time in the morning," or, "The Kurtzes always open their presents on Christmas morning."

Actually I think the real reason was that Mother never got all the presents wrapped until late on Christmas Eve.

And this year it would be even worse. We would have to wait until Christmas afternoon to open presents.

"With Cousin Esther and her parents coming, I think it would be real nice if we waited until they got here to open our presents," Mother had announced.

"Afternoon!" my sister shrieked when she heard Mother's decision. "Why!" She practically became speechless as she considered the injustice of it all. "Next thing you'll be telling us that we have to wait until New Year's."

Dad broke in, "We'll do as your mother has decided," he said firmly. No use arguing, I thought. If Dad and Mother both agreed, that was it.

After the children's pageant we came back to the parsonage. The doorbell rang once or twice as parishioners came with late presents.

"I think I'll go to bed," Grandpa announced. "I'm going to the service tomorrow."

He didn't need to announce that, I thought. Grandpa would never miss a German service. After all, Martin Luther WAS German, he would point out, generally within my mother's hearing.

We all wished Grandpa "Merry Christmas!" as he climbed the stairs to his bedroom.

Now—the high point of Christmas Eve. We all looked at Dad.

"Phil, lock the front door," Mother directed. "Harold, pull down all the shades in the kitchen."

The family gathered around the kitchen table.

"Well, how much did we get?" I asked.

"We did not get anything," Mother said sternly. "Your father received the gift."

We kids laughed. Mother was the first one to talk about what "we" received from the congregation or what "we" did in church.

Dad chuckled. "I think it is meant for all of us," he said.

Dad reached into his inside coat pocket and pulled out the envelope.

"Well, this is different," he puzzled.

"What do you mean?" asked Mother.

"It doesn't feel like a check," he replied.

He opened the envelope.

"Look at this," he said, holding out a bunch of crisp bills.

I looked at them.

"Are they all twenties?" I asked.

Dad slowly counted them out

"One, two, three, four, five, six, seven. All twenties—$140."

"That's the most we, I mean you, ever got for Christmas," Mother commented.

"How come it's in bills? Don't you usually get a check?" Phil wanted to know.

"Hard to say. Maybe Charlie just doesn't believe in checks," Dad answered.

One-hundred and forty dollars, I thought. That is a lot of money. I knew that Dad didn't get a very big salary—about $100 a month, so the $140 was almost like a month and half salary for Dad.

"That was nice of the congregation," Mother observed. "Now you can get a new suit, Henry. You really need one."

"And you could use a new winter coat," Dad told her.

"Boy," I observed. "I've never seen so much money in my life."

Our family suddenly grew quiet. We were all thinking the same thing.

"Where will we hide it?" Phil finally asked, saying what we had all been thinking. What if someone would steal it while we were at church for the candlelight service?

We knew none of the members would do such a thing.

"But you know," said Mother, "there are always a lot of visitors on Christmas Eve. You never know who might be there."

We offered suggestions.

"Under a mattress?"

Too obvious.

"Locked in Dad's desk?"

Too easy to break into.

Mother cut the conversation short.

"I'll hide it," she declared, picking up the envelope.

We didn't think any more about it as we got ready for the candlelight service. Little did we know how this would turn out.

Chapter 8

The Mystery Is Solved

I heard the side door of the house close. I opened my eyes. Christmas morning, I remembered. That must be Dad going to church to get ready for the German Christmas Day service. We kids were glad that there was just the German service on Christmas Day.

"Otherwise we'd have to go to church again," Phil told me. We figured that going twice on Christmas Eve was enough church-going for the holiday. Since Emanuel just had the German communion service on Christmas Day, we got to stay home.

"How come there's a German service?" I asked Dad one time. "Everybody around here speaks English all the time."

"You're right," Dad agreed, "but the older people appreciate a German language service once in a while. They grew up speaking German; they learned their catechism in German; and they like to sing the old carols in German. I'm not real crazy about preaching in German, but it's something I figure I can do once or twice a year."

Dad told me that when he first started in the ministry, a lot of Lutheran congregations had German services every week.

"Thank goodness, we've done away with that," he said.

As I lay in bed, I heard the house door open again. Wonder why Dad is coming back? I thought. Since service was early, I remembered that Grandpa had said something about not bothering with breakfast, that he would eat after church. I dozed off, vaguely hearing Grandpa getting ready for church.

This is weird, I thought. It just did not feel like Christmas morning. Normally we would all be up, waiting for Dad to come back from church so we could have breakfast and then open presents. But with having to wait until this afternoon to open presents, we kids were sleeping in. I tried going back to sleep, but couldn't.

This year would be different. We would have to wait until Christmas afternoon to open presents.

Well, I thought, I guess I may as well get up even though we won't be opening any presents for hours. I got up, moving quietly. Phil was still sleeping. I put on my slippers, quietly opened the bedroom door, and went into the hall. The other bedroom doors were closed.

Guess Mother and Helene are still sleeping, I thought, as I tiptoed quietly down the back stairs. Our house had a split stairway. From the upstairs, you walked down a few steps to a landing. If you went down the stairs to the left, you came to the front hall, if you went the other way, you ended up in the kitchen.

As I tiptoed down the stairs, I heard Mother's voice:

"It's got to be here somewhere."

I stopped abruptly when I heard Mother talking to herself. What was Mother talking about? Her tone told me that that she was not worried about a misplaced present.

I stood on the stairs and I reviewed what had happened on Christmas Eve. It immediately came to me—Dad's Christmas present. Mother said she was going to hide the envelope.

This is serious, I thought. I scurried back upstairs, entered our room, and began shaking Phil.

"Wake up," I whispered, "Mother needs help."

Phil sleepily rubbed his eyes and asked, "What now?"

I quickly told him what I had heard, and what I believed had happened.

"Let's see what is going on," he said, putting on his robe and slippers.

Mother was startled when we both entered the kitchen.

"Merry Christmas," she said weakly.

"Merry Christmas," we quickly replied, and then I asked, "What happened? Why are you worried?"

Mother paused momentarily, mentally deciding if she should confide in us or wait until Dad got back from church. Then she answered, "I can't find the money."

"What do you mean you 'can't find' the money?" Phil wanted to know.

"It's not where I hid it. Someone must have gotten into the house while we were at the candlelight service," Mother responded.

We thought about that for a moment. It could have happened, I thought, but there would have been signs of a break-in or something.

"OK," Phil said, "let's see if we can help figure this out. Where did you hide it?"

"I hid it in Dad's study," Mother answered, "and now it's not there."

"Let's go check," Phil said, and we all trooped into Dad's study. Most people would have called it a home office, but in parsonages it was always called the pastor's study. It was the room where Dad did indeed study, work on his sermons, read, and take care of church business. It was also where he met with church members who came for counseling and with couples planning to be married. The study was at one side of the house and had a separate entrance.

I suppose someone could have come in the study entrance, I thought.

We entered the study. There was Dad's big desk with bookcases on two sides.

"Did you put the envelope in the desk?" I asked.

"No," replied Mother, "when we discussed a hiding place last night, we decided that the desk wouldn't be a good place."

"So where did you hide it?" Phil asked.

"I put it in one of Dad's old German books. I figured no one would look at them. Dad never seems to read them," she answered.

There were two shelves of large black books, all with German titles. I remember one time Dad pointed out a big three volume set.

"That's the church history written by my great uncle," Dad explained. "He was a famous professor in Europe."

I was impressed that someone could write three big books like that ... and do it in German, besides.

I had no idea what the rest of the books were about.

"I put it in the back of the third book on the right, here on the second shelf. I figured it would be safe there. Now it's nowhere to be found. I checked through every book on the shelf, and there's nothing there." Mother was almost sobbing by this time.

"Let's double check everything," Phil said. "Was there any chance you might have put it in a book on another shelf?"

Mother shook her head. "No, it was the third book on the second shelf."

"The third book on the right or left side?" Phil wanted to know.

"The third book on the right," Mother answered.

Phil picked up the third book on the right and began going through it page by page. Nothing. He replaced the book and picked up the one next to it. Again nothing. He slowly repeated the process with each book on the shelf. The result was always the same.

He went through the next shelf as well. No envelope.

"You're certain it was a German book?" Phil asked.

"Yes, it was definitely one of his German books," Mother assured him.

While Phil was searching the books, I examined the door to the study. It was locked and there was no sign of anyone breaking in. I looked out at the steps leading to the door. No one had used the entrance since the snowfall two days ago, and there were no tracks on the steps. I looked through the windows, and there were no tracks anywhere around.

"No one could have come in through the door or windows," I said, "otherwise there would have been footprints outside."

The three of us stood there silently. Suddenly we heard a voice.

"I'm hungry. Where is everybody anyway? When do we get to open presents?" It was my sister.

"We're in Dad's study," Mother called. "We'll be right there."

"Let's wait until Dad gets home before we tell Helene," Mother decided. We nodded our assent.

We went into the kitchen where Helene was standing in her pajamas.

"I remember," she said glumly, "no presents until Esther and her parents come. But I'm hungry. When is breakfast?"

"Well," said Mother, "we're not going to have breakfast today. I thought we would have brunch when Dad and Grandpa get back from church. That should hold us until supper tonight."

"What is 'brunch'?" Helene wanted to know. "I've never heard of it."

"Brunch is a combination of breakfast and lunch," Mother explained. "You kind of combine two meals."

Helene pondered this for a minute.

"Sounds as though we're getting gypped out of a meal," she concluded. "Next thing you know, you'll combine breakfast, lunch, and supper into one meal and call it 'blupper'."

In spite of our concern about the missing envelopes, we all laughed.

"Why don't all of you get dressed. By that time, Dad and Grandpa should be back from church and we can eat," Mother suggested to us.

We went back upstairs and got dressed. Just as we finished dressing, I heard the downstairs door open and knew that Dad and Grandpa were back from church.

As we came downstairs, Dad was coming out of the study.

"Merry Christmas, Dad," we all called. Dad smiled and said "Merry Christmas" to us.

"Merry Christmas, Grandpa," we said. Even Grandpa smiled and said "Merry Christmas" to us as he climbed the stairs to his room.

Mother motioned Dad to go into the study. We three kids followed them. Mother quickly explained what happened.

"You mean it's gone?" Helene asked.

Mother solemnly nodded her head.

Dad stood looking at the bookcase.

"What shelf was it on?" he asked Mother.

Mother pointed to where she had hidden the envelope.

"Well, I may have the answer. Wait here."

Dad left the study and went out the door. We stood there, bewildered. Had Dad taken the envelope? If so, why?

"How come nobody told me about this?" Helene demanded. "Nobody ever tells me anything. I bet I can find it."

She started to look through one of the books. Just then we heard the house door open, and Dad reappeared, carrying a black book.

He held it out to Mother.

"Check in here," he told her.

Mother took the book and quickly turned to the back. A big smile came over her face as she pulled out the envelope.

"How in the world did this happen?" she wanted to know.

"Well," Dad explained, "for the German Christmas service, I like to use the special Christmas prayer in Wilhelm Loehe's *Agendum*—that's the German liturgy book. When I got to church this morning, I discovered I had taken the wrong book, so I came back and got the *Agendum*—which just happened to be the third book on the shelf. I put the other book in its place and took the *Agendum* with me to church. I never even noticed there was an envelope in the book."

Mother clutched the envelope tightly so it wouldn't get away.

"If we get a gift next Christmas, I certainly hope it will be a check," she declared. "I can't go through another episode like this."

Just then Grandpa stuck his head into the study.

"Are we going to have breakfast?" he wanted to know.

"No we're not, Grandpa," Helene quickly answered, "today we're going to have brunch."

Chapter 9

Why the Preachers Never Finished Their Card Game

The preachers never did get to finish their game of "Rook" at Mother's annual Christmas party. And, wouldn't you know, Esther and I got blamed for the whole thing which always seemed to be the case.

But I better explain exactly what happened.

It really began one night several weeks before Christmas. I had left my bedroom door open, and I heard Mother and Dad talking.

"I sure hope those two don't get into any trouble this Christmas," I heard Mother say to Dad.

I perked up my ears. They were talking about me. Actually, they were talking about Cousin Esther and me. Everybody referred to us as "Those Two", and the comment would generally be followed by some head shaking.

Esther was my favorite cousin. She was about six months older than me, and I could never remember a time when we hadn't been the best of friends. Her mother was my dad's sister, and her dad had been a friend of my dad's since college and seminary days. In fact, that's how Aunt Helen met Uncle Walter. When Dad and Uncle Walter were in college, they came to Grandpa and Grandma's home during a vacation, and that's how Uncle Walter had met Dad's sister.

Even though our two families never lived close, we did get together quite often. This was going to be a special year, since Esther and her parents were coming for the holidays.

I was really excited when I heard the news. "Boy, oh, boy," I thought. "Will that ever be fun!"

I suppose there were reasons why Mother and Dad were talking about Esther and me. We did have a history of getting into trouble. But no one would ever listen to our side of the story.

There's the time we got blamed for painting the washing machine. Well, we didn't really paint the washing machine. What happened was this: One time when Esther and her parents were visiting us, Dad had taken Mother and Aunt Helen shopping. Uncle Walter was supposed to be watching us, but he started reading Dad's back issues of *The Christian Century* magazine, and Esther and I played together.

We went down to our basement.

"What are those for?" Esther asked, pointing to some orange crates which were standing against the wall. In those days, oranges were shipped to grocery stores in wooden boxes about 36 inches long. They were divided into two sections with a board in the middle. Mother had read in one of her homemaking magazines that orange crates would make inexpensive children's bookcases by standing them on end. The magazine showed how they could be nicely painted for children's rooms.

Mother thought this was a good idea, and she had Dad ask Mr. Nelson at the grocery store if we could get some orange crates. Dad lugged them home from the store, and they sat in our basement waiting to be painted. Mother, of course, wouldn't do this, and Dad said he would paint them some time, but he never seemed to get around to doing it.

I explained this all to Esther and then complained that at this rate I would be grown up and off to college before I ever got a bookcase in my room.

"Well," said Esther. "Why don't we paint them? Painting isn't all that hard. I've watched a lot of people paint. Is there some paint around?"

We looked and found a can of green paint which had been left over from the time Dad had painted the outdoor furniture.

We agreed that green would be a good color for bookcases. We thought we would be generous and paint all three of the orange crates, so that Helene and Phil could have their book cases completed as well.

We found some paint brushes and pulled the orange crates to the middle of the basement.

"Should we spread some newspapers on the floor?" I asked.

"No," Esther responded. "We'll be neat and careful."

We did try to be neat, but we didn't know it would be tough getting the paint can open and that some paint would spill on the washing machine when we finally pried the lid off the can. That's why we tried smoothing out the paint which had spattered on the washing machine. We really hadn't planned to paint the washing machine, but we couldn't leave that one little section green, so we decided we should at least paint the one side so the paint wouldn't show as much.

And we hadn't thought that we would get paint on ourselves or the floor either.

After we finished the washing machine, we turned our attention to the orange crates. Just as we were starting, Uncle Walter called down.

"What are you two doing?"

Esther and I looked at each other. It was probably not the time to mention the washing machine.

"I'm helping Harold with his bookcase," Esther hurriedly called out.

"OK," replied Uncle Walter. "Just don't get into any trouble."

"We won't," Esther assured him.

We really didn't think of this as trouble. We were just trying to get the bookcases painted.

It was kind of tough painting the orange crates. They had paper labels on them and the paint wouldn't stick very well. We were so intent on our work, we didn't hear Mother and Aunt Helen come down the stairs.

"Walter," Aunt Helen almost screamed. "I thought you were watching those two."

"Well, they said they were just working on a bookcase," Walter said from the top of the stairs. "What harm could that be?"

"You just come down and see what a mess they've made."

Aunt Helen was right. It was a mess. Poor Uncle Walter got most of the blame for not watching us.

Besides, that was years ago. But people never let us forget about the trouble Esther and I had gotten into. If they weren't telling about the paint, they were talking about the kittens.

We really hadn't meant to be mean to the kittens. We were just playing. I guess I better tell this story too.

Our family was visiting Avoca, a little town in southwest Wisconsin which was where Uncle Walter was the pastor and where many of Mother's family lived. My Uncle Alfred, Mother's oldest brother, had a small farm at the edge of town. He had a big garden, raised chickens, and had a lot of animals, especially cats. It seemed as though there were always little kittens around.

Mother and Aunt Helen were working in the kitchen, and Esther and I were playing around, getting in their way.

"Why don't you two go outside and do something?" Aunt Helen told us.

"Can we go over to Uncle Alfred's and play with the kittens?" I asked.

"That would be fine. Let Aunt Ilma know you're there," Mother answered. "And please, don't get into any trouble."

"We won't," we called out reassuringly as we left the house. It was only a couple of blocks to where Uncle Alfred and Aunt Ilma lived. Aunt Ilma was working in the kitchen, so we called through the screen door to tell her we would be playing with the kittens. It was Esther's idea to play house with the kittens—she was the mommy, and I was the daddy, and the two kittens were the children. The kittens were not all that interested in being children when we told them to sit and be good. But we played with them and they liked that. Then Esther said, "I think they have to go potty."

Uncle Alfred and Aunt Ilma still had an old-fashioned outhouse, so that's where we took the kittens. The outhouse was a two-seater, and we each took a kitten with the idea of having them go potty in the outhouse. However, the kittens didn't like being held over the toilet seats and, as they struggled to get away, both ended up falling through the holes.

Oh, oh, we thought. Now what?

Just about that time Uncle Alfred was coming home from his mail route. (He was a rural mail carrier and would finish his work in the early afternoon.) He was coming to use the outhouse just as we were coming out of it.

"You did what?" he asked as we told him what had happened.

"*Uffda*," he said as we nodded that, yes, that's what we had done. (Using that old Norwegian expression was as close to swearing as Uncle Alfred ever came.)

Uncle Alfred delayed his trip to the outhouse, went into the house, got a flashlight and returned to the outhouse. We peered in behind him. He turned the light on the hole and could see the kittens crouching in the mess.

Uncle Alfred was the jolliest of all my uncles, but not today. He put his lips tightly together, shook his head, and I could tell he was trying to keep his temper.

He stood for a few moments, glaring at the two of us and then said, "Come with me."

Alfred went to the woodshed, and there he found a long branch.

"Let's see if those kittens are smart enough to climb up," he said as he lowered the branch into the hole. The kittens were either smart enough or had enough of the odor; they quickly clawed at the branch and scurried up out of the pit.

"Don't touch them," said Alfred. "They need a bath."

It was hard to tell what was the worst experience for Alfred—getting the kittens out of the outhouse or giving them a bath. But he got them cleaned up, and the kittens quickly moved out of our range.

"Don't you ever do anything like that again," he warned us as we headed back to Esther's house.

"What have you been doing?" Aunt Helen asked when we got there.

"Playing with the kittens," Esther answered.

"That's nice," her mother said. (Our parents would get the complete details later.) This tale too became part of the folklore of what "Those Two" did when they got together.

But back to why the preachers weren't able to finish their game of "Rook".

I should explain that each year after Christmas Mother and Dad would entertain the area Lutheran preachers and their wives. Mother would have a nice buffet supper, and afterward the preachers and wives would play "Rook". I should probably explain the game of "Rook" and why the preachers played it. "Rook" was a Parker Brothers card game. Instead of having Hearts, Diamonds, Spades and Clubs, "Rook" cards had colors: red, green, yellow, and black. Rather than having Kings and Queens, all the cards were numbered with a 14 being the highest, like a King in regular cards.

Mother never approved of playing games with real playing cards. My grandmother Olson (her mother) had been a pious Norwegian who called playing cards "The Devil's Prayer Book", so Mother didn't approve of playing with real cards. We did have a deck of real playing cards hidden in the buffet. Mother and Dad would occasionally play a game of "Gin Rummy" late at night when there was no danger of church members making an unannounced appearance. Mother always referred to the game as "Rummy", not "Gin Rummy". She didn't like playing a game which included the name of an alcoholic beverage. However, "Rook" was an acceptable game in her mind, so that's what was played in our house at social gatherings.

That particular evening, Ed Schroeder, the young pastor from one of the neighboring congregations, decided that Mother's parties could be livened up a bit, so he brought a 12-pack of beer. Mother was slightly shocked by this. She was married to a German Lutheran pastor, and all of the visiting preachers were German Lutherans; and, to a man, they enjoyed a glass of beer. Mother also really liked the young pastor, so she pretended to be upset, but just shook her finger at Ed in mock outrage and went about getting the buffet ready.

After supper, the preachers went into the living room and got out the "Rook" cards. The women sat at the dining room table, drinking coffee and catching up on the news. The men started playing. Their wives would join in later.

None of the couples had brought their kids with them. Helene was staying overnight with a friend, and Phil had gone to his job at the service station. Dad had passed around his box of Christmas cigars; Ed Schroeder had brought out the beer, and the preachers were settling in for some serious "Rook" playing and an evening of relaxation. Grandpa, who was still visiting us, didn't like all the noise, so he went upstairs to his room where he would read and smoke his pipe. Mother always worried that he would fall asleep while smoking and set the house on fire.

Esther and I were on our own. We went down to the basement, but there wasn't much to do there.

I had an idea. "Let's make some popcorn." One of the members had given the family a large container of popcorn for Christmas.

We went upstairs, through the kitchen, and pushed open the swinging door into the dining room where Mother and Aunt Helen were sitting with the other women.

"May Esther and I make some popcorn?" I asked Mother.

Mother turned from talking and said, "Yes, you may, but do it downstairs, so you don't mess up the kitchen. And be careful."

We had a two-burner gas stove downstairs. It was used mainly for heating water for clothes washing, but it was also used for cooking at times when the electricity went out.

"OK, thanks," I said. Esther and I headed back to the kitchen. I got the popcorn and our long-handled popcorn popper and we went downstairs.

I lighted the gas burner, and we put some popcorn into the popper. The popper had a round pan which was covered with a dome-shaped screen. You popped the corn by moving the pan back and forth over the flame, with the long handle keeping you away from the heat.

"I know," Esther exclaimed, "let's make some caramel corn instead of just regular old popcorn."

"How do you do that?" I asked.

"Oh, it's easy. We need some butter and syrup. There's butter upstairs, and I know there's syrup because we had it on pancakes this morning."

"That's right," I agreed. "Let's go get the stuff."

No one heard us when we went into the kitchen and got the butter and syrup from the refrigerator.

"How do we do this?" I asked.

"Let's see. I think I remember. I saw the mother of one of my friends do it one time, and it looked easy. First, pop the popcorn."

I put the popper on the gas burner and began moving it back and forth. The popping of the corn kernels soon started, and in a short time the dome of the popper was filled with popcorn.

"OK, now put the popcorn in the bowl," Esther told me.

I opened the cover and poured the popcorn into the bowl.

"Now," Esther continued, "take the cover off the popper. We'll heat the butter and the syrup in the pan and then pour it over the popcorn. That's all there's to it."

It sounded simple enough to me. We filled the pan with a generous amount of butter and syrup. What we didn't realize was that when there was that much butter and syrup in a low pan near an open flame, there was a good chance that the contents of the pan would catch on fire.

Which it did.

"Oh-oh!" I yelled. "Quick, run up and open the side door, and I'll throw it out in the snow bank."

Esther ran ahead of me and opened the side door of the house. She jumped out of the way as I ran up the stairs with the flaming pan, holding it with the long handle to keep the flames away from me. I threw it on the snow bank at the side of house.

And that would have been perfectly OK except ...

Well, except that circumstances intervened to get Esther and me in trouble again. Just as I threw it out the door, Mrs. Signer, our neighbor from across the street, was standing at her window, looking at all the cars in front of our house and wondering who everyone was at the preacher's house. Mrs. Signer couldn't see too well, and as she looked, she suddenly saw what seemed to be flames bursting out of the parsonage.

And I didn't know that in the afternoon Phil had piled up the wrappings from the Christmas presents for Wes Carley, the Village garbage collector, to pick up the next day.

You can imagine when the flaming butter and syrup hit the wrapping paper, flames shot up.

"Oh, my goodness. The parsonage is on fire!" Mrs. Signer yelled. She ran to the telephone, rang the operator and excitedly told Mildred, the night operator, to blow the fire whistle because the Lutheran parsonage was on fire.

It so happened that this was Tuesday, and Tuesday nights were drill nights for the volunteer fire department. It was a mild night, so the fire department members had the fire engine out to clean it.

"Don't worry, Lydia," Mildred assured her. "The firemen are right here, and I'll just open the window and tell them to get down there." The firehouse was right next to the telephone exchange.

The firemen couldn't believe their good luck. Going to a real fire was a lot better than a drill. They jumped on the truck. Scoop Mason, the fire chief, drove, and he turned on the flashing lights. There was no reason to turn on the siren since there wasn't any traffic. They covered the four blocks in no time and pulled up in front of the parsonage. Several of the volunteers started hooking up the hose to the corner hydrant while others headed to the front door and began pounding on it. Mother had locked the door so that no one would accidentally come in and see the preachers drinking beer.

The preachers were intent on their "Rook" game, and the banging on the front door startled them. The preachers froze—cards in one hand, beer cans in the other.

"Oh, my goodness," Mother screamed. The house was being raided. One of the members had seen the preachers drinking beer, and they would all be arrested. It was the WCTU out on a raid. It was ... no time to think!

"Quick," she motioned to the preachers, "in there," pointing to Dad's study. The preachers grabbed their beer cans and hurriedly moved to deposit the cans and cards out of sight.

"Just a minute," she called as she ran to the door.

She opened the door, and the firemen streamed in.

"We got a report the parsonage was on fire and there were smoke and flames coming out of the house," Scoop told Mother.

"Grandpa," Mother gasped.

"Upstairs," she pointed. "First door on your left."

Walt and Ed ran up the steps. They saw the closed door and saw some smoke coming out from under the door.

"This is it," said Ed, whipping on his gas mask. The Village fire department had just gotten a shipment of war surplus gas masks, and the volunteers were eager to try them out. Walt followed suit and put his mask on; they cautiously moved to open the door.

Grandpa had been smoking. He had been sitting in his big chair, puffing away on his pipe. The noise from downstairs was bothering him, so he had taken off his hearing aid to read in peace. He had gotten a bit sleepy, put down his pipe in the ash tray and dozed off.

Walt and Ed burst into the room, saw Grandpa slumped over in the chair, and immediately assumed he was overcome with smoke. The gas masks made the room seem much more smoky, so they decided that they had to get Grandpa out of the room and fast.

"Get some oxygen ready," they yelled as they grabbed Grandpa and started to move him toward the stairs. Grandpa was a fairly husky man. Ed and Walt weren't all that big, but they knew a life was at stake, so they began moving Grandpa toward the stairs.

Grandpa woke up immediately.

"What's going on?" he demanded, struggling to get free. Ed and Walt were so intent on getting him out, they didn't reply ... which was just as well since Grandpa didn't have his hearing aid on and couldn't hear a word anyone said.

Grandpa continued to struggle.

"He's probably suffering from oxygen deprivation," Ed yelled at Walt. Ed had just completed a first aid course and was eager to show off both his vocabulary and his new knowledge.

Meanwhile, Mother was making certain that the preachers had their beer cans and cards out of sight, and she didn't see what was happening with Grandpa.

The other firemen had checked the outside of the house and did not see any flames or smoke coming out. They did see where the pan had set the Christmas wrappings on fire. The wrappings were still smoldering a bit, so the firemen doused the remaining embers with their fire extinguishers.

"Never mind with the hose," they told the firemen who were connecting the fire hose to the hydrant.

Fred Conrad, our neighbor who was in charge of the Village water works, had come out to see if he had to go down to the pumping station to get some extra pressure.

"No need, Fred," Scoop Mason, the fire chief, told him. "The fire's all out."

Back at the house, the firemen had Grandpa laid out on the floor of the hallway and were holding him down as they put the oxygen mask on his face and started giving him oxygen.

When Ed and Walt finally let go of him, Grandpa sat up, tore the oxygen mask off, and yelled, "Heinrich, what are they trying to do to me?"

Grandpa used Dad's German name when he got excited.

Dad had gotten the beer cans out of sight and came out of the study with the other preachers.

"Are you OK, Dad?" he asked.

Grandpa put his hand to his ear.

"What?"

Dad saw Grandpa didn't have his hearing aid on.

"I think he's OK," he told Walt and Ed. "Let me go get his hearing aid."

Walt and Ed reluctantly moved away from Grandpa. They didn't want him to have a relapse, not when they were responsible for him.

Dad returned with Grandpa's hearing aid. Grandpa put it on and Dad again asked him if he was OK.

"I was perfectly all right until these guys tackled me and dragged me down the stairs," he said, standing up and straightening his suit.

Scoop came in to check that things were under control.

"What's going on?" he asked.

Walt and Ed explained how they had come into the smoke-filled room and found Grandpa slumped over.

"I was not slumped over. I was sleeping," Grandpa roared at them. "All you had to do was ask if I was OK."

Dad reminded Grandpa that he didn't have his hearing aid on, so it would not have done any good for them to ask.

"Yankees!" Grandpa said under his breath. "Yankees" was his term for anyone who appeared to be non-German and non-Lutheran.

"They were just concerned that you had been overcome with smoke, and I think they acted wisely," Dad told him.

Walt and Ed relaxed. They did not want to get in trouble with Dad. Walt and Ed were Methodists, and they knew all the Lutherans in town would give them a hard time if they had goofed up at the Lutheran parsonage.

All this time Mother was guarding the door of Dad's study, willing to throw herself in front of the firemen if they tried searching the other rooms. There was no way she was going to let the Methodist firemen (whose wives belonged to the WCTU) see that the visiting preachers had been drinking beer in the parsonage.

Esther and I had been keeping out of sight. We pushed open the door between the kitchen and the hall to watch. By this time we had figured out what had caused the commotion, and we were hoping no one would point to our role in this.

But the pan of burnt butter and syrup was the smoking gun of evidence against us. Fortunately the presence of all the preachers and their wives kept us safe from any immediate discipline.

"We can explain it," Esther said.

"Never mind. No lives lost," said Mother. "No lives lost" was her favorite saying in situations like these.

"Well, I guess we might as well take the truck back to the firehouse," Scoop said. "Glad there was nothing serious."

"We are too," Mother told him, relieved that the firemen hadn't pressed to check all the rooms in the parsonage, especially Dad's study. "We're sorry if there was any inconvenience."

"Nope, it's our training night anyway, so we were all set," Scoop reassured her.

The firemen left the house, and Esther and I scooted downstairs to finish cleaning up the remains of our popcorn popping episode.

The preachers and their wives began saying that it was about time for them to leave and started thanking Mother for her hospitality. Mother was beginning to regain her composure, thankful that none of the beer cans had been seen by the firemen.

Beer cans!

"Wait a minute," she called as Ed Schroeder and his wife were getting ready to leave. "Ed, you brought this beer tonight. You just take the empties with you. I can't put them in our trash."

She got a grocery bag, picked up the empties, and handed the bag to Ed.

"It was a great party, Minnie," he told her. "And I'll take care of the empties."

The last car left, and Mother and Aunt Helen began putting things away.

"Those Two," I heard Mother saying to Aunt Helen. "What will they do next?"

Esther and I decided it was bed time, so we quietly tiptoed upstairs.

Chapter 10

It Was Hardly a Silent Night

"Now," said Mother at the supper table, "tonight we are going Christmas caroling."

"Christmas caroling? Tomorrow's New Year's Eve. It's way past Christmas caroling time," I protested. "Besides, I'm very busy tonight."

"Nonsense," Mother replied. "We all know there are twelve days of Christmas. Now that Esther and Uncle Walter and Aunt Helen have gone home, we can get back to normal. And what are you so busy about tonight?"

"Aah, I ... ," Actually I had nothing planned, but anything would be better than going Christmas caroling a week after Christmas. "I promised Wayne I would go to his house and see his family's Christmas tree before they take it down." (That sounded good, I thought.) "And they're taking it down tomorrow, so I really have to go tonight."

I wondered if Wayne's family still had their Christmas tree up, or if they were going to leave it up for another week. Didn't matter. Anything to get out of going caroling.

"Oh, you've seen their tree a dozen times. Tonight we are going caroling, and I don't want to hear any more objections."

Mother had this thing about us being a musical family. Last year the Singing Dobrecht Family had made an appearance at our church's Mother and Daughter Banquet. The Dobrechts lived in Watertown, where Rev. Dobrecht was the minister at a Methodist Church. The six members of the Dobrecht Family regularly toured eastern Wisconsin, presenting programs at churches, schools, and anywhere else they could get an audience.

They sang a mixture of gospel hymns and light opera, like songs from *Naughty Marietta* and *Babes in Toyland*. Mother loved Victor Herbert, so she thought the family was wonderful.

"You know, I think our family could do something like that. We really ought to put together a program. Henry, you're so musical. I bet you could come up with something," she said repeatedly.

Mother was right, at least partially right. Dad was musical. He could play almost any instrument; he was a good singer; he directed choirs; he composed and arranged music.

Mother was a good musician, too. She would tell us how she used to play the piano for silent movies back in the opera house in her hometown. (I later discovered that the opera house was a hall over the grocery store where they showed movies on Saturday nights after the grocery store closed.) She could play almost any piece on the piano, and she had a good singing voice.

But it took more than musical parents to make a musical family. We kids were not great musicians. We struggled through piano lessons. We played in the school band. We liked music, but we just weren't particularly talented.

Then there was Phil's accordion.

This was the era of the great amateur hour radio programs. The most popular show was on Sunday night. Each week the show would travel to a different city where the program would be broadcast nationally from the stage of the biggest auditorium in the community. The best local amateur talent would perform to see if any of them could unseat the current reigning champion. And the champion who won week after week was an accordion player. Every time he won, he would receive a $1,000 grand prize. One thousand dollars—that was big money. Dad only made a little more than that all year.

Mother thought this accordion player was wonderful. Phil had a job working at the local gas station, and Mother began to convince him that he should save his earnings and buy an accordion.

"I don't know how to play an accordion," Phil protested. "And, I don't want to spend my money on one."

"Oh, you can take lessons. Think how much fun it will be. You can play all over and you can probably even earn some money doing it. It would be a lot easier than working at the gas station."

Phil continued to protest, but Mother finally wore him down and convinced him he should get an accordion. Which he did. I think it must have cost him fourteen or fifteen weeks of his earnings. So Phil took lessons. He got so he could play a couple of simple tunes, but he was never in much danger of getting on the *Horace Heidt Original Amateur Hour* radio show. Dad taught himself to play the accordion, but he probably wasn't eligible to enter the amateur hour contest. Besides, he only played hymns, and Lutheran chorales were not the type of music to excite an audience to a frenzy of applause.

But Mother was convinced there was musical talent in the family, and it was her job to uncover it. She was like Harold Hill in *The Music Man*. She knew her children could be musical geniuses if she just made them think positively about the matter.

So Mother persisted in trying to make a performing musical group out of her family. The only time we ever performed was at the Ladies Aid. The Aid was the women's group of our church. It had originally been the *Frau Verein* back when it was a German-speaking congregation, but it became the Ladies Aid when the congregation switched over to English during World War I. The ladies patriotically changed the name of their organization to the Ladies Aid, the idea being that the organization would "aid" the congregation in its work.

The Aid met the first Wednesday afternoon of the month. It was at the meeting when Mother was the program chairman that the Kurtz family made its performing debut.

There were two things which appealed to me about performing. One was that I got excused from school. The other was the prospect of the Ladies Aid lunch. To most people, the lunch wasn't all that great, but it usually had things we never had at home: Jell-O made with marshmallows and fruit cocktail, and sandwiches made with lunch meat. Our meals rarely had items which had to be purchased at the store. Most of our meals centered on vegetables Dad grew in his garden and meat which was given to us by members of the congregation. We would buy milk, flour, orange juice, oatmeal and things like that, but lunch meat and fruit cocktail were luxury items as far as our family was concerned.

So we performed. Phil played the accordion. I did a solo on the French horn. Mother accompanied Helene who performed several vocal solos, and then the family sang a couple of hymns with Dad playing the accordion. We received polite applause and were asked to stay for lunch. Our appearance was duly noted in the weekly Village newspaper, but we were not asked to appear before any other groups which was disappointing to Mother and was a great relief to the rest of the family.

Still Mother wouldn't give up. That's where Christmas caroling came in. Mother had made up her mind we were going to go caroling, and unless a blizzard roared through the Village before evening we knew we didn't have a choice.

"We've been singing carols all Christmas season, so we won't have to practice. Henry, do you think it will be too cold for you to play the accordion while we sing?"

Dad usually went along with Mother's ideas, but I could tell he didn't want to lug the accordion around the Village.

"I think it's going to get pretty cold tonight," I said, hoping that Mother would remember her fear of children coming down with pneumonia from cold weather.

"I don't know if I want to be trying to play the accordion when I'm wearing my topcoat," Dad answered.

Mother knew she had to give in on that point, so she didn't press Dad.

"How long will we have to do this? There are a couple of radio programs I have to hear," I said.

"Oh, it won't take long. We'll go to some of the shut-ins," Mother answered.

The shut-ins, I thought. Good grief, I thought, I hope not to Mrs. Schwartzbauer.

Mrs. Scwartzbauer was one of the shut-ins of our congregation. I guess every church has its shut-ins—those elderly members who rarely get out of their house because they're too old, or have something wrong with them, or they just prefer to stay at home.

Mrs. Schwartzbauer was one of those people. She claimed to be a faithful member of the congregation, but she never attended. She did manage to plant a big garden, but she could not make it to Sunday service. I just wished she would put more energy into getting to church and less effort into her garden. Her garden was a major problem in my life. She planted row after row of every vegetable I despised: rutabagas, squash, turnips—if I couldn't stand it, she raised it. And having raised it, she would call Mother and offer the vegetables to us.

Mother never refused a proffered gift from a member.

"If you turn down something, word would get around and no one would offer us anything," Mother explained to us. Since donated food formed a major portion of our meals, this was a serious matter.

So when Mrs. Scwartzbauer would call, I could hear Mother saying, "Why, our family loves parsnips. We would certainly like to have some."

As soon as I heard Mother talking like this, I would disappear as fast as I could because I knew the next part of the conversation would be: "Why certainly, he will be glad to ride his bicycle to your house and get them."

Me—I was the "he" she referred to. Eventually Mother would find me and tell me I had to go to Mrs. Scwartzbauer's and get the parsnips. Mrs.

Schwartzbauer lived on the other end of town. Maybe it was only eight blocks away, but it was also at the top of the steepest hill in town. Then when I got there, Mrs. Schwartzbauer would invite me into her house. She had a deathly fear of window peepers and had all the windows tightly covered. Even on the brightest of summer days, it felt like the middle of the night when I entered her house.

"Would you like a cookie?" she would ask. The first time I had been there, I had said, "Yes," and she proceeded to bring out a box of Fig Newtons which must have been fresh about the time the Japanese attacked Pearl Harbor. It was like trying to eat a piece of concrete.

"Oh, no," I would now respond, "Mother doesn't like us to eat between meals." (Mother made me come, so I might as well blame her for something.)

"Are you sure?" Mrs. Schwartzbauer persisted.

"Oh, definitely," I answered. "Mother's very strict about that."

"Well, I could send one home for you so you could have it after supper," she said.

"No, no, I don't think so." It was bad enough having to lug the parsnips home without having a hard, old cookie, too.

Mrs. Schwartzbauer would then start rummaging around for a sack. After finding one, we would go out to her garden where she would proceed to dig up the parsnips. She must have bushels of them, I thought. She began putting them in the sack. After she had about four of them in the bag, I began to assure her that that was a great plenty.

"Be sure to save some for yourself," I told her. Once I got them home, I knew we had to eat them. It was bad enough having them for one meal, but I certainly didn't want to have two or three meals featuring parsnips.

The sack was finally full. I took the bag, declined an invitation to stay longer, and told Mrs. Schwartzbauer that I was certain Mother appreciated the parsnips.

"Tell your mother she's welcome to more," Mrs. Schwartzbauer would call as I rode away.

So when Mother brought up singing to the shut-ins, I immediately mentioned Mrs. Schwartzbauer.

"Probably not to her." Mother said. "We'll stay closer to home and maybe go to the Reinhards, Mrs. Braatz, and Mrs. Jagnow. They're a lot closer, so we won't have to walk far."

All excuses failed. There was no dissuading Mother. We would go caroling after supper. We cleared the table and did the dishes in silence. My sister and I didn't even fight over whose turn it was to wash and whose turn it was to dry. Only Mother was cheerful.

The last dish was dried and put away, the floor was swept, and I desperately looked out the window hoping to see an unanticipated blizzard springing up.

"OK," said Mother, "let's get our coats on so we can get started."

Yeah and get it over with, I thought.

But sing we must, so we bundled up and headed out into the cold silent winter night of the Village.

"We'll start with the Reinhards," Mother announced as we started walking.

The Reinhards were an elderly brother and sister. Bertha must have been about eighty or so. She wasn't blind, but she was close to it. She took care of her brother Reuben who was a bit younger than his sister. Reuben was a nice old guy. I think he was slightly retarded, at least we always thought he was pretty simple.

Now none of us knew what had happened earlier that day and if we had, I bet even Mother would have been willing to stay home.

What had happened, as we learned later, was that in the afternoon Reuben had been outside their house, shoveling the melting ice and slush off the sidewalk. The Huehne kids came around and started picking on him.

The Huehne kids were the Village's bullies. Maybe bullies was too strong a term, but they were roughnecks and troublemakers. If you stood up to them, they usually backed down, but if not, they would make life miserable for their victims.

There were three of them. Beulah was the oldest. She was in eighth grade and she was tough. She rarely played with the other girls. Sports were more interesting to her. When the boys would choose up sides for a game of baseball or football, she was always chosen first. Beulah was good; she was tough, and she was mean.

Her two brothers were just as mean. Bub (his name was Robert, but only the teachers called him that) was in my grade. Bub was double trouble: he was mean and he was stupid. He would be sent to the principal's office at least once a week. The principal would try to get his parents to come in to talk about his behavior, but they rarely did.

The youngest was Guerdon, not Gordon he would tell everyone; it was Guerdon. No one knew where his parents had gotten that name, but then most of us didn't much care since we didn't really like Guerdon or his brother or sister. The three of them always hung around together. You never saw one or two. You always saw the three of them.

That afternoon they had found Reuben shoveling his walk, and they started teasing him. Then they started pushing snow on the walk where he had just shoveled. He told them to stop that, but they continued to push snow on the sidewalk. Then they started throwing snowballs at him. Bertha heard the commotion and came outside and began scolding them.

"You kids are nothing but troublemakers. Get out of here, or I'll call the police."

They retreated but yelled, "Watch out. We'll be back."

The Huehne kids were always making threats, but they usually didn't follow through. However, anytime something happened in the Village like a window being broken or a garbage can overturned, the Huehne kids would usually get blamed for it, but no one ever caught them.

Bertha, like most people in the Village, had had trouble with these kids before. She had had enough. She called up Wes Carley, the Village constable.

"Wesley," she told him, "you have just got to do something about the Huehne children. They practically terrorized Reuben today, and now they threatened they would come back to get us."

Wes was not a real policeman. He was the Village maintenance man. He plowed the streets in the winter, was the janitor at the Village hall, picked up the garbage and mowed the park lawn. His job as constable meant he was on duty on Saturday nights to direct traffic and take care of an occasional farm hand who had too much to drink.

"Well, Bertha, there's not a lot I can really do," he told her when she called.

"Wesley, something has to be done. We cannot let those young hoodlums pick on Reuben. Heaven knows what they might do. Maybe they will come and set fire to our house."

Wes was right. There wasn't a lot he could do. He had no patrol car, no uniform, no training. On the rare occasion when there was the need for professional police help, the Village turned to the county sheriff's department.

Wes mulled things over.

"Tell you what, Bertha. I'll talk with Leo Flannery and see what he says." Leo was the deputy sheriff assigned to the western part of the county and he lived in the Village. When police help was needed in the Village or surrounding area, Leo was the person who responded.

Later that afternoon, Wes called Bertha.

"Bertha, I talked with Leo. He's had it with those kids, too. He thinks that maybe if he gives them a good scare, they'll stop this kind of behavior. If they come around tonight, you call Leo and he'll come right over."

As we walked to the Reinhards, we were unaware of what had happened with the Huehne kids. We didn't know that Bertha was keeping a watchful eye (actually a watchful ear) for troublemakers. Like many people with a vision problem, Bertha had very sharp hearing. Even when we were some distance away, she had detected the crunching of our feet on the snow.

A short distance from the house, Dad stopped us and listed the carols we would sing.

"OK," he said quietly, "we'll start with *Joy to the World*, then we'll do *Silent Night*, and we'll end with *The First Noel*."

When Bertha heard our approach, she peered from her window. She could make out that a group of people was stopped near her house, but, with her sight problem, she couldn't determine who they were. Naturally she assumed they were the Huehne kids coming back to seek revenge.

She immediately picked up the telephone.

"Mildred," she told the operator. "Get me Leo Flannery right away. It's an emergency."

Leo had just gotten off duty and was still in his uniform.

Bertha quickly explained things, and Leo said he would be right over.

"Don't worry, Bertha," he assured her, "I am going to teach those youngsters a lesson they won't forget."

Leo had just gotten a new squad car with a big, powerful searchlight, flashing red lights, and a loud siren. He was anxious to use the new equipment.

After talking with Leo, Bertha took Reuben into the basement where she hoped they would be safe.

Blissfully unaware of what was happening, we processed to the house and climbed the steps to the porch.

"I'll knock and then we'll start singing," Mother said. She knocked and we began singing, "Joy to the World, the Lord is come ..."

Meanwhile Leo jumped into his squad car and covered the few blocks in seconds. He had the lights off, and we didn't notice the car since we were on the porch facing the house.

Just as we started singing, "And heaven and nature sing," Leo hit the siren, the flashing lights, and the searchlight; then he jumped out of the car with his pistol drawn, yelling: "OK, you kids, stay right there! This is the police!"

We kids froze, we all stopped singing, Mother screamed and Dad turned, blinking in the light.

Leo was stunned. Instead of a frightened group of Huehne kids, he had the Lutheran preacher and his family caught in the spotlight.

He quickly reached into his car, turned off the lights and the siren, and put away his revolver.

"Reverend Kurtz, I am sorry," he told Dad. He explained what had happened. We kids were disappointed that the Huehne kids hadn't been there.

"They deserve a good scare," I told my sister.

Leo knocked on the door and called, "It's OK, Bertha, come on out."

Bertha appeared, looking perplexed. She had heard the people coming up on her porch and then heard them start to sing. Now she saw her pastor and his family. She didn't know quite what to think.

"I didn't think the Huehne kids would be singing Christmas carols," she told us.

Mother decided that we were done with our caroling, and we walked back home, laughing about our adventure.

When we got back home, Mother made hot chocolate, which was a big treat for us. We recounted our caroling adventure and figured that was the end of the matter.

It wasn't.

Leo got overtime pay when he was called out after hours. To qualify he had to file a report. The time around Christmas and New Year's was one of the slowest times for local news. After Leo filed his report in the county sheriff's department, the reporter on the police beat saw it. Since there wasn't much happening on the police beat, and since the Village rarely made the news, the reporter wrote a detailed and humorous account of the big Christmas caroling police raid.

We didn't subscribe to the daily paper from the county seat, so we were totally unaware of the story. When Dad went to the post office to pick up the mail, he didn't know what the postmaster was talking about when he asked Dad if the family had been Christmas caroling lately.

When we did get a copy of the paper, we kids thought it was hilarious and felt it served Mother right. Mother was "completely mortified," to use her words. Dad chuckled about it and clipped the story to send with the next family Circle Letter.

I did point out to Mother that she had gotten her wish. We had become a famous singing family.

She was not amused.

Chapter 11

And to All a Good Night

Christmas was over. Cousin Esther and her parents had gone home. The morning after they left we all went down to the drug store to wait for the Greyhound bus which would take Grandpa Kurtz to his next destination—Aunt Elizabeth who lived in La Crosse. We waved goodbye to him as the Greyhound bus pulled out. It was quiet in the parsonage.

Then it was Epiphany. In years to come, I would know it as "Twelfth Night", but for our family it was Epiphany, the twelfth day of Christmas. Dad used to have church services on Epiphany, but it got so that hardly anyone came, so he gave it up. For us it was the time when we put away the Christmas decorations.

Earlier in the day when it was still light, we had taken down the outdoor display. Even Mother helped, instead of standing around supervising as she usually did. We removed the pine branches and put them at the side of the driveway to be picked up with the garbage the next day.

"Don't go setting these on fire," Phil laughed as we set them down.

The spotlight was put away and the *Silent Night* painting was lowered to the ground. We carried it to the garage and carefully covered it.

"We can use it next year," Dad said.

"Can we win a prize again?" asked Helene.

"I don't know if we'll be eligible for a prize with the same thing, but we can certainly put it up," Dad answered.

After supper we took down the Christmas tree, carefully wrapping the ornaments. Dad stood on a stool and gently removed the spire from the top of the tree.

"This was brought to America from Germany by my grandfather," he told us every time he put it up and took it down. "It's the only heirloom I have from him."

The candles and wreaths were removed from the windows and put away until next Christmas. All the other decorations were taken down and packed away.

Mother stood in the living room, surveying the scene.

"You know," she said, "I think you're right. This was the best Christmas in the annals of the Kurtz family."

RING THE BELL AND COUNT THE PEOPLE

Chapter 12

Mother Writes a Disclaimer

About the time World War II started, we moved from Milwaukee, Wisconsin, to the Village, a small town in eastern Wisconsin. My mother, my father, my older brother Philip, my younger sister Helene (and me) made up our family. Dad was the pastor of Emanuel Lutheran Church in the Village, and we lived in the parsonage, right next to the church building. Since the Village was a small town, we knew everyone, and everyone certainly knew us. Preachers' families tended to be in the public eye.

Anyway, World War II had been over for a few years, and life had returned to normal for most people. For some families, life would never be the same since they had a son or brother or other family member who had been killed in the War.

Inside Emanuel, the Honor Roll still hung on the side wall. It listed all the members of the congregation who had served in the War, and beside two of the names were stars, indicating they had died in the War.

But for most people, life was back to normal. Food and gas rationing were over. This meant we could buy sugar and make Kool-Aid at home. When we had a nickel, we could buy a Hershey or a Milky Way candy bar which were rarely available during the War.

Dad had even gotten a new car—a shiny grey four-door Chevrolet Stylemaster, which replaced the 1934 two-door Chevy he had driven all those years. When a busy and meaningful Christmas happened for us, I wrote down all that happened as stories and called the collection *Hardly a Silent Night*.

I hadn't really planned to write more stories after *Hardly a Silent Night*. Writing is tough work, and I certainly had enough other things to do with my time. But a lot of things had happened since last Christmas, plus I've remembered other things worth telling, so that's why you're reading this.

The family had varied reactions to the idea of more stories. My sister said there should be more things about her, since after all, she said a lot of cute things, and I wouldn't even have to make them up like I did last time. Phil said he would be just as happy if I left him out entirely. Dad just smiled and said something to the effect that if I wanted to write, I should go ahead and do it. Besides, he liked the way I talked about some of the members of the congregation.

As for Mother's reaction, she complained that I exaggerated things.

"If you're going to write more about us, I think I should have a chance to set the record straight," she intoned.

"What do you mean 'set the record straight'?" I asked.

"Well," Mother hesitated and then continued, "you know, so the members won't get upset."

Oh, the members. Mother was always worried about what the members of Emanuel might say about her or her children. (She never was concerned about what they thought about Dad. Since he was the pastor, it seemed to me that this should be her chief concern. But no, it was always what the members might think about her or her children.)

I learned long ago that it was best not to argue with Mother since I never could win an argument with her. So I told Mother that if she wanted to have her say she could write her own piece and I'd stick it in. This is what she wrote.

Mother's Disclaimer:

Before you read more of these stories, I feel there are some things you better understand. I am the author's mother, and I'm proud to have a son who writes. I haven't had a chance to read this next group of stories, but he said I would be pleased when I did.

If it's like the first set, *Hardly a Silent Night*, you'll enjoy it. But it's only fair to warn you that not everything he writes is true. Oh sure, most of the things are correct. After all, it wouldn't be right to say that he lied about things. My son wouldn't do that, especially since he's the pastor's son.

But there are some things he writes about that are not quite as I remember them, especially when he's writing about me. As he always tells the family, he never let the facts interfere with a good story.

So I think it's only fair to warn you that you shouldn't believe everything he writes, even though it sounds good. Now do you remember when he said I wanted the family to be a famous performing group? Now, I never said that (well, maybe I did once); I just thought it would be a nice thing if the family could be together and sing and play some of the songs which we do in our living room at Christmas time.

And he claimed that I was always scared my children would come down with pneumonia and that I made them wear too many clothes in winter. Well, that may be true, but if they get sick, you know who has to take care of them. He needs to listen to his mother.

I could go on and on (*author's note: she usually does*) but I won't—this time. All I want you to know is not to believe everything he writes about me. If he isn't careful, I may have to write my own book.

The Author's Mother

So with that out of the way, here are some stories about life in the Village.

Chapter 13

A Memorable April Fool's Day

I honestly can't remember where I learned about this April Fool's trick. It might have been from Bob Schultzman. Bob was the son of a neighboring pastor, a good friend of my parents. Bob was about Phil's age, maybe a year or two older. I always thought Bob was a neat guy. He was good at magic and was always able to fool people with his newest trick. I probably learned the trick from him.

Getting back to April Fool's Day—April 1 as most everyone knows. It was a day of minor annoyance for teachers as students would try to trick fellow students, or the more daring students would even try to trick the teacher; although most teachers had long ago learned what students were up to on April 1.

I had learned this trick a while back but would forget about it until it was too late to do it on April 1. This year I remembered.

It was a simple enough, but it took a little advanced planning and, in my case, it also involved cooperation from Mother. This could pose a problem. While Mother had a good sense of humor, she was always worried about the conduct of her children and how it would reflect on her. And what would members of the church think!

Here's how it worked and why I needed Mother's help. You took a spool of white thread. After threading a needle, you ran the thread up the sleeve of your shirt—it had to be a dark-colored shirt—and then poked the needle and thread through the back of the shirt. You detached the needle and left a short piece of thread on the back of the shirt. You then put the spool of thread in your pants pocket and waited for someone to say, "Oh, you have a thread on your shirt."

The person would invariably reach over to pluck it off. Of course, since it was attached to the spool of thread, it could not be lifted off, so the helpful person would give it a tug only to find that the thread grew longer.

My plan was to do this at school. In my classroom I sat in front of Ann. Ann was a meticulous girl and seeing that piece of thread on my back ... I was positive she would reach over and pick it off.

At supper the night before April 1, I broached the subject and asked Mother if she would help.

"Where did you get that idea?" my sister wanted to know. I told her I didn't remember. I think my brother Phil would have liked to do this too, but since it was my idea, he never would admit to wanting to do it.

Thankfully Mother smiled and agreed to help. "I've got a dozen spools of white thread which I hardly use." (Mother was not big on sewing.)

The next morning Mother and I set it up. Fortunately April 1 was a cool morning and I could wear a sweater without being conspicuous. As class was getting ready to start, I took off my sweater and slid into my seat. A minute later Ann sat down, took out her book and looked to the front of the room as Mr. Franklin stepped to the blackboard.

At that minute, Ann noticed the thread on the back of my shirt and surreptitiously reached to remove it. When she couldn't pick it off, she tugged at it. I pretended to be oblivious to what was happening, but put my hand in the pocket where the spool was, to be sure the thread didn't get tangled. Ann gave the thread another pull and the thread in her hand got longer. Shirley, who sat next to Ann, noticed what was going on and started to giggle, causing others to look. Meanwhile I sat looking at my textbook, paying no attention to what was going on behind me. Out of the corner of my eye I could see the thread getting longer and longer. I could sense Ann didn't know what to do. Should she stop and let all the thread hang out? Should she say something to me?

Meanwhile the giggles started turning into laughter, getting Mr. Franklin's attention.

"All right," he demanded, "what's going on?"

The room got silent. Then someone pointed to Ann who was sitting there with several feet of white thread in her hand.

Mr. Franklin strolled over, looked at the thread, at Ann, and then at me.

"OK," he said, "does someone care to explain what's going on?"

"Well," Ann began, "I noticed there was a thread on the back of his shirt and when I went to pick it off, this happened."

I didn't want to get Ann in trouble, so I burst out: "April Fool!"

"I might have known you were the guilty party," Mr. Franklin said with a smile. "Want to tell us how you did that?"

I pulled the spool out of my pocket, broke off the thread and gathered up the streamer of white thread. I then explained how it worked amid loud laughter from the class.

"Pretty ingenious," Mr. Franklin said. "If it weren't April Fool's Day, you would have gotten a couple pages of dictionary."

Copying pages from the dictionary was Mr. Franklin's standard punishment for misbehaving. I had gotten a few of those in the past, and my brother teased me about it incessantly, but I had learned many new words that way (such as "incessantly").

"All right," Mr. Franklin said, "let's get started on arithmetic. And," turning to me, "no more April Fools."

That night at supper, I reported to the family about the thread escapade.

"Did you get in trouble?" my sister wanted to know.

"No," I answered, "Mr. Franklin thought it was funny, but he did warn me not to do any more April Fool's tricks."

As we were eating, Mother mentioned that she and Dad would be at church that evening for the meeting of the Christian Fellowship. The Christian Fellowship was the congregation's adult social group.

Helene burst in. "I've got an idea. Why doesn't Daddy do this at the meeting?"

"Do what?" Phil asked.

"Put the thread on his back."

"Oh," Mother immediately said, "he couldn't do that. How would it look?"

Dad smiled. "I think it might be kind of funny. The Fellowship meetings can get a little dull. This would liven things up a bit."

Mother paused, trying to decide if she should continue to object.

I broke in. "Why not, there's a lot of white thread left."

Anyway, here's what happened. Dad got a spool of white thread, had Mother run the thread up the sleeve of the coat and out the back, leaving a one-inch piece of thread showing on his black suit coat.

Dad put the spool of thread in his pocket, and he and Mother departed for the Christian Fellowship meeting. Dad started talking to someone, probably Herb Schmuhl, the organization's president, and had his back turned to the wall so others who were gathering for the meeting wouldn't notice.

Just before the meeting was getting ready to start, he casually turned so his coat could be seen by a group of women who had been standing nearby chatting. The piece of white thread was very noticeable on his black coat.

Now there's not a Lutheran lady anywhere in Christendom who, seeing a white thread on the back of the pastor's coat, would not immediately feel compelled to remove such an imperfection. I think it was probably Verna Pretzlaff who first noticed and went over to pick it off, not even saying, "Excuse me, Pastor." Dad continued talking, trying to be oblivious to what was going on. Verna picked up the thread but it wouldn't come off. So she pulled it a bit. Dad meanwhile was controlling the spool in his pocket. More thread.

Well, once you start a job, you had to finish it, Verna decided, so she pulled again. More thread. She was faced with a dilemma. If she stopped, a much longer thread would be hanging on the back of the coat. She looked around to see if Mother was there to give guidance. Mother had gone to the kitchen to keep out of sight, most likely to keep from bursting into laughter. So Verna tugged again. More thread. Dad continued talking. Other women watched, some in slight horror. Others were silently giving prayers of thanks that they hadn't been the one to pick off the thread. Poor Verna didn't know what to do. Finally Dad turned around. There stood a very embarrassed Verna, her hands filled with white thread. Dad smiled and said, "April Fool!" and the church basement exploded in laughter. Verna still looked perplexed, but also relieved. Dad revealed the prank and told Verna he hoped she wasn't TOO angry.

At supper the next night, Dad related the whole story. Mother said she apologized to Verna, but said Verna ended up thinking it was kind of funny.

"Next year I'm going to do it at school," Helene announced.

Chapter 14

Those Cute Little Shelves

Bobby Draeger was one of my best friends, but one summer he certainly caused me a major problem. It really wasn't his fault. It was Mother who was the source of trouble. Bobby was an innocent bystander.

I guess I had better explain things. Bobby's dad was the Lutheran pastor in Rosendale, a neighboring town to the Village. Pastor Draeger and his wife were good friends of my parents. Our family and the Draegers would often visit each other.

That's how Bobby and I got to be friends. We would be together when our families visited. Sometimes he would come and stay with me for a few days, or I would visit him, doing various things together with his friend Don. One summer the three of us were in the same cabin at Bible Camp.

Once when our family was visiting the Draegers, Mother noticed that Mrs. Draeger had some new little shelves in her kitchen. Mother admired them and asked Mrs. Draeger where she had gotten them.

"Oh," said Mrs. Draeger, "Bobby made them."

Mother was astonished. "Bobby made them? They really are nice."

Mother was Norwegian, and I always felt there was something genetic about Norwegians and how they admired people who worked with wood. Mother's father was an excellent carpenter, and many of her family were skilled woodworkers.

Mother didn't feel that Dad would ever do much in woodworking. After all, he was German, and Mother felt that Germans weren't as good as Norwegians when it came to woodworking. However, Mother did feel that given the right circumstances, one of her sons could probably become an accomplished woodworker. They were half Norwegian, she reasoned.

Mrs. Draeger explained that Bobby had saved his money and had purchased a small jig saw from Sears Roebuck.

"He didn't even need a pattern for the shelves," Mrs. Draeger told Mother. "He just figured it out."

As we drove back to the Village from our visit, Mother told us all about how Bobby had made these cute shelves with his new saw.

"And he's not even Norwegian," she exclaimed.

I didn't pay much attention. If Bobby wanted to make shelves for his mother, good for him, I thought. It wasn't anything which interested me.

A few days later at the supper table, Mother brought up the subject of the shelves.

"You know," she said to me, "I bet you could make some nice things if you just had a saw like Bobby's."

I pointed out that I didn't have a saw, I didn't have any money to buy one, and in addition, I wasn't interested. I tried to change the subject.

"Besides, if you want some shelves, have Grandpa Olson make them for you," I told her.

Grandpa Olson was Mother's dad. He was a good carpenter. He made a lot of things for us.

"Well," Mother replied, "I don't know if he will be coming to visit us. Besides, he would need that type of saw to make the shelves."

Mother dropped the subject. However, a couple of weeks later she brought up the saw again.

"We just got the new Sears Roebuck catalog," she announced. "The saw like Bobby Draeger has is on sale."

"How do you know what kind of saw he has?" I asked.

"Mrs. Draeger showed it to me," Mother answered. "He paid $29.95 for his, and now it's on sale for $19.95."

I did not like the way the conversation was heading. I thought back to a year or so ago when Mother had coerced Phil into buying an accordion. It cost Phil many weeks of pay from his job at the filling station, and now the accordion just sat in the closet.

Usually I could get Mother distracted by picking a fight with my brother, but he wasn't home for supper this evening; he was off working at his job.

"But I don't have $19.95. Plus there's the mailing cost too," I protested.

Mother paused. She knew I didn't have the money. I made a little money mowing lawns during the summer, but that wasn't very much. I got 50 cents for one lawn and 75 cents for the other one.

"And even if I didn't spend anything, it would take four months to save that much and lawns won't need mowing that long," I pointed out to Mother.

Mother thought for a moment.

"Don't forget the money you make selling night crawlers," she countered.

She was right. The highway through the Village led to a number of good fishing lakes. I had developed a little business selling night crawlers—the large worms which came out at night after rains. Fishermen liked to use them for bait.

"But I only get 25 cents a dozen, and I never know if I will sell any or not, and if it gets dry, there won't be any to sell," I told her.

Supper was over. We had our devotions. My sister and I cleared the table and helped with the dishes. Mother dropped the subject.

I was worried. I knew how persistent Mother was. I thought back to how she got Phil to buy an accordion. He took lessons, but he soon lost interest, and the accordion sat in the closet except when Dad played it.

Dad could do a lot of things, I thought. I remembered the time he had done a painting of the *Silent Night* Christmas carol, and we had won the prize in the decorating contest. Or the time he had surprised Mother by making a pottery vase.

A few days later Mother brought up the subject again while we were having supper.

"You know," she said, "that sale only runs for three weeks more. It sure would be great if you could get that saw and make some nice little shelves."

"Even if I did have the money for the saw, I would need money for wood for the shelves," I told her.

"No, you wouldn't," Phil interjected. "We have all the wooden boxes."

I glared at Phil. He was no help at all. He was right: we did have all those wooden boxes which could be taken apart and used for wood. We had gotten a whole truckload of wooden packing boxes when Cousin George was working at the canning factory in the Village.

Getting back to the discussion with Mother.

"Yes," replied Mother, "there is plenty of wood. You could make all sorts of shelves and other things if you had that nice saw."

"But where would I get $20?" I asked. "Besides, there's the cost of postage too."

"Well, if you order it, we'll pay the shipping," Mother promised.

"OK," I said, "if by some miracle I can come up with $20 before the sale ends, I'll buy the saw."

I figured I was safe. There was no way I would come up with $20 in the next two weeks. It had been real dry for the past several weeks which meant that the lawns I usually mowed weren't growing, and it also meant that there were no night crawlers to hunt since they only came out after it rained. Besides, once the sale ended, maybe Mother would forget about the shelves and the saw.

Wouldn't you know. The next day it started to rain, and it rained all day, all night, and the next morning. By noon it had stopped, and the weather began to clear.

I was looking out the window when I saw a pickup truck pull into the driveway. I didn't recognize the truck.

A man got out of the truck and came to the door. I opened the door, and the man said, "I saw your sign on the highway. Got any night crawlers?"

"No," I answered, "it's been too dry. But I'll have some tomorrow."

"My name is Bud Norton. I have a guide service at Green Lake. I have a big group coming from Chicago this weekend. I'm out of bait and my regular supplier can't help me. I'm going to be coming back this way about 12 tonight. Do you think you could have 1,000 night crawlers by then?"

A thousand night crawlers, I thought. Most people only bought a dozen or two.

"If you can," he continued, "I'll give you $20."

Twenty dollars! That's about as much as I made in the whole summer mowing lawns.

I was so stunned by the offer that I said, "Yes, I think I can have that many night crawlers by midnight," and forgot that I had promised Mother I would order the saw if somehow I would get $20.

"OK," replied Bud, "see you about midnight."

I closed the door What had I gotten myself into? How could I ever collect that many night crawlers in one evening.

Then it hit me. If I did get that many night crawlers I would have to buy the saw. But if I didn't try ... well, I had given my word to the man, so I had to do my best.

Mother was talking to Dad in his study. I interrupted them as I walked in.

"I've got a big problem," I told them.

I explained the situation.

"We can all help," Mother replied. "Dad and I can go out. Phil isn't working tonight, and I'm sure he will help if I ask him."

That evening we gathered around the kitchen table. I outlined how we would do things.

"Mother and Helene can stay around here. You can make a circuit of the gardens in our block and the next. Then repeat the route about every 15-20 minutes," I said.

I had permission from the neighbors to hunt night crawlers in their gardens. All they asked is that I go along the edges and not step on any plants.

"Phil, why don't you take the athletic field. That's usually a good place to hunt," I continued. "And, Dad, maybe you could do the park. I'll get the lawns and gardens on the other side of the church. When your cans get full, bring them back and dump them in the containers in back."

Catching night crawlers is not all that easy. You had to bend over and be quick. Although they supposedly couldn't see the light from your flashlight, they could sense when someone was near. They would come out at night to dry off after a rain but would lie with their tail in the hole. You had to make a quick grab at the tail end and be careful not to pull too hard or it would break.

So off we went. Since it didn't get dark in the summer until late, we did not have a long time to hunt. But with four of us—five if you counted my sister—we should be able to do it, I thought.

Mother and Helene quit early since it was past Helene's bedtime. Dad, Phil and I kept working. It was about 11:30 when we headed home.

What an amazing sight—the large, stone crocks where I kept the night crawlers looked like a scene from a jungle film. Now I had a real job—counting them.

Around midnight I triumphantly announced, "We did it. There are 1,020 of them."

Dad, Phil and I went and sat on the front steps, waiting for Bud to appear. It was soon 12:15. No sign of him.

"What if he doesn't come?" Phil asked.

"I'm sure he will. He gave me his name and what he did," I replied. But, I thought, what if he didn't come. What would I do with all those night crawlers? That was more than I sold the entire summer.

Twelve-thirty came.

Phil yawned and said, "I think I'll go to bed."

Dad and I continued to sit on the steps.

Fifteen minutes went by. I began to worry.

"What if he doesn't come?" I asked Dad.

Before he could answer, we saw headlights and the truck pulled up in front of the house. There was Bud.

"Sorry I'm late. I had a flat tire. How did you do?" he asked.

"We have 1,020 of them for you," I replied.

"Great. I'll get my bait container from the truck."

We went to the back of the house where he filled the container and then carried it to the truck.

"Here's your $20," he said, handing me two ten dollar bills. "And thanks for your hard work. I may need to contact you again."

"Thank you," I told him. "I had a lot of help from my family."

Bud smiled and got into his truck. He waved as he pulled away.

"Well," Dad said, "I think it's bedtime. It's been quite a night."

I slept late the next morning. When I got up, I checked my billfold—the $20 was still there. It was the most money I had ever had.

Then I remembered. I had promised Mother I would buy the saw.

Darn, I thought. Why in the world had I ever promised to do that? I never in the world thought I would earn $20.

But I had given my word. Well, maybe it would be neat to have that saw. I might be able to do all sorts of things with it.

So we ordered the saw and in due course when I stopped at the post office to get our mail, there was a red parcel slip in our box.

I went to the window and handed the slip to Cap Regel, the postmaster.

"This is pretty heavy," he said. "Think you can manage it, or should you have your dad come with the car?"

"I think I can handle it," I answered. "It's not that far."

It was only two and a half blocks home, but I had to stop and rest several times, especially walking up the hill.

"Well, it came," I announced as I entered the kitchen. Mother and Helene gathered around as I placed the box on the table.

I opened the box and there it stood: a Sears Roebuck Craftsman Magnetic Jig Saw.

As I read the instructions, I found that it was not like the jig saw Uncle Alfred had where the blade moved up and down, cutting the wood. This saw had a motor which made the blade vibrate. The vibrations caused the saw to cut the wood.

"It doesn't look too difficult," I said, as I finished reading the instructions.

"You be careful. Don't go cutting your fingers off," Mother warned.

Now she tells me, I thought. Whose idea was this anyway?

I took the saw out to the barn. I got the hammer and dismantled several wooden boxes. I started practicing on some of the smaller boards. It was hard cutting in a straight line. I ruined a lot of boards trying to get some straight cuts. I got some cuts which were fairly straight, but when I tried nailing them together, the wood split. I continued trying, but did not fare any better.

I cleaned the saw, put it back in its box and brought it into the house. Where should I put it? The perfect place, in the closet right next to Phil's accordion.

I reported to Mother that thus far I had been totally unsuccessful in building little shelves for her.

"The next time we visit the Draegers, you can get Bobby to show you how to do things," Mother said encouragingly. I nodded and left the room.

A few nights later at the supper table, a different topic came up.

"Uncle Carl and Aunt Esther would like to get away for a few days," Mother said. "They wondered if I would be willing to come and stay with Dad while they and the kids are away."

When Mother said "Dad", she was referring to her father, our Grandfather Olson. Grandpa Olson lived with Mother's brother Carl and his family in a small town in southwestern Wisconsin.

"Can we come too?" Helene asked.

We all enjoyed being with Grandpa Olson. He was always glad to see his grandchildren and liked playing games with them, any kind of games, especially checkers. Phil had noted, however, since he had gotten so he could regularly beat him in checkers, Grandpa was less interested in the game. But he was still willing to play most other games we would suggest.

"If Phil can get off work, I thought he could drive the car there. Do you think you can get some time off?" Mother asked Phil.

"I probably can. Some of the guys who used to work at the station are home from college, and one of them would probably work for a few days. I'll check and see," Phil answered.

Everything went as planned. We had a good time visiting Grandpa Olson and seeing other relatives in Avoca. We had a lot of fun playing games with Grandpa. He and Phil went fishing a couple of times. My Uncle Alfred Olson was a rural mail carrier, and I rode along on his mail route.

Uncle Carl and Aunt Esther and their children returned from their trip. They thanked Mother for coming. We loaded the car and began the drive home.

"I wonder if Dad has done anything special while we were gone," Phil said as we rode along.

"He usually does while we're away," Mother said.

"Remember the time he made the vase?" I asked.

"And when he did the painting?" Phil recalled.

We all nodded. Several other incidents were mentioned.

"Have you noticed that Dad hardly ever does anything more than once?" Phil asked.

"I don't know why that is," Mother answered. "He'll do something. It will turn out fine and then he won't do it again. It always seems he does these things when we're away, and he gets bored."

We continued to ride through the Wisconsin countryside. It was late afternoon when we arrived home.

Dad came out to meet us.

"It's great having you back," he told us. "I was pretty lonely without you."

We unpacked the car and went into the house.

Mother stopped in the kitchen.

"Where did those come from?" she asked.

Dad smiled.

"Where did what come from?" Helene wanted to know.

"There," Mother said, pointing to the counter by the sink. On either side of the sink stood small, white shelves just like the ones Bobby Draeger had made.

"For heaven's sakes, Henry," Mother exclaimed. "Did you make those?"

Dad nodded modestly. "I thought I would try using Harold's saw. I guess I have a little more woodworking talent than I thought."

We all laughed because Dad was not very handy when it came to working with tools.

We crowded round, looking at them.

"Why, Henry, they're wonderful," Mother sad. "They're just what I wanted."

"See," she told me, "I told you that saw would be just the thing for making those little shelves."

I agreed. I figured I was now off the hook and wouldn't have to worry about using the saw any more.

Too bad I had to waste twenty dollars buying it.

A few days later, Mother brought up the subject of the shelves as we were eating supper.

"You know, " she said to me, "now that Dad has made those shelves, you could use them as a pattern and make some more of them. Dad would be glad to help you."

"You've got your shelves. Besides, even if I could build them, what would I do with them?" I responded.

"Why, you could sell them," Mother persisted.

"Where would I sell them?" I wanted to know.

Phil cut in "You could sell them at the tent sale."

"Tent sale? Can we buy one?" Helene asked.

"Buy what?" Dad asked.

"A tent," Helene replied. "It would be a fun to have a tent. We could put it up in the backyard, and my friends and I could play in it. We could even have a sleep over in it."

"It's not a sale of tents," Phil told her. "The merchants in town are going to sponsor a sale in a big tent."

Phil explained that he had heard at work that the business association in the Village was going to sponsor a sale where people could bring items to sell.

"The merchants thought it would be a good way to get people to come to the Village, and then while they are here for the sale, they would probably shop in the stores," Phil said. "There's going to be a section where kids can bring things to sell."

Great, I thought, now Mother will really be after me to make those shelves.

Later that week I picked up information which told about the sale. For 50 cents, kids could have a place at a table where they could sell things. Adults had to pay two dollars.

Then the idea struck me. It would be worth 50 cents, I thought. If it works out, it would be worth a lot more than 50 cents.

After I got paid for mowing Mrs. Grindemann's lawn, I took 50 cents and went down to the store and reserved a place for the sale. I did not tell anyone else what I had done.

Mother had her shelves, and as far as I was concerned, there was no need to keep the saw. I would try to sell it at the tent sale. It was mine, after all.

The day before the tent sale, I took the saw out of the box and carefully cleaned it, removing the sawdust from when Dad had made the shelves. I then got the current Sears Roebuck catalog and cut out the picture, description and price of the saw. I pasted it on a sheet of paper. Then using a black crayon, I carefully printed:

HARDLY USED
CURRENT CATALOG PRICE: $29.95 (plus shipping)
SPECIAL SALES PRICE: $25.00

I pasted the sheet on a piece of cardboard and then made an easel out of another piece of cardboard, so it would stand up. I was all set for the sale.

The instructions said that the sale would run from 10:00 in the morning until 4:00 in the afternoon and that sellers should be there by 9:30. When I arrived at the tent, a large crowd was milling around, waiting for the sale to start. I showed my reservation slip and was directed to the kids' section.

I saw a lot of my friends there, getting set up.

My friend Norm was busy unpacking several boxes of toys.

"Is there space at the table, Norm?" I asked.

"Sure," he replied. "Help yourself."

I unpacked the saw, placed it on the table and set up the easel. I was ready.

"Where did you get all these?" I said to Norm.

"They're my old toys plus some from my sister. Mom said I should see if I can sell them, to get rid of some of the clutter around the house. Where did you get that?" he asked, pointing to my saw.

"Oh, my mother thought it would be a good thing for me to have, so I could make things, but I decided I wasn't all that interested in woodworking," I told him.

I glanced around. Everything you could think of was for sale. Some of the farm kids were selling berries and vegetables. One girl had a big assortment of doll clothes. My friend Arlyn had a display of stamps.

"They're all duplicates, so I thought I would see if I could sell them," he informed me when I stopped by his table.

I was going to look at some of the other tables, when Mr. Crosley, the banker who was in charge of the sale, made an announcement.

"All right, everyone. I hope you're all set. We're going to let people in now, so everyone should get to their tables. If you have any questions or problems, see me or one of the committee members.

"OK," boomed Mr. Crosley through his microphone, "the sale is now open."

A swarm of people came through the entrance. A steady stream of people came by our table. Many kids stopped at Norm's table, and I could see he was selling a lot of things.

"Mom said the secret is not to price things too high. She said it was better to sell the things than to lug them home and that people are really looking for bargains," he told me during a lull in business.

Hmm, I thought, I wonder if my price is too high. A few people had stopped and looked at my saw, but no one asked about it.

I glanced over at Arlyn's table.

"Any business?" I called to him.

"Sold a few. I don't think there are many stamp collectors here," he answered.

"I think we should be selling toys. Norm seems to be doing pretty well," I told him.

I continued to sit at the table, but no one seemed interested.

"You're not getting any business," Norm said, "Maybe you ought to try something different, like holding a raffle."

"What do you mean by a raffle?" I asked.

"People buy a chance for a big item, but the chance doesn't cost very much. That way they may end up with a big prize for just a little money," Norm explained.

I pondered this information.

"Isn't that gambling?" I wondered.

"No, not really. Our church does it all the time at its festivals," Norm said. "Tell you what. If you watch my table, I'll run home for some lunch and then bring back some blank raffle chances. I know we have a bunch of them left over from the last church festival."

Norm returned, and I walked home for lunch.

I quickly ate a sandwich, got a piece of cardboard, a black crayon, and made a sign. I carried it back to the sale and set it by the saw.

WIN
A $29 JIG SAW
50¢ FOR A CHANCE

People began stopping by.

"The drawing will be at 4:00, at the end of the sale. You don't have to be here to win," I told people.

I started selling chances, having people fill out the forms Norm had brought.

"Put your name and phone number on the entry form," I told people. I took one of Norm's empty boxes and put the entry forms into it.

By 2:30 I had more than 30 entries, and people continued to stop and buy chances. I lost count, but by 4:00 I knew I would come out ahead.

At 4:00, I announced to those standing around, "Last chance." I sold two more and then announced that the raffle was closed.

I put all the entry forms in the box, stirred them up and asked a little girl who was standing there to select a name. She pulled out an entry form and handed it to me.

"The winner is Donald Lathrop," I announced.

"Mr. Lathrop," Norm exclaimed, "the industrial arts teacher at school."

I looked around and saw Mr. Lathrop coming forward.

"This is great, he said, "I have been wanting one of these for beginning wood working, but we never had the funds to buy it."

The crowd applauded as I handed Mr. Lathrop the saw and the packing box. I put the money in my pocket and then helped Norm pack up the toys he hadn't sold.

"That was a marvelous idea you had," I told Norm as we left.

When I got home, I counted the money. I had taken in twenty-eight dollars which meant I had made a profit. But the best thing was that I wouldn't have Mother bugging me to build more little shelves.

Chapter 15

Why There Was No Sunday Sermon

People in Waupun still talk about the Sunday morning when traffic in the city was gridlocked. Members of Emanuel thought it was a minor inconvenience, but it ended up making most church goers in Waupun late for Sunday services.

I better explain what happened.

It all started one evening last winter. We had just finished saying our table prayer at supper when Dad began.

"I sure got a surprise at the church council meeting last night," Dad reported.

"Did you get a raise?" Phil asked.

"No," Dad chuckled, "nothing that good."

"What was the surprise then?" Helene wanted to know. Helene liked surprises.

"Well," Dad began, "Matt Schielmann has an idea for the church picnic, which sounds like it could be a lot of fun."

Matt was a new member of Emanuel. He and his wife Rose had moved to the Village from Milwaukee when he retired from the Milwaukee Police Department.

"How come you decided to move to the Village?" Dad asked when they joined the congregation.

"Well, Rose's family originally settled here when they first came from Germany, and although she never lived here, she always thought of it as home," Matt answered.

"My grandparents are buried here, and we used to visit their graves," Rose explained. "The Village always seemed nice and peaceful."

"And that is what appealed to me," Matt added. "After 30 years on the Milwaukee Police Force, I was really looking forward to peace and quiet."

"I just hope it isn't too quiet for you," Dad laughed, mentioning that he and the family had also moved to the Village from Milwaukee. "But you will find it peaceful."

Matt and Rose became active in the Village. Matt joined the volunteer fire department and the sheriff's auxiliary. Rose was soon active in the Thursday Women's Club and the Music Club.

At the annual meeting of the congregation, Matt was elected to the church council.

"That is something," Dad noted. "Usually it's the same group on the council."

Now about the church picnic. Next to the Christmas Eve program, the church picnic was the other event that kids in the congregation looked forward to with great expectation.

The picnic was held at the county park, located just outside of Waupun, about ten miles from the Village. Waupun was a city of some 6,000 residents.

The church picnic took place at the conclusion of Vacation Bible School. Bible school was held the first three weeks after school let out. Each morning, the children of the congregation would gather in the church basement. They would memorize hymns and Bible verses and work on craft projects.

"Matt thinks it would be fun to have a parade of cars from the church to the picnic. He said they did that at his congregation in Milwaukee," Dad explained. "He said he thinks we could get a police escort since he's a volunteer with the sheriff's department."

"What did the council think of the idea?" Mother asked.

"They felt that if Matt was willing to do the work, and it wouldn't cost any money, it was OK with them," Dad answered.

At the next council meeting, Matt reported that he had talked with Leo Flannery, the sheriff's deputy who lived in the Village.

"Leo said he would be glad to do it," Dad later told us. "He said he could lead the procession and still get back to the Village for 10:00 a.m. mass." Leo and his family were faithful members of the Village Catholic church.

A couple weeks later at supper, Dad brought us up to date on plans for the church picnic.

"I'll tell you Matt is getting everybody excited about the picnic. He met with the Sunday School teachers the other night, and they're going to go all out to be sure there are games for all the kids.

"He is really getting people enthusiastic about the picnic. Now he thinks we ought to have a band for the service. I told him I thought there were enough musicians in the congregation that we could have a good band. I know the church used to have a band. There's a whole bunch of band music in the storage closet. Would you be willing to play?" he asked Phil and me.

"Sure," we said, "it sounds like fun."

Soon about a dozen of us were practicing every week. Some of us were in the school band, but there were other members of the congregation who also played.

"I haven't played the clarinet since I graduated from high school," Herb Schmuhl told us, "so don't get upset if I come up with a few squeaks."

"And I haven't played my trumpet since high school either," said Fritz Freimark, "and I graduated a few years before you did."

"Don't worry," Dad said to them at the first practice. Dad was directing the band. "You'll do just fine."

Dad told us that we would play for the outdoor church service, accompanying the hymns and playing the prelude and postlude. "And let me dig through the music. Maybe we can find some old pieces to play in the afternoon."

The church picnic would begin with an outdoor service in the park band shell. This would be followed by a potluck dinner and then an afternoon of games.

School ended, Bible School started. The three weeks flew by, and it was time for the church picnic.

The Sunday of the picnic came—a beautiful sunny day.

"You couldn't ask for better weather," said Mother at the breakfast table. She had gotten up early to be sure we were all ready for the picnic.

The congregation members had been instructed to come to the church for the parade to the park. There was a little grumbling from some of the members who lived east of the Village on the way to Waupun.

"Seems like a waste of time to come to the church and then drive back past our house," Fred Hammerschmidt complained.

"Oh, Fritz, it's no big deal," his wife chided him. "Besides, the children want to be part of the parade."

Matt was out by the church before anyone else was there. Dad went to talk with him.

"Look what I have, Reverend," he said. There was a box of small American flags which could be attached to the car windows.

"I got a good deal on these at the Army surplus store in Fond du Lac," he told Dad. "This will be Rose's and my contribution to the picnic."

Matt explained the organization to Dad.

"Leo will lead the parade. You will follow Leo, then Charlie Rhindflesch, the congregation president, and then the rest of the congregation will follow.

Why don't you get your car out and park it in front of the church? I'll place people as they come. Leo gave me a police light for my car, and I'll be at the end so anyone behind us will know there is a reason for the long procession."

Dad backed our Chevy out of the barn behind the parsonage and pulled in front of the church.

"Park right here, Reverend," he told Dad. "I'll start lining up the people when they come. Let's put a flag on your window."

Cars began pulling up to the church and Matt was busy lining them up.

"Here," he told me, "why don't you give flags to everyone."

I began handing out the flags, showing people how to fasten them on their side windows.

The line of cars grew longer.

"Well, the Gruemanns just arrived," said Charlie. "If they're here, everyone is here."

The Gruemann family was notorious in the congregation for being late for everything.

"I don't know what it is with those people," Dad would fume. If you start something at 7:00, they'll arrive at 7:15. If you move the time to 7:30, they'll come at 7:45."

"Relax, Henry," Mother would say, "it's their problem, not yours."

Matt had pulled his car in back of the Gruemann's and then walked to the front of the line.

"I wonder where Leo is. He should be here by now," he said to Dad,

"It's not like him to be late," Dad agreed.

Just then, Fred Conrad, our neighbor who lived across the street, came out of his house and walked up to Dad.

"Leo just called me," he told Dad. "He tried calling you, but figured you probably would be outside, so he called me and asked me to tell you that he's been called to an emergency over on the other side of Ripon. He radioed the sheriff's department and asked them to send a deputy over. He should be here shortly."

Most of the drivers were standing beside their cars. Dad went to Charlie, told him the news and asked him to relay the message to the drivers behind him.

Matt meanwhile was trying to be reassuring to Dad. "He should be here any minute," Matt said. Matt didn't let on that he was worried. The procession had all been his idea, and now this had to happen.

In a few minutes, a sheriff's squad car pulled up and a uniformed deputy got out.

"Sorry to be late," he said to Dad and Matt. "I'm just not acquainted with the western end of the county. I usually patrol over on the east side. I'm Deputy O'Gara."

Dad and Matt introduced themselves.

"You're with the auxiliary, aren't you," he said to Matt. "You got a red light on your car?"

Matt nodded.

"OK," he said to Dad, "you pull up and park on the highway with the red light flashing and I'll lead the cars. We're heading for the Waupun park, right?"

Dad said yes as he got in the car.

Phil was driving and Dad sat in the passenger side. Mother, Helene and I were in the back seat.

"All right, let's go," called the deputy.

"Now, Phil, you be careful and don't run into the police car," Mother called from the back. I could see Phil scowl as he replied, "Yes, Mother. I'll be careful."

The cars turned right onto the state highway following the squad car.

"Do you suppose he'll blow his siren?" Helene asked.

"I doubt it," Dad answered. "There's no need for that. Look back and see the big line of cars."

We looked back and saw a long line of cars, American flags flying briskly.

"I can't even see Mr. Schielmann's car," I said.

"He must be there," Phil said.

We were soon nearing the entrance to the county park.

"He's not turning into the park," Phil exclaimed as the squad car kept going straight past the entrance pillars on the road to the park.

"Just keep going. He may be going to use the back entrance to the park," Dad said.

Dad looked back. All the cars were following; none had turned into the park. Good Germans, Dad told us, they just follow the leader.

When the back entrance to the park came up, Phil slowed down, expecting the deputy to turn. But he just kept going straight.

"Blow the horn at him, Phil," Dad said, "let's get his attention, so we can get turned around."

Phil began beeping the horn just as the cars entered the city of Waupun. Charlie in the car behind ours couldn't figure out why we hadn't turned into the park or why the pastor's car was beeping its horn.

"Maybe we're supposed to have a little parade or something," said Charlie to his wife. "Well, I suppose I may as well beep my horn too."

The driver behind him heard Charlie and the pastor sounding their horns, so he began beeping as well. The rest of the drivers joined in. As the long column of cars drove down Waupun's Main Street, all the cars were beeping their horns.

There weren't a lot of people on Waupun's Main Street at that hour of Sunday morning. But those who were there stopped and stared as they saw the parade of beeping cars, American flags flying, and red lights flashing on the deputy's squad car.

"What in the world is going on?" Dad wondered. "Phil, stop at the stop light and let me out I'll run up and talk with Deputy O'Gara."

At the stoplight, Dad got out and ran to the deputy's car.

"Where are you taking us?" he asked.

"You're going to the Waupun City Park, aren't you?" Deputy O'Gara replied

"No, we're going to the county park," Dad told him.

"Oh," he answered, "we went by that, didn't we?"

Dad nodded.

"OK, no problem. We'll just take a left at the next light, go around the block and head back to the entrance."

Dad walked back to the car. The horns had stopped by this time and members were sitting in their cars, wondering what was happening.

Dad motioned for the cars to follow him and the squad car. That should have been the end of things except ... well, except that the next light was the north-south state highway and there, stopping traffic, was a National Guard military police jeep.

"Now what?" asked Mother.

"I read in the paper that the Wisconsin National Guard is traveling to Camp McCoy today for its annual training," Phil said. "We must have hit one of the convoys."

"Guess all we can do is wait," Dad said. "I'll skip the sermon today, and we'll just have the children's portion of the service."

We sat and waited. What we didn't know was that behind us, the early service at Immanuel Lutheran Church had just gotten out, and people were trying to turn on to Main Street from the church parking lot. However, they couldn't turn because our members' cars were blocking the street.

Meanwhile, the early mass at St. Joseph's had let out. Half their members were trying to turn on to the north-south state highway, but couldn't because it was blocked with the National Guard convoy. The other half were trying to get on the east-west highway, but couldn't because it was filled with the cars from our church, and cars heading for the 9:30 a.m. service at the First

Reformed Church ... plus the normal traffic on the state highway. Then cars began arriving trying to get to the Methodist church for their service. Every driver seemed to want to go a different direction, but not one could move. Total gridlock ensued.

Finally the slow-moving Guard convoy cleared the intersection, the MP's moved on, and Deputy O'Gara motioned for us to follow the squad car. Everyone tried moving at the same time. A Waupun City policeman came up to Deputy O'Gara's squad car and asked what was going on. Deputy O'Gara explained, and the city policeman worked to get our procession turned around.

It was slow getting everyone through the intersection since traffic had been backed up both ways, plus all the church members were trying to get in and out of the church parking lots.

Finally after a good twenty minutes, all the Emanuel members got turned around and headed to the park. As I looked back, I could see cars still stopped in all directions.

"I sure apologize for this," the deputy told Dad and Matt at the park. "I just don't know this end of the county. I thought for sure you were going to the Waupun City Park. I've got to go back now and help the Waupun police straighten out the traffic jam there."

The church service went well. The congregation sang lustily with the band accompaniment. The Bible School children recited their Bible verses and sang the hymns they had memorized. No one seemed disappointed when Dad announced that because of the delay, he was omitting the sermon. (Later at home, Mother said, "At least they didn't applaud.")

Then it was time for dinner. There may be better meals than the church picnic potluck dinner, but I can't remember many.

What an array of food! There was fried chicken, home-smoked ham, pork chops, sauerbraten, and a dozen different kinds of hot dishes. There was an endless array of salads: two-bean salad, three-bean salad, four-bean salad, coleslaw, lettuce, and more. And Jell-O of every color plus my favorite—whipped Jell-O. Then there were the desserts: all kinds of pies including strawberry, rhubarb, lemon meringue, coconut cream, and more. And cakes, cookies, and tortes. No one made better tortes than German women, Dad often commented.

One advantage of being the preacher's son was that our family always got to go first at events like this. But before we could eat, we had the table prayer.

Dad stood on the table and in his loudest voice said, "We'll sing the table prayer. I think you all know it."

Years later I learned that the prayer we sang had been written by Methodist Charles Wesley and set to music by a German Reformed composer, but we Lutherans had adopted it as our own and we forcefully sang:

Be present at our table, Lord.
Be here and everywhere adored.
These mercies bless and grant that we
May feast in paradise with thee. Amen.

Hardly had the "Amen" died out when the two lines started moving down the picnic tables where the food was laid out. Members of the Ladies Aid hovered nearby removing empty dishes and replacing them with full ones.

The last of the diners filed through as the first ones through the line started coming back for seconds and desserts.

"You know, Alfred, I think church picnics are better than most threshing meals," I heard Hans Buettemann say to his friend Al Schoenweiss.

The grown-ups were having their second cups of coffee, and the kids were starting to fidget, when Willard Monk, the Sunday School superintendent, climbed on a picnic table to announce the afternoon events.

"OK, everyone, let me have your attention," he called in his loudest voice. People quieted down. "First, I want to thank Matt Schielmann for organizing the procession today. We had a little more excitement than we had planned on, but we all got here safely and soundly. Let's have a big hand for Matt."

Loud applause filled the air. (I could see Dad leaning over and saying something to Mother. Later Dad told us he was sure relieved that people liked it because Matt had worked so hard.)

"And Matt asked that you all turn in your flags so we can use them again next year," Willard continued after the applause died down.

"Every student gets two tickets. You can redeem them for pop, ice cream or candy bars at the stand which the church council is running. Grown-ups can buy treats if they have any room after that great dinner.

"The Sunday School teachers are setting up the games now. We'll start with the preschoolers, then the primary, and then the older grades. There will be games for every age and prizes for all. And at 2:00 p.m., we have something new. It's a ball game between the high schoolers and the adults."

The games began. Mollie Monk, who taught the preschoolers, asked all of her students to gather around.

"Our first game is the penny hunt," she told them. She pointed to a large canvas tarpaulin with a mound of sawdust and wood shavings in the middle. "There are a bunch of pennies hidden here. There is also one quarter. When I say 'Go' you can start hunting for the pennies and the quarter. You get to keep all the coins you find."

Several mothers quickly looked at their children's Sunday clothes and wished they had remembered to bring everyday clothes.

"Too late now," I heard one say.

The children gathered at the edge of the tarpaulin, waiting for the command to start.

"OK, you have ten minutes. Ready, set, go." Hardly had the words gotten out of her mouth when the horde of little ones dove into the pile.

"I found one," said Jimmy Kohlbar, holding up a shiny penny for his mother to see.

"Good," his mother replied, "keep looking."

More pennies were found as sawdust flew through the air like a desert sand storm. Suddenly a loud scream came from the busy diggers. Everyone stopped.

"I found it, I found it," screeched Joannie Hessler, holding up a shiny 25 cent piece. "I found the quarter!"

She quickly ran to her mother, gave her the quarter and said, "Hold this for me, please. And don't lose it."

"I won't," her smiling mother assured her.

Mollie clapped her hands and said, "OK, children, one minute more and then it's time for the fish pond."

There was a frantic pawing through the sawdust in a search for any remaining coins.

"That's it," Mollie called. "Everyone out. Dust yourself off and then line up for the fish pond."

The fish pond had neither fish nor water. Rather, the children were handed a stick with a piece of string attached to it. There was a blanket hung between two trees. The child threw the line over the blanket and a Sunday School teacher attached a small gift, gave the string a tug and the child lifted up the stick to receive the gift.

Squeals came forth as each child caught a "fish" and proudly ran to a parent to show the gift.

The games continued as the time came for the older children to participate. There were all sorts of contests. There was the three-legged race where teams of two would tie their middle legs together and at the word

"Go" would awkwardly race toward the finish line. The winners were usually the pair who avoided falling.

Then there was the bag race. Contestants were handed burlap feed bags. They would put their feet in the bag, pull the bags up to their waists and would attempt to hop to the finish line. This was followed by the wheelbarrow race. One contestant would stand on his hands while his partner picked up the other person's feet and attempted to drive the person like a wheelbarrow.

Hardly had this race ended when it was time for the cracker eating contest. Participants were given six soda crackers. The object was to eat them as quickly as possible and the first contestant who could whistle was the winner. Whistling, it turned out, was no small feat after a mouthful of dry soda crackers.

On the ball diamond, the game between the high schoolers and the adults was in full swing. The adults were no match for the young people who had a number of high school players on the team.

As the games went on, there was a steady parade of boys and girls to the stand where they were exchanging their tickets for treats.

Soon it was nearing 4:00 p.m., the ending time for the picnic. Since most of the members were dairy farmers, they had to get back home, change clothes and milk the cows.

Dads began calling to their children while their wives were gathering up their pans from the potluck dinner.

As people began to leave, Mrs. Stroessenreuter began asking, "Has anyone seen LeRoy?"

We also started asking around. Where had he gone? Who saw him last?

LeRoy was a fifth grader and was always going off by himself.

"I think I saw him over by the swimming pool a while back," someone called.

"He didn't have his swimming suit, so I'm sure he's not in the pool," his mother said. "I just hope he didn't wander off in the woods."

The park had forty acres of woodland with trails and camping sites. Several boys volunteered to see if he had gone there.

"What about the river?" someone asked.

"No need to worry about that," one of the men assured the questioner. "The Rock River is only a foot deep over by the golf course."

"I remember seeing him walking over toward the golf course," one of the girls said. "I told him to look out that he didn't get hit on the head with a golf ball."

As people were standing around talking and wondering what to do next, LeRoy suddenly appeared.

"Where in the world have you been?" his mother wanted to know. "I was worried silly."

"Over there," he gestured, pointing toward the country club. "I was just walking around. Look what I found."

He reached into his pocket and pulled out three golf balls.

"Where did you find them?" one of the boys want to know.

"They were just lying there on the lawn," LeRoy answered, "right by a little flag."

Chapter 16

Dad and the Singing Hollanders

The phone rang just as we were finishing supper.

"Now who could that be?" Mother wondered.

Mother had this thing about the phone. If she wasn't expecting a call, she would look at the phone, wondering who might be calling. Sometimes the phone would ring five or six times while she stood there, listing who it might be.

"I hope it isn't bad news. What if someone died?" she might say. Or, "I hope it isn't Mrs. Gehrke. She always talks for an hour."

We kids would usually say something to the effect of, "For heaven's sake, pick up the phone and find out."

She was the same about the mail. If a letter came from someone she wasn't expecting to hear from, she would hold the letter in hand, staring at it. If it were from her sister, and it wasn't her turn to write, Mother would get anxious.

"Oh, dear, I hope no one is sick."

Or if it came from one of her brothers, she might say something like, "Why, Alfred never writes. This must really be serious."

As Mother was pondering who might be calling, Dad got up, went into the dining room to the phone and answered it.

We could hear him from the kitchen.

"Yes. This is he. No, this is fine."

A silence followed.

"Just a moment. Let me get my calendar."

Dad put the phone down, went into his study and came back with his pocket calendar where he kept all his appointments.

"Tomorrow evening looks fine. How about 7:00 p.m.? Use the door to my study. That would be the door on the right as you face the house. Fine, I'll see you tomorrow evening."

Dad talked a little longer, hung up the phone and came back to the table. We waited expectantly to see who would be coming to see him. Usually calls like this would be from a member who was planning to get married, and she and her fiancé would come to make arrangements. Or it might be a member wanting to talk with Dad about a private matter. But judging from the tone in Dad's voice, it didn't sound like he had been talking with a member of the church.

"Well," he said, sitting down before we had our evening devotions, "that was interesting."

"Who was it?" Mother wanted to know.

"It was Herman Rietsma," Dad answered.

Herman Riestma, I thought. He ran the hardware store in the Village and was a member of the Reformed Church. Why would he want to see Dad?

"What in the world did he want?" Mother asked.

"Herman and a couple of members of the Alto Christian Reformed Church are coming to see me tomorrow evening. They want to know if I would be interested in directing the church's male chorus," Dad answered.

"Why, you can't do that. You're busy on Sundays," Mother told him (as though Dad might need to be reminded).

"No, it's not a church choir. They don't sing at services. They're a group of men from the church who like to sing. I think most of the Dutch churches have men's choruses," Dad told her.

I probably should explain about the Dutch Reformed churches in the area. Next to the Germans, the Dutch—generally called Hollanders—were the largest ethnic group in the Village and surrounding area. Most of them were members of the Reformed Church, a Calvinistic Protestant denomination. Like the Lutherans, there were several varieties of the Reformed Church. The Village had a congregation of the Reformed Church in America. East of the Village was the small community of Alto which had two Reformed churches: the Reformed Church in America and the Christian Reformed Church. Both branches were rather strict. There was no unnecessary work on the Sabbath. Services were held twice on Sunday, morning and evening. Drinking was frowned on; although in communities which had a sizable Dutch population, many of the taverns had doors at the back, so patrons could enter without being seen. These were often referred to as "Dutch Doors". Most businesses in the Village were closed on Sunday;

although Miller's Drug was open in the morning so people could buy their Sunday papers and get ice cream for Sunday dinners.

Anyway, Dad got along really well with the Reformed members. He was friends with the Reformed pastor in the Village. The call from Mr. Rietsma was a little surprising, but we didn't see anything out of the ordinary about it. After all, Dad had a reputation as a good musician. He directed the choirs at church, he was a skilled organist, and he periodically was a vocal soloist at civic events.

The next evening after supper, Dad brought a couple of extra chairs to his study, closed the door, turned on the outside light, and waited for the group to arrive. The rest of the family sat in the living room. The Venetian blinds were open just a crack so we could see out.

At two minutes before 7:00 p.m., Mr. Rietsma's black Chevrolet pulled up in front of the parsonage. Four men got out.

"Good grief, it looks like they're all going to a funeral," said Phil as he watched them come to the study door. They were all dressed in black suits, with white shirts and dark ties.

"Why don't you kids go to your rooms," Mother suggested as she heard a knock on the door to the study.

We complied, figuring we would learn what had happened later.

It wasn't too long before Helene came to my room and said, "I think we can go downstairs now. I just saw them drive away."

Helene's bedroom faced the front of the house, and she had been keeping an eye on the car.

"They left," she reported.

We trooped downstairs to the living room and waited for Dad to come out of the study.

"Well," said Mother when he came out.

"That should work out just fine," Dad answered. He proceeded to tell us that the chorus met on Thursday evenings from September through May. Rehearsals ran about an hour and a half.

"Actually, the rehearsals run about an hour, but they stop for coffee about halfway through," he said.

The Hollanders were big coffee drinkers and took coffee breaks in the morning and afternoon, long before it became normal for most people.

"The men from the Village will give me a ride to rehearsals. They have an annual concert at their church, plus a joint concert with the other men's choruses from the area. Oh, yes, they sing in church one Sunday a year, but I don't have to be there. And, they pay ten dollars for each rehearsal and concert."

Mother brightened up immediately.

"That's pretty generous," she exclaimed.

"They seem to have plenty of money. Every member pays weekly dues to belong.

"Oh," Dad remembered, "they agreed that I would select the music. I'm not interested in just conducting Gospel tunes."

"Don't forget, you have all that music from the men's chorus in Milwaukee," Mother reminded him.

I remember Dad telling us when we lived in Milwaukee that Uncle Carl and he sang in a men's chorus. It was conducted by a well-known choral director who came to Milwaukee every week from Chicago to direct the group. Dad and Uncle Carl often talked about how much they had enjoyed this.

"Yes, I thought of that," Dad answered. "I'll have to dig out that music and see if they're able to handle it."

So began Dad's directing.

From time to time Dad would report on how things were going.

"There are a lot of good singers there. Most haven't had any musical training, but they seem willing to learn," he mentioned. "I've started with some easy pieces, and I'll gradually add more difficult numbers."

One day Dad was especially excited after rehearsal.

"Last night I got them to try Bach's *Jesu, Priceless Treasure*," he said. "They seemed to like it."

Rehearsals continued. It was nearing the time for the joint concert. Choruses from both the Reformed Churches in America and the Christian Reformed congregations participated.

"The two church groups have a number of differences, but they seem to be able to get along when it comes to singing," Dad told us one night at supper. "They're better than the Lutherans that way."

The joint concert would be held in the Waupun Auditorium. Eight choruses would sing. Each one would perform three numbers and then all the groups would join for a closing number.

Dad had selected three numbers: the old Gospel hymn *Let Us Gather at the River*, Noble Cain's arrangement of *Rise Up, Oh Men of God* and finally Bach's *Jesu, Priceless Treasure*.

Dad reported that he thought the concert went well. "Our group sounded the best I've ever heard them."

The following week after rehearsal, Dad gave us this report at supper.

"Well, I don't know if I'll have a job with the chorus next year," he remarked.

"Why do you say that?" Mother asked.

"It seems that some of the men from the other choruses started needling our chorus members. They were calling them the 'High Brow Hollanders'."

We all laughed. We thought that was funny.

"Why would they say that?" Mother wanted to know.

"I guess maybe the Bach number was a little too much for some of the other choruses. Our men seemed to like it OK. But you know how sensitive people can be on things like that," Dad responded.

The following week after rehearsal, Dad was all smiles.

"The men told me they had a special meeting of the chorus after church on Sunday morning. They decided that being called the 'High Brow Hollanders' was actually a compliment. One of the men said that back in Reformation times, the Reformed were called Protestants as an insulting term, but they adopted it as a name of honor. The chorus unanimously voted to keep me as director," Dad reported.

Rehearsals continued. Dad introduced other numbers including a selection from Handel's *Messiah*.

The annual concert had a big audience at the church. Our family had received a special invitation, and we were shown to seats of honor in the front.

During intermission, Mr. Rietsma went to the lectern.

"Last summer the chorus decided to ask Reverend Kurtz if he would direct our group. I think I speak for all the members when I say that we have not only enjoyed singing for him, but we have learned a lot about music. We took up a collection and would like to present Reverend Kurtz with this gift certificate as a token of appreciation."

He motioned for Dad to come up and then handed him an envelope.

Dad shook hands with him, thanked him and the chorus, and told the audience how much he enjoyed directing the chorus and what a great bunch of singers they were. There was loud applause.

The next fall, Dad again directed the chorus, introducing some additional numbers. For the joint concert, he decided they would do *For Unto Us a Child is Born* from *Messiah*, the concluding chorus from Bach's *Nun Dunket Alle Gott* and an arrangement of the old Dutch hymn *We Gather Together*.

Dad suggested that we might like to attend the concert.

"You'll probably be the only Lutherans in the audience, but I think you will enjoy it," he told us.

We rode with Dad to Waupun, some ten miles from the Village. Phil had to work that evening, so Mother, Helene and I went with Dad.

We found seats toward the back of the auditorium.

"No reserved seats for us this time," I said to Mother.

"Shh," Mother said. "We don't want to be conspicuous."

"What does 'conspicuous' mean?" Helene wanted to know.

Mother again said, "Shh," and added, "I'll tell you later."

The concert seemed to go on and on. Except for Dad's chorus, most of the music sounded pretty much the same.

After the concert was over, we waited around for Dad. I noticed he was talking to a man.

"I wonder who that is," I said to Mother. "He isn't a chorus member, and he doesn't look like one of the Reformed preachers."

In a few minutes Dad joined us, and we went out to the car. When we got in, before I could ask about the man, Helene demanded, "OK, now what does 'conspicuous' mean and why shouldn't we be that, whatever it is?"

We all laughed and Helene got indignant.

"What's so funny, just because I don't know what a word means?"

Mother explained that since our family were the only Lutherans in the audience, she didn't want to draw attention to us by parading up in front.

This satisfied Helene, and I changed the subject by asking who Dad had been talking to at the end of the concert.

"That was very interesting," Dad answered. "He's what they call a field man for Calvin College."

"The college has a farmer?" Helene asked.

Again we laughed, and again Helene was indignant.

"Farmers work in fields," she pointed out.

"Well," Dad said, "this is a different kind of field. It means he goes out and talks with people and congregations who might be interested in Calvin College."

Dad explained that Calvin College was located in Grand Rapids, Michigan, and was supported by the Christian Reformed Church.

"The choir I direct is a part of the Christian Reformed Church," Dad explained. "Anyway, he told me he was quite impressed with the singing of our chorus. He told me that at Christmas time, Calvin College presents Handel's *Messiah*, and the college invites various church choirs to be in the chorus. He asked if our chorus would be interested in singing there."

"What did you tell him?" Mother asked.

"I told him that this sounded great, but I couldn't answer for the chorus, especially since I was a Lutheran pastor."

"Did you feel conspicuous?" Helene wanted to know.

"No, but I told him to send a letter to Mr. Rietsma, and it would be up to the chorus to decide."

There was no chorus rehearsal the next week. Members took the week off after their big concert. A week later after the next rehearsal Dad reported on the invitation the chorus had received.

"The men were really excited about the invitation. It was the first time any chorus in this area had ever been invited to sing there. I gather that this is quite an honor," Dad told us.

"Are they going? Will you go too?" Mother asked.

"No, I won't be going. The men are trying to figure out if they can make the trip. Most of them are dairy farmers, and it is difficult for them to get away. The way they were talking it sounds as though some of the men will stay home and take care of the milking so others can go. My guess is that more than half of them will be able to make the trip."

Dad added that since the *Messiah* presentation was in December, they had about six months to make arrangements.

"But there's no doubt that they will go. It means that we'll have to do a lot of rehearsing which means I'll really have to prepare as well. Aside from *For Unto Us a Child is Born*, I've never directed anything from *Messiah*."

A week later at the supper table, Dad gave a report.

"It looks as though about fifteen of the chorus members will be able to go. The farmers have made arrangements either to have chorus members do their milking or have family members take care of things. We decided that the whole chorus will practice selections from *Messiah* and do a special Christmas concert at the church."

Never had a group practiced harder. Rather than take the summer off, the chorus continued practicing throughout June, July and August ... except when our family went on vacation.

"The extra income will come in handy," Mother remarked.

Summer turned into autumn. Dad would walk around the house, humming selections from Handel.

"Well, the men have things figured out. They decided they will go in three cars. Some of them have relatives down in South Holland near Chicago, so they will drive there the first night, stay overnight and then head to Grand Rapids. There are a couple of rehearsals and then three concerts on Thursday, Friday and Saturday nights. On Monday, they'll drive straight home," Dad said.

"Why don't they leave on Sunday and get home sooner?" Mother asked.

"Oh, no," Dad explained, "with the Christian Reformed, there's no traveling on Sunday. They'll stay and go to church and then leave bright and early on Monday."

Everything went according to schedule. At the next chorus rehearsal, Dad got a full report.

"This was one of the biggest adventures most of these men have ever had. Some of them had never been out of Wisconsin before. Things went great. They had a wonderful time and ..."

Dad got up, went to his study and came back with the program.

"Look at this. Here's how the chorus asked to be listed on the program."

We all looked at the program. There it was:

The High Brow Hollanders, Alto, Wisconsin

Chapter 17

The Mystery at the Gas Station

Crime was not a major problem in the Village. Old timers would talk about when people "thought" that Jesse James and his gang had ridden through the Village, but since they hadn't tried to rob the bank, no one was certain if indeed the notorious band of criminals had been there.

Then there was the time back in the 1930's when the John Dillinger gang had stopped at the Texaco station. At least, that's what people thought. The way they told it was that one afternoon this big car with Illinois license plates pulled into the station. They parked the car at the side of the driveway, and a woman got out to use the restroom. They didn't buy any gas, but the people in the station noticed there were three or four men in the car.

"Looked to me like it could have been the Dillinger gang heading up to northern Wisconsin," said one of the guys who was at the station. Of course, no one knew for sure.

"I sure wasn't going to go out and ask them," he said later.

But criminal activity was virtually unknown. The Village had no police force. Wes Carley was the Village constable, but this was only a part-time duty for him since his main job was being the Village maintenance man. He plowed the streets in winter, mowed the park lawn in summer, collected trash year around and maintained the Village hall.

The only reported criminal event in recent memory really wasn't a crime at all, but resulted in a degree of hilarity for residents of the Village. It involved the disappearance of Willard Monk's '39 Ford.

Willard was the Sunday School superintendent at Emanuel. He and his wife Mollie lived in a small house just west of the Village business section. Willard worked at Herb Schmuhl's grocery and dry goods store, and Mollie was a clerk in the post office. Both jobs were located a few hundred feet from their home, so they always walked to work. Their car would sit in the garage, often going unused for weeks at a time.

One Thursday evening they had been invited to have supper with Mollie's cousin and his wife who lived out in the country. Willard went to the garage to get the car. To his amazement it was gone.

He ran into the house, excitedly calling to Mollie, "Our car has been stolen! I've got to call Wes."

Wes had just gotten home from his Village duties when he got Willard's excited call. Willard quickly explained the situation and asked Wes, "Should I call Leo Flannery?" Leo was the county deputy who lived in the Village and was called upon if there appeared to be real criminal activity.

"Relax, Willard," Wes said. "Your car hasn't been stolen. It's sitting in the Lutheran church parking lot, right where you left it on Sunday."

Then he remembered. Willard was the Sunday School superintendent at Emanuel, and he liked to get to church early to make sure everything was set for the session. It had been raining when he left in the morning, so he drove to the church and parked his car in the lot. By the time Sunday School and morning services were over, the rain had stopped and the sun was shining, so Willard and Mollie walked home, oblivious to the fact that their car was standing in the church lot.

Now that's the kind of criminal activity which the Village would typically face. What took place one Saturday night was really out of the ordinary. Let me tell you what happened.

It was after 9:00 p.m. on Saturday night when Phil came home from his job at the filling station. On alternate Saturday nights, he worked alone and was responsible for closing the station.

When Phil got home on Saturday nights, he would be tired from a full day's work. He would have a snack and go to bed. I was in the kitchen when he came in. Mother was upstairs, getting Helene ready for bed. Dad was in his study with the door closed. Sometimes he would be working on his sermon. Other times he would be reading. On occasion, I knew that he might be sneaking in a game of solitaire. Mother didn't know about that, and Dad had warned me not to say anything about it to her. Mother thought there was something sinful about playing cards, especially on a Saturday night when he should be working on his sermon.

"You look worried," I said to Phil as he pulled up a chair at the kitchen table and sat down.

"I had kind of a strange experience tonight," he told me. "As I was getting ready to close, a couple of guys came in. I didn't know them. They bought a dollar's worth of gas and hung around for a while, like they were looking the place over."

"Then what happened?" I asked.

"Well, nothing. One guy bought two Mars bars and watched carefully when I took out the key to open the candy cupboard."

"Mars bars? They're expensive. And two of them!" I said. All other candy bars were a nickel. However, Mars bars were a dime, and rarely did many people buy one and never two.

Before I tell you more, I should explain about the station. The filling station, or service station, was located directly back of the church. It was owned by Augie Kohls. Augie and his wife had no children, but over the years the young men Augie had hired to work at the station became almost an extended family for them.

Augie was very particular about who worked there. The high school student he hired had to have excellent grades, be well respected by the faculty and plan to attend college. As a result, former employees tended to be a successful group.

During vacations, they would return to visit. If things got busy, they would help out. In the summer, Augie would hire one of the former workers to run the station while he and his wife went on vacation. It was not unusual to have a Ph.D. washing a customer's windshield.

The alumni, as they were frequently called, went on to college and successful careers. A couple of them became school superintendents, others were teachers; a couple were business people; and one became a minister. The only exception was the son of the former pastor at Emanuel. He so thoroughly enjoyed his work at the station that he become an auto mechanic, much to his father's consternation because he had hoped his son would follow in his footsteps and become a pastor.

The station had been built in the late 1920's when Spanish architecture was popular. The two buildings had a stucco finish and a faux tile roof. One building was where oil changes and minor repairs were done. The other building had the office, storage areas, a large waiting room with chairs and a pop machine. One distinctive feature was the women's restroom. Augie used to say that it was the most attractive public restroom in Wisconsin. In addition to the toilet facilities, it had a waiting area with wicker furniture. During the summer, Augie always put fresh flowers there.

The Village was on a main highway to several resort lakes. It was about one tank of gas from Chicago to the station, and the women's restroom was a major draw for business on Friday nights during the summer.

The station was a favorite gathering place for kids and neighbors. It was especially interesting to be there when the alumni were home during vacations. One could learn all sorts of things about college life, jobs and what was happening in the Village.

But getting back to Phil's concern.

"So what happened?" I asked.

"Nothing. They stood around for a while. The one guy ate both his candy bars. They saw me look at the clock a couple of times and finally one said, 'I suppose you're getting ready to close.' I told him that yes, I was, so they left and drove off," Phil said.

"So, then what?" I asked.

"Nothing. I put the money in the downstairs safe, turned off the lights, locked up and came home," Phil answered.

"So why are you worried?"

"There was just something about these guys which didn't seem right. Why would two strangers hang around the station late on a Saturday night? I hope nothing happens. Well, I guess I'll have something to eat and go bed. I'm tired."

A little bit later I went to my room and got ready for bed. My room was at the back of the house, and the window over the head of my bed looked out over our back yard. I had a good view of the station from there.

I left my shade up that night. Usually I pulled it down since the sun would shine directly on my face in the morning. I thought if anything happens at the station, I might be able to see things from there.

I woke up a couple of times during the night. Each time, I would look intently at the station. Each time I failed to see anything but the dark buildings, faintly outlined by the streetlight.

After church on Sunday, Phil told me he was going to stop at the station and tell Augie about Saturday night and see if everything was OK. He came back in a few minutes and said Augie appreciated that he had told him about the two guys, and he would keep his eyes open for them.

I continued to keep my shade up for the next few nights, but there was nothing to be seen. I did get awakened early with the sun coming through the window, so I again pulled the shade down at night and forgot about keeping watch over the station.

I'm not certain what caused me to wake up the next Saturday night. Maybe I had heard something. I raised the shade and looked out at the station. Things appeared normal, but then I thought I saw a glint of light through the station window.

I watched for a few minutes and didn't see the light again, but I thought I saw a car parked in the shadows near the entrance to the station driveway.

I decided to tell Phil and see what he thought. I quietly opened the door of my bedroom and tiptoed across the hall to Phil's bedroom. I didn't want to wake Mother who was a light sleeper and would immediately forbid us to leave the house.

I let myself into Phil's room and gently shook him awake. I told him what I thought I had seen.

"Let's check it out," he said. "Get dressed and we'll sneak over there. And be quiet so we don't wake Mother."

I ducked back to my room, quickly dressed and met Phil in the hall. We tiptoed down the steps, into the kitchen and let ourselves out the side door. Just before we went out the door, I saw the ice pick sitting on the ledge where we had used it a few days earlier when we made ice cream. I grabbed it and whispered to Phil,

"Just in case."

We silently moved through the shadows toward the station. We knew every inch of our back yard, and we kept close to the bushes on the side of the yard. When we got within sight of the big side window of the station, we stopped and watched.

"I saw a light. There's someone in there," Phil whispered.

"And there's a car over there," I whispered back.

"Let's go call the sheriff's department, " Phil said.

"Just a minute," I told him.

I crawled over to the car, ice pick in hand. I quickly punched each of the back tires, noted the license plate number and came back to where Phil was waiting.

"Let's go. Be real careful."

We hurriedly sneaked back into the house. Phil went to the telephone. He jiggled the hand set to get the operator's attention. The night operator would often doze off since few people made calls late at night.

In a minute, I heard a faint voice saying, "Number, please."

"This is Philip Kurtz. Can you call the sheriff's department right away? There are people in Augie Kohls' station."

This time the voice was louder.

"I'll call right away, and I'll also call Leo. And you stay away from the station until the police get there."

"I will," Phil promised.

Phil and I went out in the back yard just in time to see a car with its headlights off pull away from the station and head down the state highway.

A few minutes later Leo's squad car pulled up, and we ran over to it.

We quickly explained what had happened.

"Which way did they go?" Leo asked.

I pointed to the east.

"It's a dark-colored Plymouth, either a '41 or a '45. The license number is 563-335. I don't think they'll get too far," and I told Leo what I had done.

"That was a little bit dangerous, but smart," he told me. "I'll send out a radio alert."

He went into his car, and while he was talking, another squad car pulled up.

The deputy got out of his car, looked us over (apparently deciding we weren't the criminals) and walked over to Leo's car.

Leo got off the radio and told the deputy what had happened.

"I'll go down the highway, and if they are stopped with flat tires, I'll radio for backup," the deputy said. "Check the station and see what you can find out."

The squad car took off.

"We should probably call Augie to let him know," Leo said.

"I'll go back to the house and call him," Phil said.

"Let's take a look at things," Leo said, "but first I'll pull the squad car over to the door so I can hear the radio."

"Stay behind me and don't touch anything. I doubt if anyone is in there, but we need to be careful."

Leo picked up his flashlight, drew his revolver, and we walked to the front door. Leo reached in his pocket and pulled out a pair of gloves which he put on.

"There might be finger prints here," he said.

The front door was open, and there was broken glass in the door from the smashed door window.

"That's how they got in," Leo pointed out. "They reached in and undid the lock."

Leo looked around.

"No one here. Where are the light switches?" he asked.

I pointed to the switches over the pop cooler.

Leo switched them on, and we looked around the office. Just then Phil came in.

"Augie's on his way over," he told Leo.

The cash register had been pried open.

"That was a waste of time," Phil noted. "We never keep any money in there at night."

"What do you do with the money?" Leo asked.

"We put it downstairs in the safe," Phil said.

"We'll check that when Augie gets here," Leo said, continuing his search of the office area.

"Look, they broke into the candy case," I said. The glass on the case was shattered. I looked inside.

"It looks like the only thing they took were the Mars bars," I said.

"I bet it was the same guys," Phil responded.

"What guys were those?" Leo wanted to know.

Phil recounted what had happened earlier, including how one had bought two Mars bars.

"Can you describe them?" Leo wanted to know.

Just then a car pulled up in front. Augie got out and came into the station.

Leo explained what had happened.

"I don't think they're going to get too far," Leo said, "thanks to his quick thinking," pointing to me.

Augie smiled. "Good job, both of you."

"Why don't you check downstairs and see if they got into your safe," Leo told Augie.

Augie went down the stairs in the back storeroom. He reappeared shortly.

"Nope, they didn't get into the safe. I doubt if they found it."

Just then a voice came over the radio.

"Leo, I got them. I just called for backup to transport them to the county jail."

"Do you need me?" Leo asked.

"No," came the response. "When the other squad gets here, I'll come back and fill you in. I've got both guys handcuffed in the back seat. Here comes the other squad now. Ten-four."

"Ten-four," Leo replied.

"I'll get my camera and take pictures of the break-in," Leo said, "and I'll dust for fingerprints."

Leo went to his squad car and returned with a camera and a small black bag.

I watched carefully. I had read about evidence gathering, but had never seen it firsthand. Leo took pictures of the front door, the broken candy case, and the cash register.

He took out a container of white powder from the bag and, with a small brush, dusted the door knobs, the cash register, and the candy case.

"There are a lot of prints here. I'll need to get your prints so I can tell whose might be the intruders," he told Augie and Phil.

Phil was going to be fingerprinted. Wow, I thought, this is better than a detective story.

"Anything else look as though it has been disturbed or broken into?" Leo asked Augie.

Augie had been checking things out.

"Doesn't appear to be anything," he replied.

Just then the other squad car pulled up. The deputy got out and came into the station.

"Got everything, Leo?" he asked.

"I think so. The only thing we found missing was a box of Mars bars," Leo told him.

"And that was in the back seat of the car," the deputy answered.

"You can clean up the glass and board up the door," Leo told Augie. "I'll stop over tomorrow and finish the report. I'll have to get a statement from you two," he told us.

Phil and I walked back to the house.

"Should we wake Mother and Dad to tell them what happened?" I asked Phil.

"Let's wait until morning," he answered.

The next morning I heard Dad get up. I got up too and so did Phil.

We went downstairs and told Dad what had happened.

Mother heard our voices and came down, wondering why we had gotten up so early.

"You two could have been killed," Mother exclaimed after we told her the story.

"What do you mean 'killed'?" came a sleepy voice. Helene had come down the stairs just in time to hear Mother's comment.

We repeated the story.

"Wow," Helene said, "that was exciting. Next time will you wake me up, so I can come too?"

We smiled.

"I hope there will never be a next time," Phil answered.

"Shoot," answered Helene, "I miss out on everything."

On Monday afternoon, Leo stopped at the house and took a statement from us including Phil's description of the two guys who had been at the station earlier.

"Apparently the two men we picked up are the 'Saturday Night Burglars'," Leo told us. "For the past year or so, there have been a series of burglaries at filling stations, stores and bars. They figured that the owners would not deposit their Saturday receipts until Monday, so they would break in on Saturday nights. Lots of times the break-in wouldn't be discovered until Monday morning. The sheriff told me they have confessed, so there won't be a trial. By the way, there's a reward for their capture and conviction and you boys are in line to receive it. I'll let you know."

A reward, I thought. That is something.

There was an account of the burglary and capture in the Fond du Lac paper. It referred to Phil and me as "two minor boys whose identify the police would not reveal at this time."

"If you're under 18, they often don't list names," Dad explained.

"Shucks," I replied. "I thought we would get mentioned for our part in it."

"What you did was important, even though it was a bit dangerous. The key thing is that thanks to you boys, these criminals were captured and won't be breaking into businesses anymore," Dad told me.

Several weeks later, Leo again stopped at our house.

"Next week the sheriff would like you to come to the courthouse. He wants to recognize you and present you with a reward. I'll be glad to drive the family over in my squad car," he told us.

The following week, Phil, Helene and I were excused from school. Leo picked up the family in his squad car, and we all rode to the big, red brick courthouse in Fond du Lac. I sat in the front seat between Leo and Dad. I looked at all the equipment. Leo explained the siren, the spotlight, the two-way radio and the outside rotating lights.

"I don't suppose we can turn on the siren," I said.

Leo laughed. "No, the last time I did it with your family, it caused all sorts of consternation," he said, referring to the time we went Christmas caroling, and Leo thought we were the Huehne kids, coming to cause trouble at Bertha and Rueben's house.

Everyone but Mother laughed when he recalled our adventure last Christmas.

"We're going to meet in the main courtroom," Leo explained as he parked the squad car next to the sheriff's office.

He led us into the courthouse and up the stairs. The courtroom was a large room with wood paneling and a large, high desk in front.

"The judge usually sits there," Leo explained.

Soon there were a number of officers in uniforms, a photographer and a small group of other people.

Leo introduced us to the sheriff who asked us to sit in the front row.

The sheriff recounted what Phil and I had done and how it resulted in the capture of the Saturday Night Burglars.

"Because of all of the break-ins, the county merchants' association had established a reward for the capture and conviction of those committing the burglaries," the sheriff said.

He asked Phil and me to come forward. He then handed each of us an envelope.

"The reward is $500, so each of you gets a check for $250. And on behalf of the sheriff's department, I want to thank you for your part in solving these crimes."

Two hundred and fifty dollars, I thought. I'm rich. I never thought I would have so much money. Why ... I began thinking of what I could do with it.

Just then the photographer and reporter from the Fond du Lac newspaper came up. The photographer took several pictures of us with the sheriff and Leo.

"What are you planning to do with your reward money?" the reporter asked us.

"I'll be going to college, so I plan to save it for that," Phil explained.

"And you?" he asked me.

I was ready to start telling him all sorts of things, but then the thought struck me: what if Mother came up with one of her ideas, like buying another saw or an accordion or who knows what? Better play it safe.

"I'll probably save it for college too," I hastily explained. Even Mother wouldn't dare to make me spend college money.

Chapter 18

Cousin George Decides to Leave Town

"There's a big 'Chalk the Arrow' game tonight," I announced as we finished supper. "Is it OK if I go?" I asked Mother.

"As soon as you finish the dishes," Mother replied. "Just come home when the train gets in."

Life in the Village seemed to be regulated by the arrival of trains. The Village was located on a branch line of the Milwaukee Road which ran from Milwaukee to Berlin, about twenty miles north of the Village. Actually, the reason there was a Village was because of the railroad. Back in the 1850's, when the railroad was built, there was no town between Waupun and Ripon. Since the old-time steam engines had to take on water every ten miles, and since a farmer with a team of horses or oxen could only make a five-mile round trip in a day, there was a need for a station between the two cities. So the railroad platted a site, and the Village was born.

There were four passenger trains a day in the Village: two southbound and two northbound.

The first train of the day was the southbound train which went to Milwaukee. It arrived at 7:30 a.m., and it marked the start of the day for us kids. If we weren't up, Dad would call up the stairs, "Time to get up. Didn't you hear the train?"

At 9:30 a.m. the northbound train from Milwaukee would arrive. It was the signal for housewives to begin their walk to the downtown area for the day's shopping. Since most people had very small refrigerators (some people even had ice boxes) most housewives would shop every day. Also, the 9:30 train brought the mail from Milwaukee which was the biggest mail delivery of the day. People got their mail at the post office if they lived in town. Only people who lived in the country got their mail delivered.

The passenger train was pulled by a coal-burning engine. Behind the coal car was the mail car where postal clerks sorted the mail from each town. When the train stopped, they would drop off the incoming mail bags and pick up the outgoing mail.

Behind the mail car was the passenger coach. Sometimes on weekends or before holidays, there would be two passenger coaches, but normally there was just one.

The third train of the day headed to Milwaukee and came through the Village at 5:00 p.m. If we were playing at a friend's house, this was the signal to go home for supper since our normal instructions were, "Come home when you hear the train."

The final passenger train of the day came from Milwaukee at 8:00 p.m. This marked the end of the play day for us kids.

When we heard the train, we would head for the station to watch the train come in. A few passengers would get off, usually someone who had business in Milwaukee and had taken the 7:30 train that morning.

Each evening the routine was the same. We would watch Wes Carley hand the mail bags to the railroad clerk and get the incoming bags in return. He would load them on his hand cart and take it to the post office, a block away. As the train pulled away, we kids would walk home.

"OK," I assured Mother.

"How do you play 'Chalk the Arrow'? Can I play too?" my sister wanted to know.

"It's a game bigger kids play. We choose up sides. The first side leaves 15 minutes ahead and goes off, making an arrow with chalk to show where they are going. Every time they turn a corner or go somewhere, they make an arrow. Then finally they draw a circle with arrows pointing in all directions and then everyone on the team hides. The other team follows the arrows, crossing each arrow out with chalk—which is why it's called Chalk the Arrow—and then when they come to circle, they try to find the other team. After they find them, we go back and play it again."

"Sounds kind of complicated. I don't think I want to play," my sister responded.

Dishes were done, and I walked the two blocks to downtown and crossed the street to the Miller Drug Store, where a dozen or so kids were gathered. We waited a few minutes for a few more to come and then chose up sides.

"OK," said Hale, one of the two captains, "Ann, put your hands behind your back and show a number between one and ten. Dave (the other captain) and I will guess a number, and the closest one gets to go first."

Ann did as instructed, letting several others see the number. Hale picked "2" and Dave picked "8".

"Dave wins," Ann announced. "It was 6."

Good, I thought, we go first since I was on Dave's team.

"OK, 15 minutes' head start," said Dave as we left, each team equipped with a piece of chalk.

Our team stopped every twenty feet or so to draw an arrow on the sidewalk showing the direction we were going. We left the business area and started cutting across backyards, drawing arrows as we went. Sometimes the arrows were on trees, or they led over fences.

After about ten minutes, Dave called a halt, drew a circle with arrows pointing in all directions and said, "OK, scatter and hide. They have ten minutes to find us all once they get to the circle. Remember, you have to stay within 50 feet of the circle."

We spread out, hiding where we could—behind bushes, under porches, and generally out of sight. We soon heard the searching team coming, and we all tried to make ourselves as small as possible.

"Here's the circle," I heard one of the other team members call. The hunting began in earnest. One by one our team was found.

"That's everybody," Dave called. "Our turn to hunt."

We gathered in a circle, closed our eyes and began counting to 100 as the other team took off, drawing arrows as they went. The game continued, back and forth.

As our team was preparing to hide again, we heard the whistle of the train.

"It's 8:00," I called. "I have to go home."

"Me too," came a half dozen other voices.

The "Chalk the Arrow" game broke up, and we all headed to the train station to watch the train arrive. Wes Carley stood by his cart with two bags of outgoing mail. As the train stopped, Wes handed the bags to the clerk in the postal car and received three bags in return.

Most of us were watching Wes and the mail bags and didn't notice who was getting off the train.

Just as the conductor was calling, "All aboard!" and picking up the stool which passengers used to get on and off the train, I looked over and gasped.

"Cousin George," I almost shouted.

There, walking toward me, carrying a battered leather suitcase was Cousin George. Well, actually he wasn't my cousin. He was Mother's cousin, or maybe he was her second cousin. I never remembered for sure. He was always called Cousin George by everyone in the family.

Cousin George didn't have a home. He roamed around the country, staying with relatives or friends, working here and there and then moving on.

"How are you doing?" he called when he spotted me. "Think I'll be able to stay at your house for a while?"

"You'll have to ask Mother and Dad," I replied. I knew the answer. Mother would feel sorry for him. "You know," she would say to Dad, "poor George (it was always 'poor George' when she talked about him) doesn't have a home of his own and really has no close family either. I think it is our Christian duty to give him a place to stay."

I could hear Dad reply. "Well, I suppose so. But if it turns out like last time, he's going to be gone on the next train."

In some ways, George was a welcome visitor. He was one of the handiest people I knew. He could fix most anything, do all sorts of repairs and build things. (It was Cousin George who built bookcases for us kids since we never did get the bookcases made out of orange crates which you may remember reading about). I began making a mental list of what I needed to have done. Maybe some shelves in my room, and he could fix the brakes on my bike. I knew Mother would have lots for him to do. They would be all the things she had been after Dad to get done. Dad didn't like doing these kinds of chores, so he would postpone them as long as possible.

"I thought with the canning season starting, I could get a job there," he told me as we walked from the depot to our house. "They're always short of help, and the foreman told me I could come back any time."

We entered the side door of the house and walked up the five steps leading to the kitchen.

"Cousin George came on the train tonight," I announced as George followed me into the kitchen.

Mother appeared from the living room where she had been listening to the radio.

"Why, George," she said. "It's good to see you. Henry will be so surprised when he gets home from the church council meeting."

Yup, I thought, she said "surprised". She didn't say "pleased".

"I thought I could get a job with the canning factory for the summer," George told Mother. "Herman told me that I could come back any time even though I had to leave rather quickly last year."

I remembered now. One morning I heard George get up early and leave the house. I peeked out the window and saw him walking toward the depot, carrying his suitcase. Mother didn't exactly answer my question when I asked why George had left before the canning season ended.

"Your father thought it would be better if he left now," Mother said, offering no additional details.

"You can sleep in the back room on the couch," Mother told him. "I'll get some bedding and a pillow."

The back room was a small room, located off the dining room. When I had been little, it had been my playroom. Now it had a studio couch, Mother's sewing machine and some large plants. We didn't use the room very much.

I went to bed before Dad came home from the church council meeting. I did hear Dad talking with Mother.

"I hope he doesn't embarrass us again like he did last time," I heard Dad say. "How long is he going to stay?"

"He'll probably be here through the canning season. He'll pay board and room and the extra income will help, especially with Phil going off to college next year," Mother replied. "And he can get all those jobs done around the house which you have been putting off doing."

Mother knew she had Dad there. Mother kept a list of things which needed to be done around the house. On major items such as painting or house repairs, Dad would report to the church council, and the council members would see that things got done, since the parsonage belonged to the church. On smaller things, though, the pastor was on his own.

The list Mother was referring to were small things such as fixing a switch on a lamp, getting the toaster to work properly and a bunch of other minor jobs.

"Well," Dad sighed, "I guess we can give him a chance again. But you tell him that if there's a repeat of last time, he better get his bag packed in a hurry."

"I'm sure he'll be fine. Poor George does need a home. It is our Christian duty to help him," Mother told Dad.

Dad didn't reply, but I could guess what he was thinking. It was hard for a preacher to disagree about having a Christian duty, especially when the person making this point was his wife.

I heard Mother continuing. "I know things will be better than his other visits. He knows you won't put up with the behavior he's shown before."

I heard Dad sigh.

"I certainly hope so," he said.

The next morning George joined us for breakfast.

"Any jobs you need done around the house, Henry?" he asked Dad. "I can get some things done before the canning season starts."

Dad had the list of jobs Mother had been after him to do. After breakfast, George got to work.

"If you need more tools, I know Mr. Liner (our next-door neighbor) will be glad to lend you anything you need," Mother told him. Dad didn't have many tools—a pair of pliers, a hammer, a screwdriver and a saw constituted the contents of his tool box.

"Good idea," George answered. "I remember borrowing tools from him last time I was here."

It was fun to watch George fix things. He seemed to know how everything worked.

"When you're done here, could you take a look at my bike?" I asked. "There's something wrong with the brakes, and I haven't been able to figure it out."

"Sure," George nodded, "no problem."

After lunch, George said he was going to the canning factory to see about a job for the summer.

"You come straight back after that," Mother said in the same tone she would talk to us about being home on time.

"Don't worry—I'll be right back. Besides, I spent my last dollar on train fare to get here," George assured Mother.

True to his word, Cousin George was back in a short time.

"The pea pack is supposed to start next week," George reported at supper that evening. "That means I can start paying board and room."

I thought I saw Dad's face brighten up a bit at the prospect of a little extra income.

The Village, like most of the surrounding towns, had a canning factory. Most of these factories canned peas and sweet corn; although a few of them also canned green beans.

The canning season began in late June. Virtually every high school student who was 16 or older would work at the canning factory. It was a busy place when the canning season was going on. The pea vines would be trucked in from surrounding farms where they would be shelled. Trucks would haul the fresh peas to the canning factory. Here an inspector would take a sample of the peas and test them for tenderness. The more tender the sample the higher price the farmer would receive.

During World War II, there was a serious shortage of labor, so Herman Swenson, the plant foreman (who was a member of the congregation), asked Dad if he would be willing to run the testing office. Dad was glad to do it. He felt it was a patriotic thing to do since most of the canned goods were bought by the government to feed the troops.

"And the extra income will be nice too," Mother noted when Dad told us he was going to be working there during the canning season.

At the end of the season, Herman told him that he wished Dad would work every year.

"Farmers are always complaining that the tester isn't being fair and that maybe some farmers are bribing him to get a higher score. Nobody complained about the results when you were there. They knew a preacher wouldn't take a bribe."

I asked George, "Where are you going to be working?"

"Oh, I'll probably start in the solution room where they mix the salt and sugar," he said. "But Herman said he will probably move me around when things need fixing."

Phil started to laugh.

"What's funny?" Helene wanted to know. Helene was always worried that someone might be laughing at her. "I didn't say a word."

"No, it has nothing to do with you," Phil assured her. "I was just thinking about the time when George was working at the factory during the War, and he brought home the sugar."

I remembered that story. Sugar was rationed during the War (as was butter, meat, canned goods, and many other things).

One day George brought home a paper bag full of sugar.

"Here, Minnie," he told Mother, "I thought you could use some extra sugar."

He explained that one of the 100 pound sacks of sugar had broken open and most of it had spilled on the floor.

"We had to throw that away, but there was some left in the bag, so I brought it home," he explained.

"I remember that we had Kool-Aid for the rest of the summer," I said.

"I don't remember that," Helene objected. "How come I didn't get any Kool-Aid?"

"Of course you don't remember," Mother assured her, "you were only a baby at the time."

George got most everything fixed up around the house, and then the canning season started. We didn't see much of him. He worked until late in the evening and started early in the morning.

"The busier he is, the better it is for everyone," I heard Dad say to Mother.

"Oh, Henry," Mother answered, "you know George is trying to straighten himself out."

I didn't hear what Dad answered. Maybe he just shook his head and went into his study.

When George got his first pay, he paid Mother for board and room.

"George," I heard her tell him, "let's go down to the bank and open an account for you. That way you won't be tempted."

Tempted, I thought, tempted for what?

"Good idea, Minnie," he answered.

The canning season continued. George worked long hours. Each pay day he would give Mother money for board and room and then the two of them would walk down to the bank. Mother would watch as George deposited the remainder of his pay.

"See, George, you're building up a nice savings there," I heard Mother say to him one day.

Then the pea canning season came to a close. All the seasonal workers took a break until the sweet corn canning would start. George continued to work, converting the factory for canning corn. He worked shorter hours now and ate meals with us.

The break in the canning season also meant that the summer band concerts resumed in the Village park.

The Village merchants knew they had a lot of competition for Saturday night business. Since much of their profits depended upon this trade, they were always thinking of ways to lure farmers to the Village on Saturday nights, so they wouldn't go to nearby cities like Fond du Lac, Ripon, or Waupun.

It was Herb Schmuhl, owner of the grocery and dry goods store, who suggested having band concerts on Saturday nights during the summer. Herb had played in the high school band and enjoyed music.

So the Merchants' Association made an arrangement with the school to have concerts and the Association agreed to pay Mr. Vogel, the school band director, for rehearsing the band and directing the concerts. As an incentive for the students to perform, each player got a coupon good for a treat at the drug store or the restaurant.

There were two problems to be solved. First, the Village did not have a bandstand in the park by the depot. And second, since virtually all of the band members who were 16 or older worked in the canning factory during the pea harvest, that meant that most of the band members would not be available for half the summer.

Both problems were solved. The canning factory brought in two wagons used in the pea harvest. They were placed side by side and provided a large enough platform for the band. Wes Carley, the Village maintenance man, strung up lights so the band members could perform.

The other problem was solved by having a split season. There would be concerts in the early part of June until the pea harvest began. Then the canning factory would reclaim its wagons and the students would go to their jobs. When the pea harvest ended in late July or early August, the concerts would resume.

Phil started playing in the band his freshman year, so our family began attending the Saturday night concerts. I guess this convinced Mother that no blatant sin abounded, to entice us children into dens of iniquities, so from then on we could go downtown on Saturday nights, band concerts or not.

Mother, Dad, Helene and I planned to go to the concert since Phil was playing in the band.

"Wouldn't you like to come with us?" Mother asked George at supper on Saturday night.

"Well," George paused. "Ah, maybe I'll come down a little later."

We left for the concert and settled down on a park bench. We were sitting there, enjoying the music, when suddenly Dad jumped up and started walking very fast toward the business section of the Village.

"Where is Daddy going?" Helene asked.

Mother watched him before replying. "I'm not certain," she answered. "Why don't you go and check," she said to me.

I jumped up and headed in the direction Dad had gone. It was only a short distance to the business area of town. Since it was Saturday night, the downtown area was jammed with people. I had lost sight of Dad. I continued walking quickly, keeping my eyes peeled for him.

Then I saw Cousin George heading toward one of the Village's three taverns. Suddenly it dawned on me what Mother and Dad had been discussing about George and why Mother was so insistent about George depositing his pay in the bank.

Just as George was about to enter the bar, Dad appeared. I was now close enough that I could see Dad grab George's arm. As I got closer I heard him say, "I think you should come and join us at the band concert, George."

George was startled. He looked at the bar and then at Dad.

"I think you're right, Henry," he answered, turning and going with Dad back to the Village park.

I followed them, and we all sat on a park bench, listening to the concert. It struck me that George wasn't enjoying the music all that much.

After the concert, we all walked back to our house. Dad kept a watchful eye on George. As we entered the house, Dad said to George, "Let's go to the study for a little talk."

Mother took Helene upstairs to get ready for bed. I noticed that Dad had not fully closed his study door, so I crept into the living room and sat in the chair closest to the door so I could hear what was going on.

"George," I heard Dad saying, "I thought we had an understanding."

Dad was speaking in what Mother called his "preacher" voice.

"But, Henry," George protested, "I was only going to have a beer."

"George, you know very well that if you had one beer you would soon have another and then another. The next thing you would be buying drinks for everyone in the tavern, and after a while you would be wandering up and down the street handing out money to every kid you saw. At least that's what you did last time you were here."

"How do you know all this stuff, Henry?" I heard George ask.

"In a town like this, word gets around pretty quick," Dad answered.

I couldn't hear what George said next, but I heard Dad continue.

"I think it would be best if you figure out where you are going next. I don't think it is a good idea for you to continue to stay here. I'm not going to make you leave right away, but I do want you to decide where you are going to go from here."

I heard Dad get up, so I quickly scurried away so Dad wouldn't know I had been listening.

It was about a week later when George announced that he had heard from Clara, Mother's sister in Omaha.

"Clara says that she thinks I can get a job as the maintenance man with one of the apartment buildings there," he told Mother and Dad. Clara's husband Martin was a janitor at an apartment house and knew about the opening.

"Let me check on train schedules," Dad said as he got up and headed to his study.

Dad loved trains. He had a whole drawer full of railroad timetables in his desk, so he could figure out how to go anywhere in the country. Of course, the only time he took the train was an occasional trip to Milwaukee for a church meeting. But he loved reading the timetables.

He soon returned with an itinerary for George.

"All right," said Mother. "We'll buy a train ticket here. I know Mr. Krueger, the station agent, can take care of that. I'll give you some money for meals, and I'll send the rest of your money to Clara, and she can take care of it for you."

George agreed and a few days later, we all got up early and went to the depot to see George get on the 7:30 train to Milwaukee. From there he would go to Chicago and then take the train to Omaha.

"That turned out better than last time," I heard Dad say to Mother as we walked home. "At least I didn't have to bail him out of jail."

"And the members didn't have anything to talk about this time," Mother agreed.

Chapter 19

Helene Learns to Eat a Cream Puff

"Amen," we said in unison as we finished our table prayer before starting supper. It was a special meal tonight: fried rainbow trout, with a fresh lettuce salad and baby creamed carrots, both from Dad's garden. One of Dad's pastor friends was an avid trout fisherman. When he had good luck fishing, he would often bring us some fresh trout.

"Now watch out for the bones," Mother warned us as she passed around the platter of fish.

"It was sure nice of Reverend Adams to share his catch with us," Phil commented as he helped himself to a filet. "Have you ever been trout fishing, Dad?" he asked.

"No," Dad responded, "I don't have the fancy equipment you need for trout fishing. I just stick to the old bamboo pole."

"Well, I'm sure glad Reverend Adams does," Phil answered.

No one has to encourage us to clean our plates tonight, I thought as I took a second helping of the carrots.

As we finished eating, Mother said, "And I have a special surprise for dessert tonight—tapioca pudding with fresh strawberries."

We all brightened up. Well, everyone but Phil. Phil would eat the tapioca pudding, but he would pass on the strawberries.

"Why, Phil," Mother would invariably say, "you always used to eat strawberries (or raspberries or pineapple or whatever fruit Mother happened to be serving). How come you don't like them anymore?"

Now as long as I could remember, my brother never ate fruit. Oh, he would eat an apple or maybe a banana once in a while, but otherwise, he would not eat fruit. Mother would then proceed to tell Phil that when he was a baby he would eat every kind of fruit there was.

"But now you won't eat any of it," Mother told him.

"I just don't like it," Phil answered.

"You just don't know what's good," Mother concluded, always eager to have the last word.

"I have an idea," Dad said, wanting to change the subject. "I think we should go to the State Fair this summer."

The State Fair, I thought. I hadn't been to the State Fair since we had lived in Milwaukee. I remember Mother had gotten all upset because she said I had gotten lost. She would never believe me when I told her I had NOT gotten lost. Everyone else had abandoned me.

Just to set the record straight, here's what actually happened. (Mother has her own version, but what I'm telling is exactly how things happened.)

I was four or five at the time. Our family had gone to the State Fair one Sunday afternoon with another pastor and his wife, friends of Mother and Dad. Mother hadn't seen them for a long time, so she was busy talking to them and not paying a whole lot of attention to us kids.

When we came to the farm machinery area, I was fascinated with all the tractors. There seemed to be hundreds of them. There were the red Farmall, green John Deere, orange Case, grey Ford Ferguson, and the white Oliver tractors. I was having fun crawling up on the seats, pretending to steer and drive them. I decided my favorite were the Case tractors. I liked the orange color. I went back to where they were and climbed on the biggest one.

I was having fun, pretending to drive. "Urrrrn, urrrrn," I went, turning the steering wheel back and forth. I was so busy driving, I didn't notice that the rest of the family had left.

I got off the tractor and looked around. No sign of them. Well, I thought, they'll be back, so I climbed up on my favorite Case tractor and started driving away.

As I was turning the steering wheel, a policeman came up to me.

"What's your name, little boy?" he asked. I told him.

"Your parents are looking for you. Why don't you come with me, and I'll take you to them. They reported that you were lost," he told me.

"OK," I agreed. "But I'm not lost. I know where I am."

In a few minutes, I was back with Mother and Dad and the rest.

"Don't you wander off like that again," Mother told me.

"Wander off," I protested, "I stayed right there. You're the ones who wandered off."

Anyway, that's what actually happened.

Meanwhile Dad was talking.

"Since it's Wisconsin's centennial, the State Fair is going to run for the entire month of August, not just the regular ten days," Dad explained. "I think we should pick a date and go to the fair."

I thought Mother would bring up this incident as a reason why we shouldn't go to the fair. Instead, she asked, "Can we afford it?"

Dad pointed out that he was getting some extra income this summer by directing special rehearsals of the Holland men's chorus.

"In that case, I think it is a marvelous idea," she said. "I want to meet Alice in Dairyland."

We had been hearing about Alice in Dairyland. Since Wisconsin was the leading dairy state, someone got the idea that there should be some sort of a dairy queen or princess to promote the industry. Rather than calling her the Cheese Queen or the Cheddar Princess, they decided to call her Alice in Dairyland.

"Why do you want to meet her?" we wanted to know.

"Why, haven't you read? Alice in Dairyland is the McGuire girl from Highland."

"Where?" Phil asked.

"Highland," Mother answered in a tone which implied everyone should know where Highland was. "Highland is the town right next to Avoca."

Avoca was Mother's hometown, located in the hills of southwest Wisconsin. We would often visit there since that's where Grandpa Olson and many other relatives lived.

"And," Mother continued, "I'm quite certain that her uncle is Patrick McGuire, the mail carrier from Highland, who is a good friend of Alfred's."

Alfred was Mother's oldest brother who was the rural mail carrier in Avoca. Patrick probably was a good friend of Uncle Alfred's since Alfred knew every rural mail carrier in southwest Wisconsin.

"We'll certainly do that," Dad agreed.

"Can Margie come too?" Phil asked. Margie was Phil's girlfriend.

"Sure," said Dad. "That would be fine."

Even though it was only June, we began looking forward to our trip to the State Fair in August.

We picked the date we would go. Phil arranged to get the day off from his job at the service station. Dad checked his schedule to be certain there was no council meeting or other church events.

August came and so did the day for our trip to the State Fair. We had been reading all about the fair in the *Milwaukee Journal* and listening to daily reports on WTMJ radio. Mother packed a picnic lunch.

"We'll picnic at noon and eat at the fair in the evening," Dad said. Eating out was always a big treat for us, so that was something else to anticipate.

Phil had driven out to the farm where Margie lived and picked her up. When they got back, we all got into Dad's '47 Chevy and left for Milwaukee.

"The State Fair is actually in West Allis, not Milwaukee," Dad explained as we headed south. Phil was driving and Dad was giving directions. Even though we hadn't lived in Milwaukee for many years, Dad knew his way around the city. I had only been to Milwaukee a couple of times since we had moved to the Village, so it was a big deal to visit Wisconsin's largest city.

As we neared the fairgrounds, traffic slowed. It seemed as though there were hundreds or maybe thousands of cars, all packed with fair goers and all headed in the same direction.

"Looks as though we picked a popular day to come," said Mother.

"Yes," Dad replied, "I read in the *Milwaukee Journal* that today is 'Madison Day' so I imagine that a lot of people are coming from there."

"Do you suppose the governor will be there?" Phil asked.

"It could very well be," Dad answered. "From what I have been reading, Governor Rennebohm has been to the fair quite often."

"I've never seen a governor," Helene said. "What do they look like?"

We all laughed.

"He looks like most other men," Mother told her. "I've never seen Governor Rennebohm either, so I really don't know exactly what he looks like."

We joined the line of cars edging their way into the fairground. There were parking attendants directing cars.

"Just follow their directions," Dad told Phil.

We came to a booth where attendants were collecting money. Dad reached into his pocket.

"How much?" he asked.

"Fifty cents," came the reply. Dad handed two quarters to Phil who paid the attendant.

We parked the car.

"There's a picnic grounds over there," Dad pointed out. "We'll leave the picnic basket in the car and come back for it at lunch time. Now everybody try to remember where we parked the car."

We joined the lines of people heading toward the entrance gates.

Dad bought the tickets, and we all went in.

"Now stay together. We don't want anyone getting lost," Mother said. Fortunately she didn't mention anything about my last visit to the fair.

There were so many things to see. There was the homemaking building with its exhibits of quilts, canned fruits and vegetables, and all sorts of handicrafts. There was the Four-H building with a whole array of projects from farm kids. We paused for a while and watched a young girl demonstrating how to make a cheese cake, using Wisconsin dairy products.

We walked through the farm machinery area, looking at all the latest equipment.

"They call that a combine," Dad explained, pointing to a large piece of equipment. "It won't be long and farmers won't be using threshing machines anymore."

"Look," said Mother, "there's the dairy building."

"I'm hungry," Helene said. "Can't we have something to eat?"

"Before we left, Dad gave me some money and told me I should buy everyone a treat," Margie said. "Maybe we can get something here."

"I know," I said, "let's have cream puffs."

I had read an article about how cream puffs were a popular treat in the dairy building.

"That sounds good," Phil agreed.

"And after that, let's see if we can find Alice in Dairyland," said Mother.

It wasn't a problem finding the cream puff counter—there was a great big line of people waiting to buy them.

We stood in line, waiting our turn. Helene was the first to get hers. She stood at the side waiting for the rest of us while carefully examining the large pastry filled with whipped cream.

As the rest of us joined her, she took a big bite, squeezing the cream puff. The cream spurted out the front of the cream puff just as two men in suits walked by. The whipped cream spattered the suit of the man closest to Helene.

"Oh, my cream puff," Helene wailed.

Mother quickly handed her own cream puff to Dad and went over to the man who had been hit with the cream.

"I'm so sorry," she said. "Here, let me help clean you off."

"Never mind," the man said as his companion pulled a handkerchief out of his pocket and said, "Here, Governor, use this."

Mother turned white.

"Governor," she stammered, "you're Governor Rennebohm."

"Yes, Ma'am. And who is this?" he asked, pointing to Helene.

Helene had calmed down by now, although she was still holding her empty cream puff.

"I'm Helene," she said.

"Well, Helene, I'm pleased to meet you. I'm Governor Rennebohm and I'd like to show you how to eat a cream puff. Let's see if these nice people will let me cut through the line, so I can buy you a replacement."

Quite a crowd had gathered by this time, including a photographer. The people let the governor go to the counter where he bought a cream puff and brought it back to where we were standing.

"Now," he told Helene, as he knelt down beside her, "here's how you eat a cream puff. You take off the top and dip it into the cream, using it kind of like a spoon. Then when most of the cream is gone, you can eat the rest of the cream puff without the cream spurting out."

Helene nodded and started eating her cream puff.

"Governor, I am terribly sorry about your suit," Mother said.

"Don't worry. From here I'm going to the dairy barn, so I wore my oldest suit today," the governor assured her.

The governor and his aide left, the crowd dispersed, and we finished eating our cream puffs. We all agreed that it was a great treat and we liked the way the governor taught us how to eat the cream puffs.

"Since we're here in the dairy building, let's find Alice in Dairyland," Mother said.

"I saw a sign when we came in that pointed to Alice in Dairyland," I told Mother.

We walked back to the entrance and then followed the sign. As we turned the corner, we all suddenly stopped. There in front of us was this huge animated figure of what had to be Alice in Dairyland. She must have been 15 or 20 feet tall. There she stood, talking with people.

We gingerly approached and the figure spoke.

"My, what a nice-looking family. How are you folks today?" she said, looking down at us.

"Ask her if she knows Uncle Alfred," I heard Phil whisper to Mother. She gave him a disgusted look.

"We're just fine," Dad answered.

"Are you enjoying the fair?" she asked Helene.

"It's great. I just had a cream puff," Helene answered. Oops, I thought, wrong question. Now we'll hear all about squirting the governor with whipped cream. But it didn't happen.

"You folks have a great day at the fair and remember to keep eating those wonderful Wisconsin dairy products," she said, turning away and starting to talk with another family.

"Well, that was something," Margie said. "I wonder how they do that."

"There must be a microphone inside and someone controlling it from a booth or something," Phil guessed.

"That was quite an experience," Mother agreed, "but I still want to see the real person."

"There's an information booth over there," Phil pointed out. "They'll probably know when the real Alice will be here."

We walked over to the booth and saw there was a schedule posted:

"Meet Alice in Dairyland in person," it read.

"She should be here in a few minutes," Dad noted, checking his watch.

Mother talked with the woman at the booth and reported, "She will be right over there. We should get in line."

We followed Mother's lead and joined the line. In a few minutes, we heard people saying, "Here she comes."

And Alice appeared—a striking young woman, with dark hair wearing a small tiara and a ribbon proclaiming that she was "Alice in Dairyland".

"Oh, we should have brought a camera," Mother exclaimed when she saw people taking pictures.

"I did," I replied, showing Mother my trusty Argus C-3 35-millimeter camera.

"Oh, good. Be sure to get some pictures of her."

I assured Mother I would.

The line moved slowly forward. Finally, we were there.

Alice in Dairyland (whose real name we knew was Margaret McGuire) was a tall (although not nearly as tall as the animated version), attractive brunette.

Mother immediately introduced herself and our family to her and then began quizzing her

"Now is your uncle the mail carrier in Highland?" she asked.

"Yes," Alice replied, "that would be my Uncle Pat."

"I thought so," Mother told her. She went on to explain that her brother Alfred was the rural mail carrier in Avoca and that he knew her uncle through the mail carriers' association.

As they were talking, a man in a suit came up to Alice.

"Excuse me for interrupting," he said to her. "I need to talk with you for a minute."

They stepped aside while we waited.

Alice came back, looked at our family and then asked Mother, "Will you folks be here through the afternoon?"

"Yes," Mother answered, "we plan to attend the grandstand show this evening."

"Good," she answered, then turning to Helene, she asked, "How would you like to be the junior Alice in Dairyland in the parade today?"

None of us knew what to say.

The man with Alice explained that each afternoon there was a parade through the fairgrounds and that every day a young girl from around the state was selected to ride on the float with Alice.

"We just got word that the junior princess for today has come down with chicken pox, and we need someone to fill in for her. Would you be willing to do this?" he asked Helene and Mother.

"Can I?" Helene begged, "can I, please?"

Mother paused. She was always pushing her children to do things, but now when it was thrust upon one of them, she didn't know what to say. So she did what she usually did when she didn't know what to do.

"Ask your father," she replied.

No problem here, I thought. Unless it was something bad or expensive, Dad usually would say yes to Helene. Today was no exception.

"Sure, why not? It sounds like fun," Dad answered.

Helene jumped up and down with excitement.

"What do we need to do?" Mother asked the man.

"You need to be at the start of the parade route no later than 3:30," he explained. "We have princess costumes of different sizes, so I'm sure one will fit her."

He pulled a map out of his pocket and gave it to Dad.

"Here's where you should be," pointing on the map. "We'll provide seating for the rest of the family. The parade will end up right where it starts, so you can meet your little princess there," he said, smiling at Helene.

"I'll see you this afternoon," Alice said to Helene. "Now I need to talk with all these people who have been waiting."

We left the dairy building.

"Let's go to the Wisconsin Centennial pavilion," Dad suggested. "After all, that's the main reason why we came."

"This is really interesting," I said as we toured the exhibits. "Did you know that the first European explorer came to Wisconsin in 1639?"

"That was only about 20 years after the Pilgrims landed at Plymouth Rock," Phil pointed out.

When we were done at the Centennial building, Mother said it was lunch time. We walked back to our car, got our picnic basket and went over to the area where there were tables for people who had brought picnics.

"How long until it's time for the parade?" Helene wanted to know as we spread out our lunch.

"It's a few hours yet," Mother told her. "Now you eat a good lunch, so you won't faint when you're in the parade."

Mother always worried about dire events happening to her children. In winter, she always made us bundle up so we wouldn't catch pneumonia. When we went swimming, any time the water was up to our waists, she would call from shore to come back so we wouldn't drown. Mother always called from shore. She never went in the water that I can remember.

"I will," Helene promised, taking a sandwich. We finished lunch, took the picnic basket back to the car and then returned to the fairgrounds.

Goodness, but there were so many things to see. We walked through the farm equipment area.

"Now don't you get lost here," Mother cautioned me.

"That was years ago," I responded.

There was certainly an array of tractors.

"That's the kind we have," said Margie, pointing to the bright orange Allis Chalmers. "Dad just got a new one. He really likes it."

"Look," I said, "there's the Wisconsin Conservation Department exhibit. Let's go there."

It looked like a scene from Northern Wisconsin. There was a lumberjack bunkhouse and a stream with a waterfall. We strolled down the path along the stream.

"Look," cried Helene, "there are fish in the water."

"There sure are," Dad agreed. "I see northern pike and trout."

"Reverend Adams should be here," Phil said, remembering our dinner when we had first discussed going to the fair.

Further down the path we saw cages with fox, mink and badgers.

"So that's what a badger looks like," Margie exclaimed.

We all agreed that this was one of the best exhibits we had seen at the fair.

"We can't lose track of time. We have to be sure to get Helene to the parade," Mother cautioned.

"Anyone want to see the farm animals?" Dad asked.

We said sure and walked to the livestock area. There were barns full of horses, chickens, ducks, geese, pigs, but especially cows.

"Look at them all," Dad said. "That's why they call Wisconsin 'America's Dairyland'."

There were cows of all kinds: black and white Holsteins, Brown Swiss, gold-colored Guernseys and others I didn't recognize.

"What time is it?" Helene asked as we left the cow barn.

Dad looked at his watch.

"I think maybe we should start heading over to the parade area. We don't want to be late."

Dad checked the map the man had given him and said, "Let's go this way."

Dad was a great map reader, I thought. When we were traveling, he always knew where we were and where we were going.

When we got there, the parade was beginning to assemble.

It didn't look like much of a parade. There was a high school band, busy tuning up, looking hot in their full uniforms. There were some 4-H clubs in green and white tee shirts who looked as though they would be marching. There was a group of horses with riders in cowboy and cowgirl attire. That was about it.

"Look," Helene shouted.

There came this big, horse-drawn float, adorned with a large sign reading: "Alice in Dairyland—Margaret McGuire."

Just then the man who we had met with Alice came up.

"Good, you're all here. Why don't you and your mother come with me," he said to Helene, "we'll get your princess costume and tell you where to go. The rest of you stay here, and I'll come back and take you to your seats."

We stood in the shade and waited. I noticed there were several more floats lining up.

"It looks like it will be a bigger parade than I thought," I told the family.

In a few minutes, Mother and the man returned.

"Oh you should see her," Mother exclaimed. "She really looks cute."

She turned to me. "Be sure to get pictures."

There was a small set of bleachers near the start of the parade.

"We call this our reviewing stand. Why don't you sit there," the man said, pointing to the top row of the seats. "Since today is Madison Day at the fair, the governor and quite a few state officials will be here in the reviewing stand."

"Oh, dear," Mother said softly, "I hope he got his suit cleaned up."

We all smiled and the man looked at Mother quizzically.

Dad explained what had happened earlier.

"Don't worry. Governor Rennebohm is a good sport, and he probably got a big laugh out of it," he said.

"I certainly hope so," Mother replied.

We climbed to our seats. Soon the reviewing stand was filled.

"I wonder who all these people are?" Mother said to Dad.

"Well, there's the governor, the lieutenant governor, and that," pointing to a man with a big mustache, "is Fred Zimmermann. He's been Secretary of

State as long as I can remember. He was governor when I moved back to Wisconsin after I got out of the seminary. I suppose the rest are state legislators and other officials."

"Goodness, isn't it something that we're sitting here with all these important people," Mother reflected.

The parade began passing by the reviewing stand. We all stood as a group of American Legion members marched by with the United States and Wisconsin flags. Then came the West Bend High School band, loudly playing *On Wisconsin*.

"I wonder how many times *On Wisconsin* has been played this year," Dad commented as the band marched by. Since the governor stood for *On Wisconsin*, everyone else in the reviewing stand stood as well.

Then came the 4-H clubs and the other units of the parade.

"Here comes the Alice in Dairyland float," Mother said. "Get your camera ready," she told me.

As the float came by, the governor looked at Helene, smiled and called out, "Hi there, little cream puff girl!"

Helene looked surprised, smiled and waved back. We all laughed, and I got a picture of Helene waving.

We went back to the parade staging area to wait for Helene. The floats returned, and the man helped Helene down. We all said goodbye to him and to Alice.

"Well," said Dad, "I think we should get some supper and then go to the grandstand so we can get good seats for the show tonight."

Eating out for supper at the State Fair! Wow, I thought, that was a treat! But where to go? There must have been a hundred places to eat.

"Oh, look," said Mother, "there's a dining hall run by Epiphany Lutheran Church. I bet that would be good."

"That would be like eating at a church basement potluck," Phil answered. "Besides, I bet Epiphany is Wisconsin Synod." (Our brand of Lutheranism was the American Lutheran Church and the Wisconsin Synod didn't have anything to do with us.)

"Let's try this," Dad said, pointing to a tent which advertised 20 different kinds of sandwiches. "We can all find something we like there. Remember, 50 cents is the limit for a sandwich and a drink."

"Do we have to have milk to drink?" Helene wanted to know.

"No," Dad answered before Mother could reply. "You can have anything you like."

"I'm going to have Grandpa Graf's Root Beer," I said. That was a root beer only available in Milwaukee, and it was a real treat.

We all decided on which sandwiches we wanted, Dad ordered, paid for everything and when the sandwiches and drinks came, we all sat at a long table under the tent.

We finished eating, stopped at one of the public restrooms and heeded Mother's admonition to be sure we washed our hands.

We climbed the stairs to the grandstand. Since we were early, we got good seats right in the middle. In front of us was a large stage.

"How come there are bleachers behind the stage?" I asked. It seemed strange that people would sit, looking at the back of the stage.

"They won't be using them tonight," Dad said. He explained that the Green Bay Packers played some of their games here.

"The football field runs between the grandstand and those bleachers," Dad explained.

"But if they're the Green Bay Packers, how come they play here? And why don't they call them the Green Bay-Milwaukee Packers?" I asked.

Dad said that for many years the Packers had played part of their schedule in Milwaukee.

"They may be the Green Bay Packers, but I think they really belong to the entire state of Wisconsin," Dad said.

The grandstand began filling up. A band began a pre-performance concert. The band finished and left the stage. Another, smaller band seated themselves in front of the stage.

As it began to get dark, the stage suddenly blazed with light, a man in formal wear came on stage and the show began.

There were all sorts of acts—singing, dancing, acrobatics, a comedian, and what I liked best were the Flying Wenningers. They did all sorts of trapeze acts, flying through the air, letting go of the trapeze and being caught by another member of the troupe. Round after round of applause greeted their performance.

Then came the grand finale with all the cast members parading on to the stage. The band struck up *On Wisconsin*, and everyone in the grandstand stood and sang and cheered. As we finished, the lights on the stage went off, and the air was filled with fireworks.

I had never seen such a display. Finally, on the ground at the side of the grandstand, the word "Forward" was spelled out as the band again played *On Wisconsin*.

We all stood and cheered.

"Well," Dad said, "that was quite a show. Now let's all stay together as we go to the car."

There was a big crowd leaving the grandstand, making its way to the parking lots. We found our car and climbed in.

"You OK to drive?" Dad asked Phil.

"Sure," he responded, "you just tell me where to go."

We inched our way out of the parking lot. It took a while, but we were soon heading north.

"That was quite a day," Dad commented. "You won't forget today, will you, Helene?"

There was no response. Helene was sound asleep.

It was late when we got home. We climbed out of the car. Dad carried Helene inside, and Phil took Margie home. Dad was right, I thought, it was quite a day.

The next day when we got our *Milwaukee Journal*, we were amazed to see a picture of Helene with the governor. Dad read the cutline out loud, "Governor Rennebohm gives a lesson in cream puff eating to a young constituent."

"I'm not a constituent," Helene protested, "I'm a Lutheran."

Chapter 20

What Was in Mr. Schiffler's Barn

"Martin wants to know if I can stay at his house for a couple of days," I said to Mother.

Martin was a friend of mine who lived on a farm a mile or so north of the Village. His family belonged to our church, and his parents were about as close of friends as my parents had in the congregation.

"I think that would be OK," Mother answered. "I'll call his mother to see that it's OK with her. When were you thinking of doing this?"

"Oh, maybe next week," I answered. Martin and I hadn't really set a time. I would often play with him out on his farm; although this would be the first time I would stay overnight.

Mother called Martin's mother, and the arrangements were made.

"How would it be if I rode my bike out there? I can carry the stuff I need in my Boy Scout backpack, and that way I'll have my bike there, so Martin and I can go riding," I suggested to Mother.

I was certain that Mother would raise objections as she usually did. I could just hear her come up with things like, "That's a long way—I don't know if you can make it," or, "That might be dangerous—what if one of the farmer's bulls got out when you were riding by," or all sorts of other reasons she would come up with.

To my surprise she offered no objections.

"That would be fine," she agreed.

The next week, I took my backpack and rode off on my Schwinn bicycle. It took me only 15 minutes or so of easy pedaling to get there.

Martin and I had a lot of fun together.

"Right now is a slow time for farm work," Martin told me. "The peas are all harvested, and the sweet corn hasn't started yet. The threshing is done for the grain, and it will be a while before it's time for another crop of hay. So there's just the usual milking and feeding the animals."

On a dairy farm, there was work to do seven days a week. Cows had to be milked morning and night. Pigs had to be fed. Eggs had to be gathered. Young livestock had to be fed and watered.

"How come you still have horses?" I asked Martin when we were in the barn. "Your dad has a tractor."

We were standing in front of the stalls holding two big black Belgian horses.

"Dad says it's real handy to have a team of horses. They can haul the stone boat when we pick up rocks in the spring. He says that if we get a bad snow storm and the milk truck can't get through, we can hitch up the horses to the sleigh and take the milk cans in. Actually Dad is just like my Uncle Art. They both grew up using horses, and they just like having them around. Uncle Art has a pair just like Dad's."

We left the barn and got on our bikes.

"Let's go this way," Martin said, pointing to a small side road.

"Where does it go?" I asked.

"You'll see," Martin answered as we pedaled down the road between a field of corn and the pasture where the herd of black and white Holsteins was grazing. We rode through a small grove of trees and then the road ended in the yard of what looked like an old farm. Martin motioned for us to stop.

"Shhh," he said, putting his finger to his lips.

There was a house, a large barn and a few smaller buildings. We got off our bikes. I followed Martin as he pulled his bike into the grove of trees.

"Who lives here?" I whispered. "It doesn't look like anybody is using the buildings."

"This is the old Schiffler place," Martin answered. "No one had lived here for years until Mr. Schiffler came back last year. Dad has rented the land from him for a long time. Mr. Schiffler seems to be a nice enough guy, but he really keeps to himself. He always seems to be working in his barn, but I don't know why. Let's see if we can peek in the barn."

We sneaked up to the barn on the side opposite the house. We crawled up to the window and were about to peek in when ...

"Hey," called a voice, "what do you think you're doing?"

We both stood up.

"Oh, hi, Mr. Schiffler," Martin stammered. "Oh, we're just out, kind of exploring around."

"Exploring? Looks as though you're doing some window peeking here." His voice sounded a bit testy.

"Oh, we're just curious. I was just showing my friend around," Martin answered.

"Who's your friend?" Mr. Schiffler asked.

Martin introduced me and added, "His dad is the preacher at the Lutheran church."

Mr. Schiffler paused for a moment.

"So your dad is the preacher at Emanuel," he finally said.

I nodded. There was another pause.

"Say, boys," his tone seemed to grow more friendly. "Why don't you come in the house. I bet you'd like something cold to drink."

"Sure," replied Martin, "we'll get our bikes and be right there."

As Martin and I walked back to where we had parked our bikes, I asked him, "What do you make of this?"

"I think he's a pretty nice guy. He just doesn't seem real sociable."

We rode our bikes to his house and laid them on the ground. Mr. Schiffler was at the door.

"Come on in. Never mind the mess. I don't have anything fancy—no Coke or root beer. However, I've got Watkins mix, so I can make you either orange or cherry."

"Great, I love Watkins," I answered.

Watkins products were sold mainly to farmers. The Watkins man would go from farm to farm selling an array of products generally to the farmer's wife. There would be vanilla and spices, a lot of home remedies and my favorite—a flavored syrup you would mix with water and make a wonderful drink. We never had it at home since the Watkins man never seemed to call on people in the Village.

"I'll have cherry," I said.

"Me too," Martin said.

"Sounds good. I'll have the same," Mr. Schiffler said. He took a bottle of the syrup, mixed it with water and then added ice from the refrigerator.

We all sat at the kitchen table.

"So your dad is the preacher at Emanuel," he said again.

I again nodded.

"You know, I really should belong there. That's where I was baptized and confirmed. Maybe I'll have to come one of these days," he said.

"We're open every Sunday," I said. We all smiled.

"When were you a member?" Martin asked.

"It was a long time ago," he replied, "a long time before you two were born."

He grew silent, took a long drink from his glass and looked out the window.

"Tell you what. Finish your drinks and I'll show you what's in the barn so you won't have to go around peeking in the windows."

Martin and I looked at each other, quickly gulped down our drinks and jumped up. We followed Mr. Schiffler out of the kitchen and across the yard. He stopped at the side door of the barn, took a key ring out of his pocket and unlocked the padlock on the door. He opened the door, and switched on the light and motioned for us to follow him into the barn. The stanchions for the cows had all been taken out—probably a long time ago.

We stopped and stared. What in the world!

"Well, boys, what do you think?" Mr. Schiffler asked.

There in front of us was a freshly painted circus wagon. I had seen pictures of circus wagons, but had never seen a real one.

"Where in the world did you get that?" Martin finally managed to ask.

"It's a long story," Mr. Schiffler replied. "Here, let me show it to you and then we'll go back to the house and I'll tell you the story."

We walked around the wagon, looking at its big wheels and its high driver's seat. We noticed there were railings on each side of the top.

"It's a band wagon," he explained. "It was used in the circus parade. Musicians would store their instruments and music in it while the show moved from city to city. During parades they would sit on top and play."

"Wow! It's really something." said Martin. "This sounds like it's going to be an interesting story."

We left the barn. Mr. Schiffler closed and carefully locked the door. We followed him back to the house. Inside the house he fixed more glasses of Watkins drink and then joined us at the kitchen table.

"Well," he began, "it's a long story. It goes back 50 years. My father had the farm here. It wasn't all that good of a farm. It didn't have as good of land as your dad's and uncle's farms have," noting this to Martin, "so he had to work extra hard to try to make a living for us. There was my parents and me. When I said he worked hard, I mean we all worked hard.

"Father made me drop out of school after confirmation. I was 15 at the time. He told me that I had enough schooling to be a farmer, and besides I was learning too much English. Everything was pretty much German around here. I was confirmed in German. All the church services were in German, and most of the people my parents associated with were Germans. Of course, I only spoke English in school, but Father thought that was too much.

"Anyway, I stopped going to school and worked on the farm with Father. I didn't much care for farming. I liked taking care of the horses OK, but I sure didn't like the rest of the work—milking the cows, taking care of the pigs, plowing, making hay, fixing fences ... there was always plenty to do.

"I did this for a year or so, all the time trying to figure out what I could do to get off the farm and start doing something I liked. I finally came up with a plan.

"I had seen posters around the Village that the Ringling Brothers circus was going to perform in Fond du Lac. I knew the circus had a lot of horses, so I figured that if I got over to Fond du Lac I might be able to get a job with the circus.

"But there were a lot of problems to figure out. I just couldn't go to Father and announce that I was going to join the circus, and would he please give me a ride to Fond du Lac. That wouldn't work.

"It turned out that the day the circus was performing in Fond du Lac, Mother and Father were going to go to a farm auction in Fairwater. Father was looking for some more milk cows and figured this would be an opportunity to get some at a good price.

"Now this was in 1898, and the Spanish-American War had started. I decided that when Mother and Father were at the auction, I would leave them a note saying I had taken the train to Milwaukee and was going to join the army.

"That's what I did. Left the note, took a few clothes, a couple of dollars I had saved and walked to Fond du Lac."

"You walked all the way to Fond du Lac," Martin said. "Why, that's 20 miles."

"Well, it was quite a hike—took me five hours or so, but I got there without any problem. I found the circus. It turned out that most of the men working with the horses were German, so I got a job right away. I soon found out that the Ringlings were German as well. Their name had been Ruengling when they started their show down in Baraboo some 20 years earlier.

"So I started work right away. I helped drive the horses as they loaded the wagons on the railroad cars, and we took off, headed for Green Bay."

"Wow," I said. "I've read a lot of stories about boys running away to join the circus, but this is the first time I ever knew anyone who actually did it."

Mr. Schiffler smiled and continued his story.

"I got to know Mr. Al Ringling quite well. He saw I was a hard worker and enjoyed working with horses. It wasn't long until he made me a driver which meant that when we had a parade, I would wear a fancy jacket and drive the band wagon at the head of the parade."

"A wagon like the one you have in the barn?" Martin asked.

"The wagon in the barn is the very same one I drove. I'll get to that shortly," he said.

"About a year or so later, I wrote to Mother and Father, telling them I had not joined the army, but was working with a circus. I didn't say which circus or where I was. I wasn't 18 years old yet, and I figured that if Father found out where I was, he might come and bring me back to the farm. I wanted to let Mother know I was OK. You have to remember at that time there were maybe 50 or 100 circuses traveling around the country, so if Father wanted to search for me, it would take some doing.

"Well, the years went by. I kept getting more responsibilities with the show; although I continued driving the wagon because I really enjoyed it. In 1908 I met a wonderful woman. She was a bareback rider in one of the acts. She liked the fact that I was good with horses. It wasn't long until we got married. A couple of years later we had a son. We named him John after my father. I would write to my parents now and then, letting them know how things were going. I never gave them an address, so I really didn't know what was happening with them. Anyway, I let them know they were grandparents and sent them a schedule of where we would be playing. We were back in Wisconsin that summer, and when we pulled into Delevan, there was a letter waiting for me. It was from my father, written in German which was the only language he knew for writing. He was glad to hear about his namesake, but also told me that my mother had passed away the previous year. I felt bad that I didn't know about this, but it was my own fault.

"Well, long about World War I, things started to change. The Ringling Brothers had bought the Barnum and Bailey Circus some years earlier, but had operated it separately. In 1919, a lot happened. Mr. Al Ringling died and then the other brothers decided to merge the two circuses into one, the Ringling Brothers, Barnum and Bailey Circus.

"After the merger, all sorts of things changed. For one thing, we no longer had our winter quarters down in Baraboo. And another thing was that circus parades were ending, so that meant the fancy horse drawn wagons weren't needed anymore. We still used a lot of horses to help put up tents and to load railroad cars, so I still had a job. When it came time to head to winter quarters, we took a lot of the old wagons and parked them in the sheds in Baraboo before heading to our new winter quarters, first in Bridgeport, Connecticut, and then to Sarasota, Florida.

"My wife was still performing as a bareback rider. Most of my work was now with the performing horses since there weren't parades anymore. My wife was teaching our son to be a performer. She said there was no future for him just working with horses. He needed to be a performer.

"It was in 1922 when my son was about your age," he said, pointing to us, "when John was riding with his mother. I don't know what happened, but John slipped off the horse. He got hit on the head by the horse's hoof. We took him to the hospital, but there wasn't much they could do for him. Two days later he died."

We sat there, stunned at his recitation.

"From then on, things started going downhill. I blamed my wife for what happened. She got real depressed. One thing led to another, and one day she packed up her things and left. It was about three years later that I got the papers that she wanted a divorce. There wasn't much I could do but agree.

"Well, things got worse for me. I started drinking more than I should have. I got a couple of warnings from my boss that I better straighten out. I tried, but I couldn't do it.

"Then one day, the big boss himself, Mr. John Ringling North, who had taken over after the last of the brothers died, sent word that I should come to see him in his office. The office was located in one of the circus's railroad cars which was parked on a siding along with the other support cars.

"When I got there, he sat me down, stood in front of me and laid down the law like even my father had never done when he was mad at me. I can still hear his words ringing in my ears: 'Now look,' he told me, 'you've been a good employee here. You go way back with the show. You knew all my uncles. If you had been one of our ordinary workers, you would have been out of here long ago. But enough is enough. This is your last chance. You straighten out your life and quit drinking, otherwise you will be out of here.'

"Well, that got my attention as you might guess. The circus was my whole life, and it was my home. I did start getting my life back together. I quit drinking, started going to Alcoholics Anonymous—I found out there was a meeting of them right with the circus—and things got better for me. Even Mr. John Ringling North told me he was glad that I had straightened out my life.

"During this time, my father had died, and I found out that I had inherited the farm. I rented out the land to your dad. I let my cousin live in the house if he would take care of things and keep the buildings repaired; so that all worked out OK.

"I was getting on to retirement age. I thought of staying in Florida where most of the circus people lived. But something kept telling me to come back to Wisconsin where I had grown up. My cousin had died, and the house was vacant.

"So I decided to come back here," he said to Martin. "You remember when I came back here."

Martin nodded.

"But what about the wagon?" Martin asked.

"I'll get to that," he answered. "Before I left the circus, I asked Mr. John Ringling North what had happened to the old circus wagons. He said a lot of them had just worn out and had been discarded, but that a few of them were still left at the old winter quarters in Baraboo. I asked if the band wagon I had driven was still there and if so, could I buy it? He said he would check and get back to me.

"A couple of weeks later he told me that the band wagon was still in Baraboo and if I wanted it, I could have it, but I would need to get it out of there. So I arranged to get it trucked up to the farm here, not knowing for sure what I would do with it.

"Once it was here, it sat in the barn for a few months. It brought back a lot of memories for me, most of them bad. But then I got the idea of fixing it up. It would keep me busy and maybe I could have it as sort of a memorial to my son.

"So," he concluded, "that's the story of the wagon."

"You mean, you fixed it up all by yourself?" I asked.

"Pretty much. I took some of the iron work to George Vercke, the Village blacksmith, to have it repaired, but most of the work I did by myself. I had a lot of time, and I knew that wagon pretty doggone well after all the years of driving it."

"What are you going to do with it now?" Martin asked.

"I don't know. I heard that Chappie Fox was talking about starting a circus museum in Baraboo. Maybe I'll see if he wants to have it there. Otherwise, I'll just keep here for the time being. Meanwhile, I would appreciate it if you boys wouldn't talk about it. I don't want a bunch of nosey people poking around here."

We nodded agreement. Mr. Schiffler followed us as we left the house and got our bikes.

"You boys come back and see me again. It gets kind of lonely here," he called as we rode away.

Little did he know, or did we know, that we would be back sooner than he thought we would.

Chapter 21

Cousin Esther and the Poor Little Piggies

I was standing in our front hallway, waiting for my friend Rich to deliver the *Milwaukee Journal*. People in the Village got one of two daily newspapers. About half the people got the *Commonwealth-Reporter*, the daily published in the county seat of Fond du Lac some 20 miles from the Village. The paper was cheaper than the *Journal* and had local news. However, subscribers had to go to the post office to pick it up when it arrived each afternoon between 4:00 and 5:00. We got the *Journal*. It was delivered to the door each day, and a lot of people liked the convenience; plus the *Journal* was a larger paper, had better sports coverage and (which was very important to me) had better comic strips.

We did like getting the Fond du Lac paper to keep up with the local happenings, but as Mother pointed out, we couldn't afford both papers. "Why, that would be six cents a day," she explained.

We solved this dilemma by trading papers with our neighbors, the Signers. The Signers lived across the street from us. I shoveled their walk in the winter and mowed their lawn in the summer. I'm not certain how we decided to trade newspapers, but we had been doing it for a long time. I felt that we got the better end of the trade. The Signers were retired, so when they got the Fond du Lac paper, they would sit down and usually finish reading it before supper and by 6:00 or 6:30 p.m., Mrs. Signer would walk over and leave the paper at our side door.

Our family, on the other hand, would rarely finish reading the paper that quickly. Sometimes when Mother was busy, it would be three or four days before she would get the papers read, and then I would take quite a bundle of papers to the Signers and leave them on their porch. But the Signers were very patient about this, and the trade worked well.

As I stood looking out the window at the side of the front door, I saw Rich ride his bicycle up the front walk to deliver the *Journal*. I opened the door, reached for the paper, said "Hi" to Rich, and watched as he wheeled off on his bike.

I took the paper into the living room, sprawled out on my favorite chair and pulled out the "Green Sheet". The *Journal* printed its comics on green paper called the "Green Sheet". Well, it was called the "Green Sheet" by everyone but Grandpa Olson. Grandpa was slightly color blind, and he always referred to it as the "Blue Sheet".

I curled up in the chair and started reading. As I was engrossed in the latest episode of "Mark Trail", I realized that Mother and Dad were talking in Dad's study. I quietly put down the paper and started listening.

They were talking about the letter Dad would be writing in the family Circle Letter. What would Dad be telling his eight siblings (along with Grandfather Kurtz, who all got the Circle Letter) about us now? Hopefully nothing too embarrassing.

"I suppose you could mention what those two just did," I heard Mother say. I perked up my ears. They were talking about Cousin Esther and me. We were "Those Two" who were always accused of getting in trouble and causing problems.

It's true, when we were little, we did get into trouble when we got together. But that was a long time ago. We were fairly grown up now and didn't cause many problems. Well, maybe the last episode was an exception. I felt it was just an unfortunate accident. Here's what happened.

You'll remember that Esther was my favorite cousin. She was about six months older than me, and we had always been best friends. Her mother was Dad's sister and her father was Dad's best friend going back to the time when they were in college and seminary.

Esther and her mother and dad lived in a small town in southwest Wisconsin where her dad was the pastor at the Lutheran church. The town also was my mother's hometown, so there were a lot of her family living there as well as Uncle Walter, Aunt Helen and Cousin Esther. I felt I was related to half the people there. Grandpa Olson lived there as did several uncles and aunts, cousins, second cousins, great aunts and uncles and other relatives.

As usual this summer, we went there for part of our vacation. This was a small town, about half the size of the Village where we lived. Early one evening we went to Uncle Alfred and Aunt Ilma's, Mother's brother and sister-in-law. Normally we would have walked the three blocks to their little farm at the edge of town. However, we drove there in Uncle Walter's car since after our visit we were planning to go to the neighboring town where a frozen custard shop had just opened.

"What's frozen custard?" Esther asked me.

"It's like ice cream, only better," I told her, recalling when we lived in Milwaukee. Milwaukee was famous for frozen custard, a rich soft ice cream. It was always a special treat when we got to have a frozen custard cone.

Mother and Dad and Uncle Walter and Aunt Helen were busy visiting with Uncle Alfred and Aunt Ilma. Aunt Ilma had made a pot of coffee, and we could see them sitting around the dining room table, chatting away. Uncle Alfred was a great storyteller, and we would frequently hear laughter coming from the house.

Esther and I were playing outside when we wandered over to the fenced yard on the other side of the house. There was a high fence designed to keep Alfred's chickens from escaping. Now, in addition to the chickens, there were two pigs behind the fence.

"I didn't know Alfred raised pigs," Esther said.

"He usually doesn't," I explained, "but one of Uncle Carl's pigs had too many babies, so he told Alfred he could have the two baby pigs if he would bottle feed them."

Uncle Carl was another of my mother's brothers. He had been a bachelor uncle who had stayed with us when we lived in Milwaukee where he had been a school teacher. After we moved from Milwaukee, he got married and had two children. He decided he had had enough of teaching and moved back to his hometown to take over the family farm.

"What will he do with them then?" Esther wanted to know.

"He'll fatten them up and then butcher them this fall," I replied.

"Butcher them! Oh, the poor little piggies," Esther cried.

"But the ham and bacon will sure be good," I told her.

We went over to the fence, and the two pigs came over, sticking their snouts through the large holes of the chicken wire.

"I bet they're hungry," Esther said.

"Let's go ask Uncle Alfred if we can feed them," I answered.

We went into the house and asked.

"You can give each one an ear of corn," Uncle Alfred said, "but that's all. And don't do anything else," he added remembering some of our earlier escapades.

"OK," we assured him. We left the house and went to the corn crib where the corn was stored.

"Let's find some nice big ears for the piggies," Esther said.

We found two ears and took them over to the fence. The two pigs came running up when they saw we had corn. We pushed the ears through the fence, one for each of the pigs and watched as they noisily gobbled the kernels off the cobs. They soon finished and looked at us, wanting more.

"That's all," I told them. The pigs continued to stand there with their snouts sticking through the openings in the chicken wire, waiting to see if we would bring more food.

We left them standing there and walked over to Uncle Walter's car.

"I sure wish they would hurry up and come," Esther said. "I really am anxious to try frozen custard."

We climbed in the car and sat on the front seat. I was on the passenger side and Esther was in the driver's seat.

"Daddy showed me how to start the car," Esther said. "This is the starter," she said, pointing to a small pedal on the floor. "This is the gas pedal; this is the brake and this ..." Pointing to the other pedal, she paused. "I think it's something called a clutch. I don't know what it does."

We sat for a few minutes.

"I sure wish they would come," I said.

"Me too," Esther agreed.

We continued to sit.

"I got an idea," Esther said. "Why don't I start the car and maybe then they'll stop talking and come out."

I nodded in agreement.

The key was in the ignition. Esther reached her foot forward to the starter pedal and pushed it.

The car was in reverse gear, and as Esther pushed the starter, the car jumped backward. As she pulled off her foot in surprise, she hit the gas pedal, and the car lurched back hitting the fence while two surprised pigs watched in astonishment.

One, two, three fence posts went down before the car stopped. The two pigs, frightened by the noise, leaped over the fallen fence and disappeared just as all the grown-ups came rushing out of the house.

"Oh, dear," I heard Mother scream. "Are you two hurt?"

They quickly surrounded the car. Fortunately, neither of us was hurt. The back bumper of the car had knocked down the fence poles, but aside from a scratch or two from the fence wire, the car and the occupants were unscathed.

"What happened to the pigs?" Aunt Ilma asked, once we explained about the car.

Everyone looked around. There was not a pig in sight. Pete Gilbertson (another of Mother's relatives) who lived across the street from Uncle Alfred's had been watching the events from his front porch.

"Ya looking for your pigs, Alfred?" he called.

"Yes," Alfred replied, "did you see where they went?"

"Yup, they headed that way," Pete said, pointing toward the downtown area.

"We better get down there and see if we can find those pigs," Alfred said. "Ilma, you call Max Swensen and tell him to be on the lookout for the pigs." Max was the town marshal.

Dad, Uncle Walter, Esther and I climbed into Alfred's car, and we took off for the business section of Avoca, some four blocks distance.

When we got downtown, which consisted of a block of businesses, the pigs were nowhere in sight.

"Where in the world could they have gone?" Alfred wondered.

About that time Max appeared. Alfred explained what had happened.

"They couldn't have gone too far," said Max. "They've got to be around here somewhere."

"There's one of them," cried Uncle Walter, pointing to the alley between the tavern and the hardware store.

We started running after it, but the pig was faster. He scurried away and disappeared behind the hardware store.

"You two go down this side," Max said to Dad and Uncle Walter. "Alfred and I will go around the other way, and we'll see if we can head it off. You kids stay here and watch for the other pig."

The pig was thoroughly frightened by now. He darted from behind the hardware store and headed toward the railroad depot.

"There it is," called Max. "We'll get him now."

All four men ran toward the depot. By this time, three or four guys who had been in the tavern came out to see what was going on. "After all," as one of the men later told Alfred, "it isn't every day that you see two Lutheran preachers chasing a pig on Main Street."

The pig took off across the tracks and headed into the field, leading to the park.

Max stopped. "We'll never find them this way. Those pigs could end up on the highway and cause an accident. I'm going to get the firemen out to help us with the hunt."

He walked to the bank and went inside to use the telephone. Almost immediately the fire siren sounded. Max came out of the bank and walked the half block to the firehouse as men started assembling.

"There's no fire, but we need help in capturing two runaway pigs," he told the volunteer firemen.

"Pigs?" several asked in astonishment. "You called us out to find pigs?"

Max nodded and explained that they might end up being a traffic hazard.

"Let's get going. The last we saw, one pig was heading through the field, toward the park. I'm guessing the other one must be around there as well. I figure if we form a line back of the depot and start walking toward the lake, we should find them."

The men followed instructions. Dad, Uncle Walter and Uncle Alfred joined the line as it moved across the field toward the park by the lake. Esther and I joined the line, walking with the men through the field. No sign of the pigs.

When we got to the park, we stopped. Several men scouted around the park, but reported no pigs.

"Where in the world could they have gone?" Max wondered.

"Maybe they did head for the highway," one of the firemen suggested. "I'll get my car and a couple of us can look for them."

"Good idea," Max responded. Two men walked back downtown.

The rest of us stood around waiting for instructions from Max.

"This probably won't make the pigs appear, but tell you what. If you find the pigs tonight, I'll donate one of them for a pig roast at the firemen's picnic next fall," Alfred announced.

Everyone cheered ... well, everyone but Cousin Esther.

"The poor piggy," I heard her say.

"Well, we appreciate that, Alfred, but it won't help us find the pigs. And we better find them before we have an accident, and we end up not having a pig roast. Let's go back to town and keep looking," Max told the group.

We all trudged back to town. I was getting tired and hungry, and I didn't care if we ever found those silly pigs.

When we returned to the business area, the men spread out and continued the search. No pigs. The two men in the car returned, reporting there was no sign of the pigs along the highway.

"We checked the ditches along the roadway too," one of them said.

Everyone stood around on Main Street, wondering what to do next.

"Well," Max said, "I think we've spent enough time trying to find these pigs. If anyone catches sight of them, call Alfred."

The men agreed and began walking home.

We climbed into Alfred's car.

"Sure beats all," Alfred said. "Where could those little rascals have gone?"

We drove to Alfred and Ilma's home and parked the car. Alfred went to check the damaged fence.

"Look at this," he called. We ran to where he was. There, sleeping quietly against the chicken coop, were the two little pigs.

"They must have gotten tired and decided to come back home," Esther concluded. "Poor little piggies."

Ilma, Aunt Helen and Mother came out of the house to see what the excitement was all about.

"Thank goodness, you found them," Aunt Ilma said. "I was worried you would spend all night looking for them."

Alfred and Ilma walked to the house. The rest of us climbed in Uncle Walter's car.

"I suppose this means we aren't going to have any frozen custard tonight," Esther said as we drove away.

By way of answer, Uncle Walter pulled the car into the parsonage driveway.

"Guess not," I said to Esther.

I figured we would really be in trouble for knocking down the fence and letting the pigs get away.

However, after we had gone to bed that night, I heard Aunt Helen scolding Uncle Walter.

"You really can't blame those two this time," I heard her say. "After all, if you hadn't shown Esther how to start the car, none of this would have happened."

I didn't hear what Uncle Walter said in reply, but I did hear Aunt Helen say: "And another thing, you should never have left the keys in the car. You have got to learn to be more careful."

Poor Uncle Walter, I thought. Esther and I cause the problem, and he gets the blame.

Chapter 22

The Greatest Village Event Ever

When we got back from vacation, the Village was filled with excitement. The big news was the planned Centennial celebration. It seemed that everyone in town was talking about it.

"Augie said that there are going to be 50 or 100 exhibits in the park," Phil reported one evening at supper. Augie owned the station where Phil worked and was a member of the businessmen's association, the main sponsor of the celebration.

We soon began hearing about all the other details. Many of the men in town were growing beards to help create an old-time look. Organizations like the Boy Scouts and Girl Scouts planned to have booths. There would be a carnival with all kinds of rides.

Mother was excited when she heard there would be a talent show.

"You know," she said at supper one evening, "I think our family should enter."

Dead silence followed her suggestion.

"What were you thinking of, Minnie?" Dad asked, finally breaking the uncharacteristic quiet which had fallen on our supper.

"Well, I thought maybe we could sing or play instruments or something like that," Mother answered.

"I'll be tied up with the high school band," Phil chimed in. "I won't have time."

"I know I'll have to work at the Boy Scout booth," I said. "I doubt if I'll be able to participate."

Amazingly it was my sister who thought it was a good idea.

"I can sing," she said. "I know all sorts of songs."

Phil and I didn't care who else from the family entered the contest as long as we didn't have to participate.

Mother looked thoughtful.

"Well," she finally said, "I'll look into that and see what the rules are for entering."

We continued to hear more about plans for the event. Every day after work Phil would report on what he had heard at the station.

"There's going to be a steer roast," he said one evening.

"What in the world is that?" Helene wanted to know.

"From what I understand, the firemen are going to dig a big fire pit in the park, and then they'll have a whole beef steer on a spit with a motor which will keep turning it around. Someone said it would take two or three days to roast the entire steer."

"Then what happens?" Helene asked.

"Well, then they'll make sandwiches out of it and sell them to people, I guess," Phil answered.

Helene pondered this for a time.

"I wonder what it will taste like?" she finally said.

More plans were announced.

"There are going to be a bunch of historical exhibits," I reported one evening. "I was talking to my friend Rich, and he said his dad was going to display his Indian artifacts in one of the store windows downtown."

"They've asked the churches to have exhibits in the store windows too," Dad put in. "Herb Schmuhl said we can have both the grocery and the dry goods windows if the church wants to use them. I thought I would ask the Luther League and the Lutheran Players to come up with exhibits."

The Luther League was the young people's group at the church. The Lutheran Players was the adult social organization at Emanuel. During the 1930's, the University of Wisconsin had encouraged small communities to organize theatrical groups. Since most small towns did not have movie theaters and this was a long time before television, the thought was that theater groups would provide the opportunity for people to perform plays and provide inexpensive entertainment. The Lutheran Players was organized and performed an annual play in the high school gymnasium. Gradually, the Lutheran Players had lost interest in performing plays and sponsored other activities such as an annual strawberry festival.

Other events were announced. There would be a street dance on Friday evening. The governor had been invited to speak on the opening day, although it did not look as though he would be able to make it.

"If he comes, maybe he can show everyone how to eat cream puffs," Helene suggested. We all laughed.

Most of the talk centered around the parade planned for Saturday afternoon, the last day of the celebration.

Phil said the high school band from the Village would lead the parade and that there would be high school bands from all the neighboring communities.

"I heard there will be a bunch of high school bands here," Phil said. "The parade is going to assemble at the athletic field, go up the Back Street and then cut over to Main Street. We'll march all the way through town, and then follow the state highway to the Back Street and then return to the athletic field."

"I wish I could be in the parade," said Helene. "I sure had a lot of fun being in the State Fair parade."

It was then that Mother surprised us by announcing that while Helene wouldn't be in the parade, she would be in the talent contest.

"I talked with Mr. Wesley at his store yesterday. He says there is no age limit, so Helene, how would you like to sing? I can accompany you on the piano."

Helene beamed while Phil and I relaxed. At her age, she loved being the center of attention. We were relieved Mother hadn't insisted on some sort of a family entry.

Later that week I was riding my bike with my friend John. His dad ran the feed mill in the Village and was also the Village president. John mentioned that his dad was in charge of the parade.

"Dad is real pleased about all the bands that will be here. There are going to be a lot of floats as well. Every organization in town is having a float and a lot of the businesses are too," he told me. "Dad says the only trouble is that there aren't any real historic things in the floats."

"What do you mean 'historic'?" I asked.

"Oh, you know, things from the history of Wisconsin or something," John answered.

It was then that I got an idea. I didn't say anything to John, but when I got home I called Martin.

"Martin," I said, when he answered the phone. "I need to talk to you right away. Can I bike out and see you?"

"Sure," he replied. "Just get here before milking time. I have to help Dad."

I told Mother I was going to ride out to Martin's, but I would be back for supper. I left quickly before she could start interrogating me.

I probably set a record for biking to Martin's farm, that is, if anyone kept records of that sort of thing.

"What's up?" Martin asked when I got there, slightly out of breath.

"You know Mr. Schiffler's wagon?" I began.

"Couldn't forget that," Martin answered. "Why?"

I explained about the parade and how they were looking for something to do with Wisconsin history.

"Circuses are a big part of Wisconsin history," I told him. "Wouldn't it be great if Mr. Schiffler's wagon could be in the parade?"

Martin nodded and was silent for a few moments.

"You know, with Dad's horses and Uncle Art's team, we could probably do it. Of course, an empty band wagon would look sorta silly," he said.

"What if we got the band from the church picnic, at least the ones who won't be marching with the high school band?" I answered. "There would be a half dozen or so."

"Let's go talk to Dad and see if he would be willing to do this. I know if he will, Uncle Art will have his team there, too."

We ran to the barn where Martin's dad was feeding the calves. We breathlessly explained things to him. When we paused for breath, he asked, "What wagon are you talking about?"

"Oops," said Martin, "we forgot to mention about Mr. Schiffler."

"Well," he said after we had told him about how Mr. Schiffler had redone the circus wagon, "so that's what he's been working on. I've seen him coming and going and have wondered what has been keeping him so busy.

"But if you guys can persuade him to have the wagon in the parade, I'll talk with Art and see about having our teams pull the wagon. We can practice out here."

He stopped.

"I have two questions: first, does Mr. Schiffler want to do this? And second, do the people planning the parade want to have the wagon in it?"

Martin and I looked at each other. We had been so excited about our plans we hadn't thought about these questions.

"Well, we don't have all the details worked out, but we'll get busy and get the answers to your questions," I answered.

"OK, just let me know as soon as possible, so Art and I can begin practicing with the horses."

We left Martin's dad in the barn and went and sat under one of the big elm trees on the front lawn.

"I don't think there will be any problem getting permission to have the wagon in the parade. I know that Mr. Jurgens is looking for something special and an authentic circus wagon would really be special," I said. "I think the hardest part may be getting Mr. Schiffler to go along with it."

"I think you're right," Martin agreed. "Let's go talk with him right now."

We got on our bikes and pedaled down the road to his house. Mr. Schiffler was pushing his hand mower on the front lawn when we got there.

"Hey, boys, good to see you. How about a cold drink? I'm about worn out mowing the lawn. It would sure be nice if someone would invent a power lawn mower," he called as we rode into his yard.

We followed him into his kitchen as he made a pitcher of cherry Watkins drink and then poured three glasses. We went outside and sat on the steps.

"What brings you fellas here?" he asked, wiping the sweat from his forehead with his sleeve. "You wouldn't be looking for a job mowing lawns, would you?"

"Not today," Martin answered. "We've got something important to talk to you about."

Martin proceeded to tell him about the parade being planned in the Village, how we thought it would be great if his wagon could be in it and that his dad and his Uncle Art had teams of horses to pull the wagon.

Mr. Schiffler sat silently as he listened to Martin and continued to sit there, saying nothing after Martin had finished. I considered telling him how great it would be to have his wagon in the parade, but thought the better of it since it was obvious he was thinking it over. Finally he spoke.

"I'm inclined to do it, but let me think about it. One thing I need to know is that they want to have the wagon in the parade. From what you tell me, you haven't talked with anyone about it yet. Is that right?"

"No, we haven't, but we can do that tomorrow," I assured him.

"Tell you what. You come back tomorrow with the OK, and we'll talk about it some more."

"OK," I agreed, "we'll do that."

"Thanks for the drink," Martin said. "See you tomorrow."

We got on our bikes, waved goodbye as Mr. Schiffler went back to his mower, and we rode back to Martin's house.

"Can you come to town tomorrow?" I asked Martin. "We can see John's dad and make the arrangements."

"I think so. I'll ride in after we're done with morning chores," Martin said.

It was about 10:00 a.m. when Martin rode up to our house.

"Let's go down to the feed mill and see if we can talk to Mr. Jurgens," I said to Martin. Mr. Jurgens was the president of the Village and was also in charge of the parade. He operated one of the two feed mills in town where farmers would have grain ground and mixed for their livestock. He was also the father of my friend John who had told me about the parade.

It was only a block and a half to the feed mill, so we walked there. Mr. Jurgens was in his office when we came in.

"Could we talk to you for a few minutes?" I asked.

"Sure, boys, come on in," he said, motioning us into his office. Martin and I both knew him since Martin's dad was a customer, and I frequently went to their house to play with my friend John.

"What can I do for you boys today?" he asked.

We explained about Mr. Schiffler and the circus wagon and how we thought it would be a good addition to the parade.

"That is real interesting. I had heard that Fritz Schiffler had come back to the old farm, but since he isn't raising any livestock, I haven't had any contact with him," Mr. Jurgens said after we told the story. "I think that the wagon would be a great addition to the parade."

We talked some more about the two teams of horses and having a band on the wagon.

"I can see a couple of problems," Martin said. "If we drove the wagon and horses into town from the farm, I think the horses might be tired out before the parade starts. Plus everyone would see it coming into town, and it wouldn't be much of a surprise."

Mr. Jurgens nodded and thought for a moment.

"I think we can solve that problem. I'll talk with Neal Tank. He has that big trailer that he uses to haul his excavating equipment. I think he would be willing to bring it into town. We could do it after dark and store it in the old lumber shed back of the feed mill."

"So, we can tell Mr. Schiffler that it's OK with you to have the wagon in the parade?" I asked.

"Not only is it OK, we will have it at the end, and it will be the highlight of the parade," Mr. Jurgens answered. "You talk with him, and I'll make the arrangements for getting the wagon hauled in. Let me know if you need any help."

Martin and I were smiling as we walked back to my house.

"Wow, that was easy," I said. "He seemed really enthusiastic to do this."

"Yeah, I thought so, too," Martin answered. "Let's go back to my house and tell Dad and then go see Mr. Schiffler."

When we got home, I ran into the house and told Mother that Martin and I were going to his house and I would be back later in the afternoon. Again I left the house quickly before Mother could start asking questions.

When we got to the farm, we found Martin's dad and told him that Mr. Jurgens was excited about having the wagon in the parade.

"I'll talk with Art about his team. You boys go see Mr. Schiffler and check that he's OK with everything."

We jumped on our bikes and rode as fast as we could to Mr. Schiffler's farm. When we rode into the yard, we saw him outside, still mowing his lawn. He stopped when we got there and walked over to us.

"I am thinking about getting a goat," he told us. "It would sure be easier than mowing this lawn. Well, what's up?"

We told him about our conversation with Mr. Jurgens.

"Yup, I knew his father when we used to go to the feed mill," Mr. Schiffler said. "I've been thinking about this, and I have a couple of questions. First, I think we need a band. It would look sorta silly driving an empty wagon. Second, I won't do this unless you boys ride with me."

I spoke up.

"We've thought about the band, and I think we can come up with one."

I explained about the church band, and I was certain that we could get enough players to fill the wagon.

"I would be in the band," I went on, "and Martin could ride with you and help with the horses since he knows the teams."

Mr. Schiffler again looked thoughtful and was silent for a few minutes.

"That would be nice."

He was quiet again and after a few moments said, "Martin, you tell your dad that he should bring the teams over so we can practice. And we need to practice once or twice with the band playing so the horses get used to the music.

"You fellas get busy on lining up things, and I'll finish this lawn mowing. By the way, you don't know anyone who's got a goat for sale, do you?"

We laughed and got on our bikes.

Martin and I didn't see each other for a while. He was busy with farm chores and, in his spare time, working with the horses. Meanwhile, I had talked with Dad about our plan and asked him to help with the band.

"Phil and the other high school students from the church band will be marching in the parade. But I can play on the wagon, and I think we can get the adults to play," I said.

"I'll talk with Herb and the others, and we can practice a few times. I'll see about getting some music. How many will the wagon hold?"

"I think six or seven would be about right," I answered. "Mr. Schiffler says we need to practice a couple of times with the horses so they'll be used to the music."

Things went well. We had our practices, and a couple of days before the parade we all went out to Mr. Schiffler's place. Martin, his dad and Uncle Art were there with the two teams of big Belgian horses. Everyone was amazed at the circus wagon.

"When you talked about a wagon, I thought you might have an old hay wagon or something like that," Herb said. "This is really amazing."

Finally the time had come. The day before the celebration began, the downtown was more active than on the busiest Saturday night. Volunteers were setting up booths for organizations and businesses to display their services or to sell their wares. Other volunteers were building a stage across from the park where events would be held. A big pit had been dug and a motorized rotisserie had been installed where an entire steer would be barbecued. Carnival rides were being assembled on the street where my friend Galen's dad had his business.

Thursday was the start of the three-day celebration. There was a band concert in the park. People milled around visiting the booths and watching the firemen as they prepared to roast the steer. The carnival rides were busy. The beard judging contest was held with winners declared in various categories.

Friday afternoon was filled with activities. The talent contest was held in the afternoon on the big stage. There were all sorts of acts: marimba players, barbershop quartets, accordion performers (but no sign of Phil) and then Herb Schmuhl, the master of ceremonies, announced: "Our next contestant is little Helene Kurtz who will sing *Now is the Hour.*"

Helene and Mother walked to the stage. Mother sat down at the piano. There was laughter from the audience as Helene stood and looked up at the microphone which was two or three feet above her head.

When Herb saw this, he quickly walked over, picked up the microphone, and held it in front of her so Helene could sing into it.

She probably didn't really need a microphone, I thought as she sang. She really belted out the song. Loud applause filled the air when she finished.

Other acts followed. The judges conferred and handed the results to Herb.

"The judges have made their decisions. There will be third, second and first prizes. The third-place prize is five dollars and the winner is ..." Herb paused for a moment. "The third-place winner is Helene Kurtz."

There was loud applause. I watched as Helene walked across the platform to collect her prize. Mother beamed from the side.

We didn't even pay any attention to the other prize winners. We all crowded around Helene and Mother, congratulating them.

In the evening, I rode out to Mr. Schiffler's with Neal Tank in his truck. With some difficulty we loaded the wagon using the power winch on the flatbed truck.

"I'll follow you in my pickup and help you unload it," Mr. Schiffler told Mr. Tank.

It was after dark when we drove into town and unloaded the wagon in Mr. Jurgens' shed.

"I'll be here the first thing in the morning to give the wagon a final touch-up before the parade," Mr. Schiffler said. "And I might even have a surprise or two."

I hardly slept that night, waiting for the morning to come and the big parade.

When I got up, I had a quick breakfast, told Mother and Dad to watch for me in the parade, and then hurried the two blocks to the shed where the wagon was waiting. As I looked down Main Street, I was surprised that people were already starting to gather for the parade.

It's more than two hours until it starts, I thought.

Mr. Schiffler was already in the shed when I arrived. He was busy polishing up the wagon.

"This reminds me of the days when we used to get ready for the circus parade," he said. "Of course, then there would have been 20 or 30 wagons all lined up."

"Well, there may not be 20 or 30 wagons, but this is going to be some parade," I answered. "I hope we get to see everything."

Mr. Schiffler continued working. In a little while, Mr. Jurgens stopped by.

"When the horses get here and you get them hitched up, you can come down to the athletic field," he instructed. He reached into his folder and handed Mr. Schiffler a number.

"Here's your number. Look for your assigned place and wait for the parade to start. If you have any questions, look for me. I'll see you at the athletic field," he concluded as he left.

The musicians began arriving. I introduced them to Mr. Schiffler. Several mentioned that they remembered his parents.

"I remember your mother always brought in her eggs to sell to the store," Herb mentioned.

We heard the sound of trucks outside the shed. I looked out. There was Martin and his dad in their pick-up truck with a horse trailer attached. Behind him was Martin's Uncle Art with his pickup and horse trailer.

It took a while to get the horses hitched up to the wagon, but it was finally done.

"The horses should be OK, but just to be on the safe side, Art and I will walk behind the wagon during the parade in case the horses get spooked because of all the people at the parade," Martin's Dad told Mr. Schiffler.

Mr. Schiffler nodded and then motioned for Martin to follow him. They went to the back of the wagon where Mr. Schiffler opened a storage compartment.

"Here, try this on," he said to Martin, handing him a brightly colored jacket.

"What's this?" asked Martin.

"It's a jacket I had made for my son. I've kept it all these years, and when I heard about the parade, I thought it would fit you. I have my old circus jacket too," he said, pulling it from the compartment.

"OK, everyone, let's climb aboard—it's parade time."

"Wait a minute," Herb said. He opened a suitcase he had with him.

"I thought the musicians should have some sort of a uniform. I found these old capes in our storeroom. I haven't the faintest idea where they came from, but they've been sitting around for years."

We put them on over our shoulders and climbed on the wagon. Martin and Mr. Schiffler crawled up on the front seat. Uncle Art opened the doors, and we rolled out of the shed to the Back Street, took a right turn and drove the two blocks to the athletic field. We found our assigned spot. I started looking around as the parade was assembling.

I had never seen so many bands. Our Village high school band would lead the parade. There were bands from all the neighboring towns: Markesan, Green Lake, Rosendale, Ripon, Waupun and even from Goodrich High School in Fond du Lac—three bus-loads of band members. There was a cacophony of noise as the bands tuned up and practiced.

There were all sorts of wagons and floats. I could see Mr. Franklin getting his group of students organized. They would be doing square dances on the platform of a truck. He had invited me to be part of the group, but I had explained that I would be doing something else.

I smelled smoke and looked at another float. It was Mr. Vercke, the Village blacksmith. There was a fireplace with a real forge, complete with a bellows operated by his assistant. I learned later that during the parade he made rings out of horseshoe nails and his wife, Myrna, handed them out to little girls along the parade route. Helene was very proud that she had gotten one.

I continued surveying the parade lineup. What in the world was that? It looked like a giant camera. It was! Joan Photo Service from the Village had constructed a large replica of a Kodak folding camera. I could see several of the women who worked there, handing out pictures of the float.

And fire engines! Not only from the Village but from the neighboring communities: Alto, Eldorado, Fairwater and other towns. Hope there won't be any fires today, I thought.

I was looking at all the other floats and marching units when I heard Mr. Jurgens on the loud speaker.

"All right, everyone. If I could have your attention, please. We are about ready to get the parade underway. Please listen carefully. Leo Flannery will lead the way in his police car. The Village high school band will follow. Each unit should follow in sequence. Stay about 25 yards between each unit. The parade will stop every few minutes, so that the bands can perform and so spectators can get a good look of the performing floats like Mr. Franklin's square dancers. We will make a circle of the town and return back here to the athletic field. Be alert and watch. If the parade stops, be sure you stop. OK Leo, lead the way."

The parade got underway. Since the circus wagon was the last entry, we got to sit and watch the parade pass by. Martin's Dad and Uncle Art stood with their teams, patting them so they wouldn't get impatient.

Finally it was our turn to move out and we began playing. We had three different songs which we repeated throughout the parade: *Barnum and Bailey Favorite, Hot Time in the Old Town Tonight* and a new piece, *Beautiful Wisconsin*. Since the French horn part was basically rhythm, I had all the pieces memorized, so I could watch the crowds as we moved along the parade route.

There were loud cheers when spectators saw the wagon. When the parade stopped, people crowded around the wagon, taking pictures. Martin and Mr. Schiffler were continually waving. The band played and played until my lips were numb.

I had never seen so many people in the Village. There were more people here than there were for the parade at the State Fair, I thought. Later I would hear that the police said there were more than 10,000 people at the parade. For a Village of only 700 people, it was truly an amazing crowd.

We crossed the railroad tracks and headed east to where the state highway curved. The entire route was jammed with spectators. We rode around the curve and then took the Back Street to the athletic field where the parade concluded.

At the athletic field, people crowded around to get a better view of the wagon. Martin and I were constantly being asked by our friends how come we got to ride on the wagon. Other people were asking whose wagon it was and where did it come from.

In the midst of this, a man came up to the wagon and started talking with Mr. Schiffler. I should know him; I knew he wasn't from the Village, but he looked familiar. Then it hit me. It was the man who had been with Governor Rennebohm at the State Fair.

What was he doing here? I heard Mr. Schiffler saying. "I think you should talk to Mr. Jurgens about that. He's in charge of the parade."

I was sitting right behind the driver's seat, so I said, "You probably don't remember me, but our family met you at the State Fair when my little sister got whipped cream all over Governor Rennebohm."

The man looked at me and laughed.

"Yes," he responded, "I could never forget that."

"Do you want me to find Mr. Jurgens for you?" I asked.

'That would be great," he answered.

I put down my horn and got out of the wagon. I knew Mr. Jurgens had to be here somewhere. It took me a while but I finally located him.

I quickly explained that a man from the governor's office was here and wanted to see him.

He had a puzzled look on his face as he followed me to the wagon.

"Mr. Jurgens," the man said, "I'm Bill Williams, an aide to the governor in charge of Centennial special events."

He went on to say that the Governor's Office was planning to award trophies for the best community events during the Centennial Year.

"Someone from the office is attending every Centennial event in the state. I was very impressed with your entire parade. When I saw this circus wagon at the end, I was awestruck. Wisconsin has had so many circuses start here, but no other town has had a wagon like this—not even Baraboo or Delevan, and they're the two biggest circus cities in the state.

"It's going to be a few months until winners are announced, since there still are still some celebrations to be held. Then the committee will review all the reports before making the recommendations to the governor. My guess is that you are in line for a trophy."

All of us on the wagon were listening as he spoke.

"Well," said Mr. Jurgens, "I don't know what to say. It would certainly be an honor if our Village would be selected as a trophy winner."

"I'll let you know what happens," Mr. Williams said. "Congratulations on a great parade."

The crowd was leaving the area. The visiting bands had boarded their buses and were returning home. Mr. Schiffler drove the wagon back to the shed, and we all got off. Martin's Dad and Uncle Art unhitched the horses and loaded them in the horse trailers.

"Neal will bring the wagon back on Monday," Mr. Schiffler told us.

While the parade was over, there were still other events on the schedule such as the fireworks that evening. But as far as I was concerned, the celebration was over.

"It's been quite a day," I said to Martin.

"It certainly has," he agreed as he got into the truck with his dad.

It was in the middle of October when Mr. Jurgens got a letter from the Governor's office. The Village newspaper reproduced the letter which read:

> *Congratulations! I am pleased to inform you that the Village has been awarded the Governor's First Place Trophy for the best parade in towns of under 1,000 population.*
>
> *The committee thought your community did an outstanding job of organizing and carrying out the parade. The committee especially noted that the inclusion of the restored circus wagon was the highlight of the parade and reflected the importance of the circus in the history of the state.*

The letter went on to say that the trophy would be presented later in the fall at a public event in the Village.

The letter was signed:

Oscar Rennebohm
Governor

Chapter 23

The Halloween Hunt Goes Askew

The Halloween Hunt this year was among the most memorable in Village history.

Before I tell you what happened, I better explain about the Halloween Hunt.

The Hunt was the Village's oldest tradition. It had started early in the 20th Century.

When it started, Halloween was a time when there was a lot of vandalism. This was particularly true in rural areas and small towns. Every community had tales about Halloween activities. Some events were minor and humorous, but often antics would get out of hand, and serious problems would occur.

The most common prank was tipping over outhouses. This was before indoor plumbing, and every home, whether in the country or in town, had an outhouse.

"Yup," one of the old timers recounted, "I remember hearing how a bunch of guys decided to go and tip over Old Man Schunk's privy. They snuck up there in the dark and three guys went to push it over. What they didn't know was that Old Man Schunk was sitting in the outhouse, waiting for them. And he had his shotgun loaded with rock salt, ready to shoot. They pushed it over from the back, so he couldn't get out the door. Darned if he didn't fire through one of the holes. Those guys got out of there pretty doggone quick!"

Or there would be the tale of the farmer's buggy hauled to the top of the barn and left there for the farmer to figure out how to get it down.

Some incidents were more serious. One common prank was cow tipping. Cows would settle in for the night in the pasture, carefully lowering themselves to the ground with their feet tucked under them. Cow tipping involved creeping up on the sleeping cow and pushing her over. The cow would be unable to get back on her feet. This meant in the morning, the farmer would need to get help in getting the cows upright.

These and other acts of vandalism had become a serious problem in the Village. That's when the Halloween Hunt got started.

There were various stories on how it began. One was that a wise teacher at the high school had suggested that if the school could keep students occupied on Halloween night, they would have less time and inclination to get involved in pranks. Another story was that the high school principal started it. Still another version was that the Village constable suggested it to the school. However the Halloween Hunt started, it was instantly accepted by students and had developed into an annual event. Originally the Hunt had been just for high school students, but now junior high students were included.

The Hunt went like this. The students were divided into eight teams, four teams of boys and four teams of girls. The Village was divided into four sections. The state highway ran east and west while the railroad tracks ran north and south. This resulted in the Village being divided into four fairly equal sections.

The Hunt would begin at the high school gym. In odd numbered years the boys' teams would hide, and the girls' teams would hunt. The next year, it would be reversed. Each hiding team was assigned to one of the quadrants a few days before Halloween. This allowed the team captain and co-captain to find a hiding place.

On Halloween night, everyone would meet in the high school gym. The hiding teams would get a half hour's head start. The school bell would ring, and the hunting teams would begin to hunt for those who were hiding. Just before the hunting teams left, each one was assigned to a quadrant.

If the hiding team was discovered, the two teams would return to the school. After one hour, the school bell would ring. If the hiding team had not been found, the team members would come out of their hiding place and return to the school along with the hunting team. There were no prizes—just the bragging rights of either finding the hiding team or escaping detection.

When everyone returned to the gym, there would be a party with refreshments and a dance. By the time things ended, everyone was tired and ready to go home with little thought of pranks or vandalism.

The residents of the Village enjoyed the Halloween Hunt. They viewed it as sort of a community-wide game of Hide and Go Seek. They would watch from their windows as groups would go searching through the neighborhood.

Most people in the Village agreed that this year's Hunt was probably the most memorable. A few of the old-timers disagreed, claiming that the '25 Hunt was the one to remember.

"That was when we got the early snow on Halloween night," Old Man Reuter told the guys at the station. "Heck, it was hardly a hunt at all that year. The boys were hiding, so when the girls came to hunt, they just followed the tracks in the snow. The whole thing was over in ten minutes."

But back to this year. Halloween night came. We all gathered in the high school gym. Mr. Rolfs, the high school principal, was at the front of the gym.

"OK," he announced, "it's just about time for the girls to hide. Girls, you have a half hour for your teams to get to your hiding places. I'll ring the school bell, and the boys will begin searching. After one hour, I'll ring the school bell again, and the teams that haven't been found will come back to the gym. Remember, don't leave your hiding place until you've either been found or until you hear the school bell." (The school was located on a hill, and the bell was located high atop the building, so when the bell rang, it could be heard all over town.) "OK, girls, go and hide."

There was a rush up the gym stairs as the girls' teams hurried to get to their hiding places. The boys stood around the gym, speculating where the girls might be hiding. They waited for Mr. Rolfs to tell where the teams would be hunting. This was never announced in advance so the team captains couldn't scout out possible hiding places.

Mr. Rolfs looked at his watch.

"OK, boys. In a few minutes, I'm going to ring the bell. As soon as it starts ringing, you can begin your search. When you hear the bell ring again, come back to the school. Remember, keep searching until you hear the bell, unless you've found your group. But before that, I'm going to give you your assignments. I have put each section of the town on slips of paper. Mr. Wilson has the slips in his hat. Each captain will draw a slip, and then I'll ring the bell."

The captains drew their assignments, and Mr. Rolfs went up the gym stairs to the corner of the first floor where the rope for the school bell hung down. The pealing of the bell sent the teams scurrying up the steps and out the front door of the school. The faculty would spend the hour socializing, waiting for the students to return.

"In the old days, a teacher would go with each group," Mr. Franklin told the others. "Now the students are on their own."

"I'm glad that has changed. I would sure hate to be hiding out in a marsh or a cold barn," said Miss Carnow, the English teacher. She was from Milwaukee and had some reservations about small-town life. She decided to go to her room and correct some papers while they were waiting for students to return.

The other teachers stood around, drinking coffee and talking. The hour passed. No students had returned.

"Looks as though the girls found good hiding places," Mr. Wilson remarked. "No one has come back yet."

Mr. Rolfs looked at his watch. "I have about two minutes before nine. I'll go and get ready to ring the bell."

He walked up the stairs from the gym to where the bell rope hung. He looked at his watch and noted it was exactly 9:00 p.m. He gave the bell rope a hearty pull and, "What in the world?" he exclaimed. Instead of the bell pealing, the rope came sliding down from the ceiling and was now piled up in front of him. He ran down the stairs to the gym.

"Find Walt," he yelled, "the bell rope broke."

Walt was the school janitor. But he was much more than that. As far as the school and the Village were concerned, he was pretty much Mr. Indispensable. During the years of World War II, he had served as the high school coach. He would drive a school bus if the regular driver wasn't available and would generally drive the bus to away athletic events. If a referee failed to show up for a game, he would be pressed into service. He would even take over a class if a teacher got sick or had to leave unexpectedly. All that plus keeping the school building up and running. During the winter he would open the school gym on Saturdays so kids could come in and shoot baskets. Whenever there was any sort of problem at school, the usual reaction was, "Get Walt."

It just wasn't at the school where he was active. He was also the assistant chief of the volunteer fire department. In the winter he would help flood the park so kids would have a skating rink. In the summer, if the businessmen's association decided to sponsor fireworks on the Fourth of July, Walt would be the one to set them off. Not much happened in the Village that didn't involve Walt.

One of the teachers headed to the boiler room where Walt would usually be found.

"Wait a minute," called Mr. Franklin. "Walt said he was going home and would be back later to lock up."

"Call his house," Mr. Rolfs said, "we need to ring the bell to get the kids back. No one is going to come out of hiding, or quit hunting until the bell sounds."

Mr. Wilson went to the office to call Walt.

"Let me go up in the belfry to see if I can ring the bell without the rope," said Mr. Thomas, the coach.

"Good idea," said Mr. Rolfs, "but be careful. I don't know how good the ladder is up there."

Coach Thomas and Mr. Franklin climbed the stairs to the third floor and found the ladder which led to the trap door. This was the access to the belfry.

"Should I come with you?" Mr. Franklin asked the coach.

"Stay here and hold the ladder. I'm guessing there probably isn't a lot of room up there."

He climbed up the ladder and disappeared through the trap door. Mr. Franklin waited. Suddenly he heard a crash and the sound of breaking wood.

Mr. Franklin quickly climbed up the ladder.

"What happened, Coach?" he asked, calling to him through the trap door.

"The ladder up here collapsed and I'm trapped. I can't move, and I can't see a thing. I'm afraid to try moving too much because I can't see anything and I might fall. Get some help and some light," Coach answered.

Mr. Franklin hurried down the stairs to the office where Mr. Rolfs was standing. He reported what had happened. Mr. Wilson had just said that there was no answer at Walt's house. Just then Miss Carnow emerged from her room.

"Why hasn't the bell rung? It's been an hour. We can't leave the students out there," she said.

Mr. Rolfs turned and went into the office.

"First, I'm going to call the fire department to see if they can get Coach out of the tower. Then," turning to Mr. Wilson, "I want you to call Reverend Kurtz and ask him to ring the Lutheran church bell. Maybe when the kids hear that, they'll come back to the school."

Mr. Rolfs picked up the phone. When the operator answered, he said he wanted the fire department called but explained there was no fire. Moments later the fire whistle sounded to summon the volunteer firemen to the station.

Meanwhile, Mr. Wilson called the Lutheran parsonage. Dad told us later what had happened.

"I was certainly surprised when I got Mr. Wilson's call, asking me to have the church bell rung. I told him that I would call Ornie and see if he could do it," Dad told us.

Ornie was the church's janitor. He lived across the street from the parsonage. Fortunately, Dad got hold of Ornie before he went to answer the fire alarm. Ornie was a volunteer fireman and was just getting ready to go to the fire station.

"I'll ring the bell first," he told Dad. "Then I'll find out if they need me at the fire."

A few minutes later, the church bell started ringing. Now the only time the church bell at Emanuel would ring other than before services was when someone died. The congregation had the custom that at the death of a member, the church bell would ring. This would be followed by tolling the bell, with a stroke for each year of the deceased's age. Usually when this happened, people would figure out who had died, but if they didn't, they would call the parsonage.

But tonight the bell kept ringing. There was no tolling.

Soon the parsonage phone started to ring.

"Did someone die?" the caller would ask.

Each time Mother would patiently explain the situation.

Meanwhile, downtown at the fire station, Chief Mason had received word why the department was being called.

"We'll need ladders, portable lights and our axes. Probably a half dozen men can handle things. Why don't you guys come (pointing to the first arrivals) and the rest can go back home. I don't think we'll need any more. Let's go," he said.

The men climbed aboard the fire truck and took off for the school, some four blocks away.

Mr. Rolfs met them at the door of the school, explained the situation, and the firemen carried their equipment up the stairs where Mr. Franklin was waiting at the bottom of the ladder.

"Don't worry, Coach," Chief Mason called, "we'll have you out in no time."

Walt was one of the firemen who had responded to the call, so he volunteered to go up to see what the situation was with Coach.

Walt took one of the portable lights with him as he crawled up the ladder.

"I think we're going to need a saw to get Coach out," he called. "Mr. Franklin, could you go down to the boiler room and get a saw from my work bench?"

Meanwhile, both the hiding and hunting groups had heard the church bell ringing.

"It doesn't sound like the school bell," whispered Patricia Vandenhoefel, one of the hiding group captains. "You don't suppose the boys are trying to trick us so that we come out before the time is up?"

"Does anyone know what time it is?" asked Angie Brueggemann, her co-captain. "Who's got a watch?"

No one had a watch, but several guessed the hour must be up.

"Let's go back," one of the girls said, "I have to go to the bathroom."

Meanwhile the boys were wondering why the bell was ringing.

"That's the Lutheran church bell, isn't it?" Ron Bumpers, our team's captain asked me.

"Sure sounds like it," I agreed.

"We've looked all over. I don't think we'll find them," Ron said. "Besides, I'm certain the hour is up."

One by one the teams straggled back to the school, certain that the time had expired. No hiding teams had been found.

As the students came to the school, they were surprised to see the fire truck parked in front of the building, lights flashing. A group of adults watched what was going on. A couple of firemen kept them out of the school. The firemen explained what had happened.

The firemen finally allowed the students to enter and told them to report to the gym.

Meanwhile, up in the belfry, things were not going well. Mr. Franklin had brought the saw to Walt. Walt called down to Ed, one of the firemen who was standing at the bottom of the ladder with Mr. Franklin.

"Ed, bring another light and come up here. This looks complicated."

Ed got another light and crawled up the ladder. About that time Mr. Rolfs came to see what was taking so long.

"Are you OK, Coach?" he called up.

"I'm OK, but it's not exactly how I planned to spend Halloween night," came his answer.

"All the students are back, so we don't have to worry about ringing the bell tonight. We can probably get along without it for a couple of days, so let's just get Mr. Thomas down from there," Mr. Rolfs directed.

"Well, I wasn't planning to replace the rope tonight anyway," Walt said as he worked to saw the boards which were holding Coach captive.

Just then, Miss Carnow came running up the stairs.

"Mr. Rolfs," she panted, out of breath from running up all the stairs from the gymnasium. "Patricia Vandenhoefel's team hasn't come back. You've got to do something. Those poor girls might catch pneumonia out there."

Mr. Rolfs paused. What more could go wrong? he thought.

"Excuse me, Mr. Rolfs, but I have a suggestion."

Mr. Rolfs looked at the fireman who had just spoken.

"I'm looking for all the help I can get, J.B.," he said

"Let's get my truck. It's got the loudspeaker on it. We can drive through the quadrant where they're hiding and tell them to come back to the school."

J.B. was the telephone company's maintenance man. He also used the telephone truck for Village events and if an emergency developed.

"Good idea," Mr. Rolfs answered. "Get your truck, and I'll meet you in front of the school." J.B. left and Mr. Rolfs turned to Miss Carnow.

"Miss Carnow, do you remember which quadrant Patricia's team is hiding in?"

"I think you said they would be in the northwest section," she answered.

J.B. lived a couple of blocks from the school. By the time Mr. Rolfs got his coat on and went outside, J.B. was waiting for him.

The northwest quadrant was the largest of the four quadrants. It ran about ten blocks east and west and four to five blocks north and south. It included the canning factory, some open fields and a marshy area.

J.B. handed the microphone to Mr. Rolfs.

"Push the button and speak into it," he instructed. "Tell me where to drive."

"Let's start by the tracks and move west paralleling Main Street," Mr. Rolfs suggested.

As they began slowly driving west, Mr. Rolfs began announcing, "Patricia, this is Mr. Rolfs. The hunt is over. Please return your team to the school."

"See anyone?" he asked J.B.

"Nope. I'll keep driving and you keep talking."

They slowly moved down the street until it ended.

"Take the street to the canning factory," Mr. Rolfs suggested. He kept repeating the announcement.

J.B.'s truck had a searchlight on it and he began moving it back and forth as Mr. Rolfs continued announcing. They could see lights going on in houses as people who had gone to bed early were awakened by the announcements and were looking out their windows to see what was happening.

It was at the edge of the canning factory grounds when J.B. halted his truck.

"There they are," he said as the group of girls came walking down the street.

Mr. Rolfs got out of the truck and walked up to the girls.

"The rope to the school bell broke, so we couldn't ring the school bell," he explained. "That's why we had them ring the Lutheran church bell."

"Well, we heard the church bell, but since your instructions were to come back when we heard the school bell, we just stayed where we were," Patricia explained. "No one had a watch, so we didn't know that the hour was up."

"That's fine," Mr. Rolfs assured her. "You followed instructions and there's no problem. We were just concerned that you were all OK. Let's go back to the school for the Halloween party."

The fire truck was pulling away from the school as J.B. and Mr. Rolfs returned.

"Look as though everything is OK," J.B. said. "I'll take the truck and go home."

"Thanks for your help, J.B.," said Mr. Rolfs as he got out of the truck.

In a few minutes Patricia and her team arrived at the school, much to Miss Carnow's relief.

"I was so worried about all of you," she told Patricia.

Coach Thomas was in the gym with the other teachers.

"No worse for wear," he told Mr. Rolfs, "but next time I don't think I'll be so quick to volunteer."

"It's certainly has been a Halloween Hunt we won't forget," agreed Mr. Rolfs.

Chapter 24

The Mysterious Missing Gold

"I'm going to the station," I called to Mother as I put on my winter coat. I was waiting for her usual response of: "I don't know why you spend so much time at that station. There are so many better things you could be doing." No, this time all she said was: "Be sure to wear your boots."

That's a relief, I thought, as I followed her direction and slipped on my overshoes, exited out of the side door of the parsonage and walked across our backyard to Augie Kohls' Texaco station.

Mother didn't understand that the main reason I spent time at the station was the storytelling. The station was a gathering spot for guys at the east end of the village. As I trudged through the snow, I hoped Old Man Miller would be there. I think his name was Bill, but we kids always referred to him as Old Man Miller. It wasn't disrespectful, but rather a reference to the fact that he was probably the oldest man in the Village. I knew that last year he had ridden in the high school Homecoming parade with a sign on the convertible that said he was the oldest graduate of the Village high school: "Class of 1879" the sign said. I remember thinking "1879? Wow! He must have been born during Civil War times."

Four retired guys were sitting there—George, Chuck, Jim and Old Man Miller. Augie was standing by the cash register so he could keep watch for customers pulling up to the gas pumps. It was pretty quiet, I thought as I found a seat. There was a little discussion about how much snow had fallen, but that didn't lead to any storytelling. Mostly they were just sitting there. I decided that here was my chance.

"Mr. Miller," I began, "when you were growing up here, what did you and your friends do for fun? There certainly wasn't any radio or television."

Mr. Miller looked at me and smiled.

"That's for sure. And there weren't any phonographs or electric lights or indoor plumbing or even paved streets.

"I was born in 1862, right during the Civil War. My parents had moved here shortly after the Village was started when the railroad came through. Dad was a doctor and pharmacist. He figured a brand-new town would be a good place to start a business.

"Of course I didn't remember anything about the Civil War, but when I was growing up there were a lot of Civil War veterans here. There was a chapter of the G.A.R.—the Grand Army of the Republic, sort of like the American Legion—and members would march in the Fourth of July parade. One thing I especially remember is that a bunch of the veterans had learned to play baseball when they were in the Army. We kids thought it was a great sport. Somehow we managed to get some bats and balls. No one had gloves in those days. So we spent a lot of time playing baseball.

"One thing I especially remember was hunting for gold."

"Hunting for gold?" Chuck broke in. "There's no gold around here."

"Nope," George agreed. "Never heard about a Village gold rush."

Mr. Miller smiled.

"No, there was never a gold rush, but there were plenty of stories about buried gold."

"I can remember hearing tales about buried gold," Augie agreed, "but no one ever found any."

"Why did you go hunting for it?" I asked.

"Well," Mr. Miller went on, "we had heard a story about missing gold. Now you realize this was still pioneer territory. When I was growing up, the old timers in town referred to Main Street as the Military Highway. It seems back in the 1830's when this was pretty much Indian country, the government had set up Army forts at Prairie du Chien, Portage and Green Bay to safeguard the water route from Lake Michigan to the Mississippi, which was the main transportation route. Of course, that couldn't be used in the winter when it was frozen. So the government decided to build a road to connect the forts. It started at Green Bay, or Fort Howard as it was called then, went down along the east shore of Lake Winnebago to where Fond du Lac is now, then came west through here long before the Village was settled and then went southwest to Fort Winnebago at Portage.

"Anyway, as the story went, the Army sent a shipment of gold coins from St. Louis to Fort Crawford at Prairie du Chien for the Army payroll at the three forts and for payments to the Indians as part of the land purchases. Normally it would have been sent up the Wisconsin River to Fort Winnebago, then portaged over to the Fox River and down to Fort Howard at Green Bay. But winter was early that year and the rivers were frozen. That meant they had to go overland on the Military Highway to bring the gold in order to pay the Indians and the troops."

"When was this?" George asked.

"It must have been in the late 1830's since the Military Highway was built a little bit earlier," Mr. Miller answered.

"Now there were all sorts of versions of the story. One was that the wagon was attacked by Indians and the troops buried the gold to save it. Since there's no record of any Indian attack around here, this probably never happened. Another version was that the wagon went off the road into the big marsh west of town and sank. That could have happened, I suppose. Another tale is that a gang of outlaws sneaked in at night and stole the gold, buried it, planning to come back when the coast was clear, but never got the chance."

"Any of this true?" Jim wanted to know.

"Probably not. But when you're a kid and hear stories like this ... well, you know how kids like to think about hunting for buried treasure, so two or three of us spent a lot of time one summer looking for that buried gold."

"How did you do it?" I asked.

"Well, we took shovels from home and started looking around the marsh, trying to figure out where there might be a good hiding place for gold. We also spent a lot of time talking about what we would do when we found it. We dug a lot of holes—not very deep since it as it was hard digging in the marshy dirt."

"And you just kept looking?" George chuckled.

"Well, there really wasn't much else to do in the Village," Mr. Miller answered.

"Sort of like it is now," George laughed.

"No, a lot worse. No radio, no cars, hardly anyone would even take the train to Ripon or Waupun. So looking for buried gold was a little more exciting than sitting around town."

"Did you ever find any?" Jim asked.

"No, not exactly," he answered.

"What do you mean 'not exactly'?" Jim replied.

"Well, one day when we were digging, I turned up a piece of metal. I picked it out of the dirt. I started cleaning it off and it was golden. I was really excited. The other guys watched as I cleaned it off. Turned out it wasn't a piece of gold. It was a gold-colored button which said 'USA' on it."

"What was it?" Jim asked.

"We took it to the school teacher in the Village. He looked at it and said it was likely a button from a soldier's uniform when the Army was building the Military Highway."

"Do you still have it?" Jim persisted.

"I kept it and a few years ago I gave it to my grandson. Then the darn fool lost it."

"Where did he lose it?" George asked.

"I asked him the same thing. He had been showing it off to some of his friends and said he thought he had put it back in his pocket. We never did find it."

"Hey, Jim," George said, "when the snow is gone, let's get our shovels and go look for the button."

Everyone chuckled at the idea of the two old guys going around town with their shovels looking for the missing button.

"Do you think there might really be gold buried somewhere?" I asked.

"You know, that story keeps popping up. A few years ago the newspaper down in Lone Rock along the Wisconsin River ran a story about some evidence turning up when they were building a bridge across the Wisconsin River. The Milwaukee paper picked up the story, too, and there was some talk in the Village about the old story of buried gold around here."

"I remember hearing that," George said, "but nothing was found."

"Nope," Mr. Miller agreed, "but the *Reader's Digest Magazine* printed an article that talked about ten tales of missing gold and this was one of them."

"So maybe there is missing gold?" Chuck wondered.

"It could be, but probably not around here," Mr. Miller agreed.

"Yeah," Chuck laughed, "nothing ever happens here."

Well, maybe nothing ever happens here, but we sure heard a lot of good stories. I realized it was about suppertime and I had to get home. At least I would have a story to tell at supper tonight.

Chapter 25

What Happened to the Huehne Kids

W e had finished our table prayer at supper, and as we were passing the food around, Dad began the conversation with, "Anything new at school today?"

"Bub Huehne got sent to the principal's office," I answered.

"That's hardly news," Phil said. "It happens every week."

Phil was right. Bub Huehne was always getting sent to the principal's office. There weren't many things which Mr. Franklin couldn't handle by himself, but Bub Huehne was the exception.

I better explain. There were three Huehne kids. Beulah was the oldest, several years older than Bub who was in my class. Beulah was tough. She was better in sports than most of the boys. No one could push her around. Bub, his real name was Robert, but only teachers and the principal called him that. Bub was mean, picking on younger kids and not paying attention in class. Guerdon—his name was not Gordon, he would tell people, it was Guerdon—was a few years younger. Guerdon, who if you called him "Gordon" would immediately correct you and usually include a few choice words of profanity. The three of them always hung out together. People were always accusing them of causing trouble like breaking windows and things like that; although, they were rarely caught doing these things.

Mr. Franklin was our teacher. He was a great teacher who went out of his way to help kids. Yet he never seemed to be able to get through to Bub. Almost every week Mr. Franklin would reach the point of exasperation and end up sending Bub to see Mr. Rolfs, the principal. Mr. Rolfs would talk with Bub who would sit there, seemingly not paying attention. Mr. Rolfs would then call Bub's parents, or at least try to call them to have them come to the school. Usually they wouldn't answer the phone, and when they did, Bub's mother would always have an excuse why her husband and she couldn't come to the school.

Mr. Huehne didn't have a regular job. He would work in the canning factory during the summer, do odd jobs around town and whatever other work he could find. He also spent a lot of time hanging around the Village's three taverns.

"So what happened with Bub this time?" Phil asked.

"Nothing much. He came back from the principal's office, took his seat and sat there. Those Huehne kids are sure a bunch of losers," I responded.

"You know," Dad interrupted, "maybe there are some things we don't know about."

"What do you mean?" I wanted to know.

"Well," Dad explained, "I've been thinking about them."

That's a surprise, I thought. Why would Dad be thinking about the Huehne kids?

"They really should be attending Sunday School and confirmation class here," Dad went on.

"I didn't know they were Lutheran," Phil said. "I didn't think they belonged to any church."

"I was going through the church records, and I noticed that both Beulah and Robert were baptized here," Dad said.

"What about Guerdon? Wasn't he baptized?" Helene wanted to know.

"There's no record on Guerdon. Maybe he wasn't baptized. I don't know," Dad told her. "Anyway, the other day I went to call on them to see if I could get the kids to come to Sunday School and confirmation class."

"I didn't know that," Mother broke in. "What happened?"

"Nothing," Dad replied. "I knocked and I saw Mrs. Huehne peek through the corner of the curtain. I knocked again, but she never answered the door. I felt like she was scared to come to the door."

We all agreed that it was a pretty sad situation, and since no one had anything else to add, we began talking about other things.

A week or so later at supper, Dad announced that he was going to meet with Mr. Rolfs to discuss the Huehne family.

"Are you coming to school?" Helene wanted to know.

"No, Mr. Rolfs thought it would be better if he came here," Dad replied. "He's going to stop over tomorrow night."

Nothing more was said. We knew better than to ask questions when it involved Dad's work as a pastor. We also knew that we didn't discuss things like this with anyone outside of the family.

"A lot of what Dad does with members is confidential, so even if we know about it, we should never mention it to anyone," Mother had warned us on more than one occasion.

The next evening Mr. Rolfs came to Dad's study. The study was Dad's office where he did his church work such as meeting with parishioners, working on sermons and doing all of the other things involved with a pastor's duties. The study was a separate room and had its own entrance so people did not have to go through the parsonage to see Dad.

The next evening at supper we waited to see if Dad had anything to report on his meeting with Mr. Rolfs. He had a brief comment.

"Mr. Rolfs was interested in what I had to say. He too has been concerned about the Huehnes and really doesn't know what to do. He said he was going to give it some thought and would get back to me."

About a week later at supper, Dad mentioned, "I had a call from Mr. Rolfs today about the Huehnes. He wants me to come to a meeting at the school. He's going to have Mr. Franklin, Miss Robin and Leo Flannery, and he thought I should come as well."

Having Mr. Franklin there would make sense since he was Bub's teacher. And Miss Robin was Guerdon's teacher.

"But why Mr. Flannery?" I asked. Leo Flannery was the deputy sheriff who lived in the Village. "Are they in trouble with the law?"

"No, nothing specific, but there have been a number of complaints about the Huehne kids. You remember what happened last Christmas time."

Everyone but Mother started to laugh. That was when our family had gone Christmas caroling the week after Christmas, and the people where we were caroling had thought we were the Huehne kids and had called Leo.

"Mr. Rolfs thought it would be helpful to have him there along with the teachers. Since I'm the one who initiated the subject, Mr. Rolfs asked me to be there as well," Dad explained.

Nothing more was said. We kids were anxious to know what would happen, but we also realized that Dad would probably not be able to tell us any details.

The meeting was held at the school one evening in the following week. At supper the next evening, Dad only mentioned that it had been a good meeting, but that he really couldn't say anything at this time.

One morning at school a couple of weeks later, we saw a stranger enter the building. None of us recognized the woman.

"Who's that?" I asked my friend Ron. Ron's dad was on the school board, so I thought he might know.

"Don't know," said Ron, shaking his head. "I don't recognize her."

Mr. Franklin had just started our reading class when there was a knock on the door of the classroom. We all peered at the door as Mr. Franklin went to answer it.

"It's Mr. Rolfs," Norm whispered to me. "I wonder why he's here?"

Mr. Franklin turned to the class.

"I need to talk with Mr. Rolfs for a few minutes, so finish reading the chapter. I'll be right outside the door, so don't get too rambunctious," he said with a smile.

The door closed. A few minutes later, it opened and Mr. Franklin reentered the room.

"Robert," he said to Bub Huehne, "Mr. Rolfs would like to talk with you."

What did he do now? was the thought going through the minds of everyone in the class. Usually Bub was sent to the office after he had caused trouble in class or on the playground.

"Don't worry, Robert. You're not in trouble," he said to a relieved-looking Bub. "Just go to the office."

Class resumed. Bub was gone for about a half hour, and when he returned, we were all itching to know what had happened. He said nothing. Mr. Franklin said nothing. The rest of us sat at our desks wondering what was going on.

I mentioned the incident at the supper table. Phil reported that Beulah had also been excused from a class to go to the office, and Helene said she thought she had seen Guerdon in the hall later in the morning.

Dad said nothing and after some speculation on our part, we finished supper talking about other topics.

A couple of weeks later, another stranger came to school .She was carrying what looked like some sort of a suitcase.

"I think I've seen her before," I said to Norm, "but I sure can't remember."

"That's Miss Threweg, the county nurse," said Alice. "Remember, she was the one who came and told us why we had to take goiter pills."

A number of years ago, researchers at the University of Wisconsin had discovered that the reason so many Midwestern school children had enlarged thyroid glands or goiters was a lack of iodine in their diet. Eventually this problem would be cured by introducing iodized salt, and the goiter pills would be discontinued.

"Maybe she's here to tell us about something else," said Allen who was standing nearby. "That way we'll get out of class."

No such luck. Class started without any word from Mr. Franklin about being dismissed from class to hear Miss Threweg. A short time later, there was a knock on the door. Mr. Franklin answered it, then stepped back into the room and said, "Robert, will you go to the office, please?"

Bub got up and left the room. We resumed our reading lesson, continuing to wonder what was going on with Bub and the other Huehne kids.

At supper I reported what had happened. Neither Phil nor Helene mentioned anything about Beulah or Guerdon. Dad again said nothing.

A week or two later, there was another visitor at the school. We saw her park her car in front of the school. We watched through the classroom window.

"Do you know who that is?" I asked Alice. "She's driving a Fond du Lac County car."

Alice's Dad was Leo Flannery, the deputy sheriff. Since he worked for the county, I thought Alice might know.

"No, I don't recognize her. I wonder if Bub will get called to the office again?" she answered.

Class started. Nothing happened in the morning. It was just after lunch when Mr. Rolfs came to the door and asked Bub to come to the office with him.

"This is very strange," I whispered to Norm.

"I wonder what's going on," he agreed.

At supper, we all had the same report: all three Huehne kids had been called out of class that day. Again Dad said nothing.

It was about a week or so later at supper that Dad said Mr. Rolfs had called and asked him to come to a meeting at the school the next evening.

"I know you are all interested in what is going on," he told Phil, Helene and me, "but I think you understand why I can't tell you anything at this time. I will say that I am hoping that some positive things will be happening soon."

We had all sorts of questions we wanted to ask Dad, but we knew that we had to wait until he could tell us more.

Several days later the Fond du Lac County car was again parked in front of the school. We were very surprised when we looked out of the window and saw Bub and his mother get into the car with the woman who had been at the school before.

When class started, Mr. Franklin had an announcement.

"I know that many of you have been wondering what has been going on lately with Robert. As you probably noticed, Robert isn't here today, and I need to tell you that I owe Robert an apology."

We looked at one another. Mr. Franklin owed Bub an apology? I thought it was more likely the other way around for all the times Mr. Franklin had to send him to the office.

"Yes," Mr. Franklin continued, "I owe him an apology, and I plan to do so the first chance I have."

Mr. Franklin then proceeded to tell the class that he, Mr. Rolfs and several others had been meeting to talk about Bub's behavior. He didn't mention Dad or Deputy Flannery.

"We talked with the county nurse and the county social worker. It was the county nurse who noticed that Robert seemed to have hearing problems. She came and tested him and discovered that he was quite hard of hearing. He can hear OK when you talk directly with him, but not when it's a situation like a class setting. The social worker said that probably accounted for his behavior problems.

"Now I have to admit I should have been smart enough to figure this out, but I didn't. That's why I owe Robert an apology. I believe his behavior problem in class is largely due to the fact he isn't able to hear everything.

"Today Robert and his mother went to Fond du Lac with the county nurse. He's going to be fitted with a hearing aid. The nurse feels that if he has one, he'll participate in class discussion more and his behavior should improve as well," said Mr. Franklin.

"Now," he continued, "when Robert comes back to our class, I don't want anyone here to make fun of him, to say things to him about his hearing aid or anything else. Having a hearing aid is no different than wearing glasses."

"And one more thing," Mr. Franklin's voice grew unusually stern, "if I catch anyone making fun of him or teasing him, I guarantee that you are going to be in bigger trouble than you can imagine."

We all nodded. No one wanted to take this kind of a chance.

At supper that evening, Dad smiled when I reported that Bub was going to get a hearing aid.

"I think we have made a lot of progress in helping the Huehne children," Dad said. "There are some other things happening which I can't tell you about now, but I am hoping there will be good news sometime soon."

We wondered what Dad meant, but again we knew we couldn't ask.

The next day Bub was back in class. We noticed he had something on the back of each ear. None of us said a word. Bub didn't say anything either, but we noticed he did seem to pay more attention than usual. As we left for recess, I noticed that Mr. Franklin motioned for Bub to stay, and I saw them talking as I walked out the door of the classroom.

After recess, Mr. Franklin had an announcement.

"I talked with Robert, and he wants to say something to the class. Robert."

Bub stood up at his desk.

"I wanted you to know that a couple of weeks ago when the county nurse was here, she checked my hearing and found out I had a problem hearing things, especially in class. So yesterday, Ma and I went with the county nurse to Fond du Lac, and I got these things for my ears. The county nurse said it was like getting glasses, only they're for the ears, not the eyes. I guess that's all I gotta say," he said, looking at Mr. Franklin.

"Thank you for telling us about this, Robert. I hope you will be able to hear better. It may take you a while to get used to it, just like it took me a while to get used to wearing glasses," Mr. Franklin told him.

At supper I reported what had happened at class. Dad mentioned that he had another meeting coming up, and that was all that was said.

Dad went to the meeting, but didn't say anything to us about what took place. We wondered, but said nothing, not to our friends or at home. We figured when Dad could tell us something, he would. Otherwise, it was better not to ask questions.

Weeks went by. Bub was doing better in class. He had not been sent to the principal's office since he had gotten his hearing aids.

At supper one evening Dad said Mr. Rolfs had called and asked him to come to the school the next evening.

"I hope we can get things resolved pretty soon," he said "I seem to be spending a lot of time on the Huehnes, and they're not even members. But it's for a worthwhile cause."

We continued to wonder what was going on. Dad went to the meeting, but again, there was no report.

It was a week or so later at supper, right after our table prayer that Dad had an announcement.

"I know you all have been wondering about all the meetings I have been attending about the Huehne kids. You know about Bub and his hearing aid. From what I understand, that has been real helpful. But a lot of other things have taken place, and I thought you would like to know," Dad said.

What he told us made us feel bad about how we had viewed the three Huehne children.

"You all know how tough Beulah is and how the three of them always go around together. Mr. Rolfs and Mr. Flannery were the ones who began to put the pieces together.

"They called in the county social worker and through her interviews, she found that there were all sorts of problems at the Huehne home."

"What sort of problems?" Phil asked.

"A whole range of things," Dad answered. "It turns out Mr. Huehne has quite a drinking problem. When he drinks, he usually will do things like hitting his wife or the kids. One of the reasons Beulah is so tough is that she stands up to her father and protects her mother and the other kids. Apparently a lot of times she ends up getting hit.

"Mrs. Huehne is totally frightened of her husband when he has been drinking. They don't have a lot of money to begin with and Mr. Huehne's drinking uses up a lot of his income.

"As we found out more and more information, we decided what steps had to be taken. The children were our biggest concern. We knew we had to do something because we felt it was only a matter of time before they would get into trouble."

"I think they've already gotten into a lot of trouble," I said.

"I don't think we should be too judgmental," Dad told me. "They have had a tough life."

"Well, what happens now?" Mother asked. Apparently Dad had not told her any of the details.

"Leo said he would sit down with Mr. Huehne and explain to him that he was in serious trouble, that Leo would give him a choice: stop drinking, start attending Alcoholics Anonymous meetings, or Leo would get a warrant for his arrest, and he would likely end up in jail."

"Wow," Phil said. "That sounds pretty tough."

"It is, but you and I have never seen Leo's tough side. Remember, he's been with the sheriff's department for a lot of years. He's an experienced police officer," Dad answered.

Dad continued, "Leo did meet with Mr. Huehne. Mr. Huehne didn't want to talk with him until Leo threatened to arrest him and take him to the county jail. Then he got more cooperative. He agreed to try Alcoholics Anonymous and Leo said he would arrange for a member to take Mr. Huehne to the meetings in Ripon. And Leo told him that if he heard he wasn't attending the meetings, he would be in serious trouble.

"Now," Dad went on, "there are still some other issues. The family is in bad shape financially. I'm sure you kids have noticed that the Huehne children don't have very good clothes."

"It must be especially tough for the girl. What's her name?" Mother asked.

"It's Beulah," Phil answered. "I've noticed her clothes aren't very nice."

"The Ladies Aid has that special fund to help people in need," Mother said. "They don't use it much at all, and the money just sits there."

"Why don't you talk with the president of the Aid and see what she thinks?" Dad to said Mother. "Maybe the Aid would be willing to make a donation to buy her some new clothes."

"I'll talk with Mrs. Jungman. I'll be glad to take Beulah clothes shopping," Mother replied.

"Now if we can just figure out how to help them with their finances," Dad answered.

Things worked well. Dad heard from Mr. Rolfs that Mr. Huehne was going to AA meetings. Mother had talked with Mrs. Jungman about what the Ladies Aid could do. It turned out that the president had the authority to authorize a gift from the fund on her own.

"The Aid apparently approved that years ago so that Aid members wouldn't start gossiping about who was being helped," Mother said.

Dad talked with Mr. Rolfs who arranged to have Beulah excused from school. Mother and Mrs. Jungman took her to Fond du Lac where they went shopping at the Hills Department Store.

At supper that night, Mother went into great detail about the clothes they had bought.

"She got some of the cutest outfits. Does she ever look nice. And while we were there, Mrs. Jungman suggested that Beulah should get her hair done at the Hills Beauty Salon. She even said she would pay for it. So we did that too. I don't think Beulah really knew what to say. She asked who was doing this and Mrs. Jungman told her that the Ladies Aid of the church had a special fund for things like that. Beulah was just amazed."

The next night at supper Phil reported that Beulah was in school with her new clothes and new hair-do.

"You should have seen all the boys looking at her. You would have thought there was a new girl in school or something," he said.

Mother smiled at Phil's comments.

"Now if we could just do something to help the family with their finances," Dad sighed.

The days went by. I noticed that the Huehne kids were rarely a topic of discussion at our supper table.

Except one night.

We were just starting supper when I said, "I think I have an idea for the Huehnes."

"What do you mean?" Phil asked.

"You know, Dad had mentioned that he is concerned about their finances. Well, I heard something today that might help," I answered.

Dad put down his fork and looked at me.

"What would that be?" he asked.

"Well, when I was at the locker plant today, getting some vegetables for supper, I heard Mr. Brueggemann saying to Mrs. Brueggemann that he sure wished they could get some extra help at the locker plant. I knew it wasn't any of my business, but I asked what kind of help they were looking for. Mr. Brueggemann said he needed someone to help in the cutting area, wrapping meat and things like that. I thought maybe this is a job Mrs. Huehne could do," I said.

Dad looked thoughtful.

"I think I'll stop and talk with Mr. Brueggemann and explain things. Mr. Brueggemann is a good church man and that should help."

It worked out well. Mrs. Huehne got the job and turned out to be a good worker. Mr. Brueggemann thanked Dad for suggesting her. It looked like that was the end of the story.

It turned out it wasn't.

One night we were just finishing supper when the phone rang. Dad went and answered. We could hear him as we sat at the supper table.

"Yes, I will be home. Yes, I'm certain Mrs. Kurtz would do that. About 7:00 p.m. will be fine. Just use the study door—that's the door on the right as you face the house."

We heard him hang up the phone, and then he returned to the table. We all waited for him to say something.

"Well, I never know what to expect when the phone rings. That was Beulah Huehne. She wants to come and see me this evening and she asked you to be there too," he said, looking at Mother.

We kids were really curious, but we kept out of sight. Beulah didn't stay long, and after we heard her leave, we all came to the living room, hoping that Dad and Mother would tell us why Beulah had been there.

Dad and Mother came out of the study. Both were smiling.

"What was that all about?" we all asked.

"Beulah said she just couldn't get over the fact that the church cared enough to provide the new clothes for her. She said it really changed her life. She decided that she wants to be confirmed and become a church member. She asked if she would have to go through two years of confirmation class," Dad said.

"What did you tell her? Phil asked.

"I told her that I thought she was an adult and that she could join the adult instruction class which I'll be starting next month. She seemed relieved to know that," Dad said.

"Why did she want Mother there?" I asked.

"I think it's because I got to know her when we went shopping," Mother explained. "She was just more comfortable with me being there."

We kids started to leave.

"Oh," said Dad, "a couple of other things. She said she was going to see that Bub would start confirmation class and that Guerdon would start Sunday School. And she also added that we'd better believe that they'll be there."

Mother smiled. "This certainly has turned out wonderfully well."

She thought for a moment.

"You know, it's just too bad this didn't happen earlier. Then maybe we never would have had that terrible incident at the Rakows."

The rest of us smiled, remembering the time it was hardly a silent night.

Chapter 26

Ring the Bell and Count the People

"Well," said Dad after we had said our table prayer and began eating supper, "I have some news."

We paused with our meal. Dad rarely made announcements of this type. He would usually mention things in an offhand manner or more likely, one of us kids would bring something up.

"Did you get a call?" Phil asked.

Pastors' families were always anxious that the pastor might receive a call to a new parish. I knew that Dad had not received a call, at least I was pretty certain he hadn't received one. I picked up the mail from the post office every day, and I would have seen an envelope from the district president's office. Most of the letters Dad got from the office were machine addressed and contained routine district announcements. If an envelope came from the district office that was individually addressed and was a fairly thick envelope, one could figure out it was probably a call. No such envelope had arrived lately, so I was pretty sure that Dad was not going to tell us he had received a call.

"No," replied Dad, "no call."

We all breathed a sigh of relief. No one wanted to move. We liked living in the Village. Being a pastor's family we knew that someday we would probably move, but for now we were happy to stay.

"So what is the news?" my sister demanded. She did not like secrets, especially when she felt she should know things before anyone else.

"Ornie is resigning," Dad told us.

This was NEWS. Ornie had been church janitor for a long time, longer than we had lived in the Village.

"How come he's resigning?" we wanted to know.

"He told me this afternoon and said I should tell the church council at its meeting tonight," Dad explained. The church council was the congregation's board which handled the various business aspects of the church. "Ornie said he has been doing it for all these years, and he feels it's time to step down."

"I didn't think the church janitor's job is all that difficult," I said. "He has to clean the church each week, mow the lawn in the summer and shovel the sidewalk in the winter."

"And he has to ring the bell for services and count the people too," Phil added.

"I think he is just a little tired of having to be at every service every week," Dad guessed. "He certainly doesn't get a big salary either."

"I wonder who will take the job," Mother said. "You know ..."

She was interrupted by sobs from my sister.

"What in the world are you crying about?" Mother asked.

Helene brushed away her tears.

"That means I won't get gum anymore."

The rest of us laughed. Helene was indignant. This was not a laughing matter.

Each Sunday morning Ornie would stop by the parsonage and pick up the bulletins for the service. Helene would always hand them to him, and he in turn would give her a pack of gum. Since we kids rarely had money of our own to buy such things, the loss of her weekly package of gum was a serious matter for her.

"That's all right," Mother responded. "Maybe it's just as well. Chewing gum really isn't good for your teeth."

This did not satisfy Helene at all. But she brightened up.

"Maybe the new janitor will do like Ornie did," she decided.

We continued to eat supper and the conversation turned to other topics.

Several weeks later Dad mentioned that no one had applied for the janitor's job.

"Ornie talked with me yesterday and said he would sure like it if the church found a new janitor," Dad reported. "I suppose we could run an ad in the Village newspaper to see if there is anyone in town who would take the job. It would be nice if a member of the church would take it."

No applications were forthcoming. The janitorial position remained unfilled.

One night at supper when we were discussing the situation, I startled the family with a suggestion.

"Why doesn't our family take the job?" I asked. "We're at the church all the time anyway. I mow the lawn at the house here and shovel the walks. It wouldn't be all that hard to do the church as well. Any time there are services or meetings, Dad is always there, so he could open the church and turn on the lights, just like Ornie does."

Dad seemed interested.

"It doesn't pay a whole lot, but the extra income would help," Dad noted.

"We would need to do the weekly cleaning and we could all help with that," I continued.

"What about ringing the bell and counting the people?" Helene wanted to know.

"Well," I answered, "I think I could do it."

"That's a pretty big bell. It even lifts Ornie off his feet when he stops the ringing," Phil pointed out.

That was true. It was a big bell. One thing you didn't want to do was to have the bell stop ringing with a weak clang or two. No, the bell had to be brought to a stop, so the last ring would be a firm sound.

"I can give it a try. Ornie will show me how to do it," I said.

We talked it over some more and decided it would be worth trying.

"The council meets tonight. If there are no applications, I'll mention it and see what the councilmen think. I see no objection, so hopefully they'll go along with the idea," Dad said.

The next day Dad reported that the council had approved hiring our family as the church janitors.

"They seemed glad that we were willing to take the job," he commented.

"They probably figured that now they won't have to give you a raise this year," Mother countered.

Helene sighed, "I suppose that means no more gum on Sunday mornings."

We exchanged glances and decided it was probably not the time to comment about oral hygiene.

Ornie showed us how things were done.

"Come to the church on Sunday when I ring the early bell, and I'll show you how it's done and let you try it," he told me.

The church bell was rung at 8:30, a half hour before Sunday School started. It would then be rung again at 9:00 to mark the start of Sunday School and then at 10:30 at the start of services.

The next Sunday I climbed the balcony steps a little before 8:30. Ornie was there waiting for me. He looked at his watch.

"Two minutes," he said. He showed me the two ropes.

"The heavy rope is for ringing the bell. The lighter rope is when you toll the bell at funerals and announcing deaths," he explained.

I had forgotten about funerals. The church had the custom that when a member died, the janitor would go to the church, ring the bell for a few peals and then slowly toll the bell, one stroke for each year of the person's age. When this happened, the telephone in the parsonage started ringing with the question "Who died?" or "Did Mrs. Ruenglin die?"

"You have to count carefully when you're tolling the bell," Ornie told me. "Everybody in town counts, and you better get the age right, otherwise you'll hear about it. I remember when Mrs. Loefler died. She was 102. I was certain I had counted right, but three people told me I had tolled the bell 103 times."

Ornie looked at his watch and said, "OK, you grasp the rope high and give it a good pull to get it started."

He proceeded to pull the rope, and the big bell began pealing out its sound.

He rang it a few times and then motioned for me to take the rope.

"Keep pulling it even," he told me. "I usually ring it about 40 times."

I continued to pull the rope.

"OK, now, to stop it, you need to quit pulling the rope and then hold it tight. You want to have the bell sound strong until the end, not kind of dribble off," Ornie said. "Now, stop ringing and hold on."

I did as instructed and was immediately pulled about three feet off the floor, but the bell stopped on a strong note.

Ornie chuckled.

"It lifts me off the floor too; although not that high. You've got the idea about how it works."

So our family took over the janitorial duties. I found I was doing most of the work: cleaning the sanctuary and basement every week, mowing the lawn in summer and shoveling in winter, ringing the bell and counting the people in attendance at services.

One evening in fall, the phone rang. Dad answered it.

"I'm sorry to hear that. I'll be over in a few minutes. By the way, how old was she?" I heard him say.

Dad hung up the phone.

"Mrs. Stoffhager died. I'm going over to the house to have a prayer with the family."

Dad looked at me. "You'll have to go to church to toll the bell. Remember, you ring it first for about one minute and then toll it. She was 79. Let me write it down so you won't forget."

I went to the church, turned on the balcony light and climbed the steps. The rest of the church was totally dark.

I grabbed the bell rope, gave it a good pull and the sound of the big bell broke the quiet of the Village evening. After five or six pulls, I grabbed the rope and got lifted off the floor. I then reached for the smaller rope.

The bell was rung by pulling the rope around the wheel which swung the bell back and forth. In tolling the bell, the rope which was tied to a large hammer hit the inside of the bell.

I began tolling the bell.

One, two, three ...

I slowly counted the strokes.

Don't miscount, I told myself.

43, 44, 45 ...

I kept tolling.

Finally, 79 and I stopped.

I climbed down the stairs, turned off the lights and walked next door to the parsonage.

"Good job," Mother told me. "I counted 79, just as it was supposed to be."

The next day Dad told me that the funeral would be in three days, and I would have to get excused from school in the afternoon to toll the bell for the funeral.

"I'll write a note to Mr. Franklin," he added.

I was further surprised the day after the funeral. When I came home from school, Dad handed me an envelope.

"What's this?" I asked.

"Fred Forest, the funeral director, stopped by with it for you."

I opened the envelope. Inside was a five-dollar bill with a statement which said: "Janitor expenses for funeral."

Hey, being church janitor isn't all that bad, I thought. Five dollars, why, Phil only makes ten dollars a week at his job at the gas station.

I immediately began mentally evaluating the physical condition of our older members. Not that I wished any harm to them, but ...

"May I keep this?" I asked Dad.

"Yes," Dad assured me. "I would not mention it to kids in your class, however."

I nodded.

Several weeks later at supper Dad started talking about the church council meeting that evening.

"I'm going to finally tell the council that it's time to discontinue the German Christmas Day service," he announced.

"Do you think they'll agree?" Mother wondered.

Emanuel had been founded by German immigrants. Up until World War I, all services had been in German. English services were gradually introduced. When Dad first came to Emanuel, there were German services every other Sunday. Slowly the number of German services was reduced, and for the past several years, the only remaining German service was on Christmas Day. We kids liked it since that meant we didn't have to attend the service. We figured that we had gone twice on Christmas Eve and that was enough.

"Well," Dad rejoined, "last year we had five people there plus the organist, janitor and preacher. Since then, Mrs. Stoffhager and Mr. Heinzmeier have died. August Stolzman is bedridden, so that leaves only Mrs. Ausmann, and she's so deaf there would be no use preaching a sermon. And oh, yes, Rolland Berwald who only comes because he likes to sing *Oh, du Froeliche.*"

"I sure hope the council sees the point," Mother said.

Now there was something I hadn't thought of. If there was a German service, I would have to go and ring the bell. Counting the attendance was not a problem. If there was no German service, there would be a regular service, and I would also have to go.

The next day Dad reported that the council had approved dropping the service.

"A couple of the councilmen said we may as well not have any service on Christmas Day since everyone had gotten out of the habit of going to Christmas Day services. I need to come up with a plan to assure a good attendance."

A couple of nights later at dinner, Dad started talking right after we said the table prayer.

"I think I know what we can do for Christmas Day," he began. "I am going to ask Gordy to give the sermon."

Gordy was a member of the congregation who was studying for the ministry.

"Last Easter he preached at the sunrise service, and people really thought he did a good job. I think they would like to hear him preach again. Phil, would you be willing to do the liturgy?"

Dad had been encouraging Phil to take an occasional role in the service, hoping that he might begin considering the ministry.

"Oh," Phil hesitated a bit, "I guess I could."

"Then we'll have the junior choir and senior choir sing. That means all of their families will come, so we should have a pretty good attendance." Dad smiled at the thought.

So it was decided. No more German Christmas Day service. There would be a Christmas Day service with special music and a guest preacher.

"And," Dad announced, "this means I can sit with the family, which will be a special treat for me."

"Ah, just a minute, Dad," interjected Phil. "Since I have to do the liturgy, I will be sitting up in front by the altar."

"And I'll be singing in the junior choir," Helene pointed out.

"And I'll be singing with the senior choir," Mother added.

Dad looked at me.

"Well, Dad, if you want to sit up in the balcony with me while I ring the bell and count the people, I'll be glad to have company," I answered.

So Christmas Day came. The service went well; Gordy had a good sermon. The choirs sang. The attendance was much better than the council had expected.

And no one noticed that Dad was sitting in the front pew by himself.

Chapter 27

The Year Comes to an End

It was New Year's Eve. We were sitting at the supper table. There were just four of us. Phil wasn't there. He and Margie were going out for supper and to a movie.

"Well," said Mother as we were eating, "this is what it will be like when Phil goes away to college. There will just be the four of us at meal time."

"When will that be?" Helene wanted to know.

"It won't be until next year," Mother replied, looking a little sad.

This hadn't occurred to me before. I knew Phil would be going to college after he graduated from high school. Mother was always talking about when we kids would go to college. We were constantly encouraged to save our money, so we would have a bank account when we were ready to go.

But college seemed like such a long way away. And now Mother was talking about when Phil would be gone. I realized why Mother looked sad. But I thought, this was no time to be sad. It was New Year's Eve—the end of a great year, and the start of a brand new one.

For many people, New Year's Eve was a big party night. For the parsonage family, it was a quiet evening. We used to have a church service. Dad called it Sylvester Eve. I remember asking him one time who Sylvester was, and Dad had to admit he didn't know for certain.

"I guess he might have been an old-time saint. It's just that New Year's Eve has always been called Sylvester Eve," Dad answered.

However, several years ago, the church council had decided to cancel the service since it was getting so hardly anyone came anymore.

"People would rather go out and party," Mother complained. We kids didn't mind. We figured we had gone to enough church services during the holiday season, especially now that there was a service on Christmas Day.

Although we just were planning to spend a quiet evening at home, there was one event to be observed. At midnight I would go to the church and ring the bell. It was a custom in the Village that the churches would ring their bells at midnight to welcome the New Year. Since Emanuel had the biggest bell, it led off the bell ringing. The other church bells would then join in: the Evangelical United Brethren, the Methodist, Bethel Reformed and St. Brendan's Catholic.

"Can I stay up until midnight to hear the bells ring?" Helene asked.

"That's pretty late for you," Mother replied. "Let's see if you stay awake until then."

To pass the time after supper, the four of us played "Rook". I thought again about why Mother was OK with "Rook" and not regular playing cards with suits and faces. Her strict Norwegian Lutheran upbringing simply made her label them as sinful. If I asked her why playing cards were sinful, Mother was never able gave a good answer.

"Dad plays solitaire," I once pointed out.

"Well, that's different," Mother answered. She did not go into detail on why it was different, so I decided to drop the subject.

"It has certainly been a good year," Dad reminisced as he shuffled the cards. "What did you like best?"

"I liked going to the state fair and being in the parade and having the governor show me how to eat a cream puff and winning the prize for singing at the centennial celebration and ..." Helene paused for breath, trying to think of what else she had done.

"Yes," Mother agreed, "it has been quite a year for us. And I'm glad that our Christmas this year was nice and peaceful, not like last year."

The rest of us smiled, remembering everything which had happened a year ago at Christmas time.

Mother was right, I thought, Christmas was a lot quieter this year compared with a year ago.

We talked more about the past year. About the Sunday School picnic, the time when the station was burglarized, about Cousin George's stay with us and when the pigs escaped from Uncle Alfred's farm and all the other things which had happened the past year.

We all agreed—it had been quite a year.

"What do you suppose the New Year will be like?" Helene wondered.

"We'll just have to wait and see, won't we?" said Dad as he dealt the last card and picked up his hand.

THE MISSING LIBRARY BOOKS

Chapter 28

The Fat Envelope in the Mailbox

There it was—a fat Number 10 envelope addressed to Dad with the return address of the district president's office. It was not a routine church mailing, I knew. I had seen an envelope like this before. It was not good news as far as I was concerned. Thoughts flashed through my mind. Maybe it was just some district business. Maybe it wasn't what I thought it was. Maybe I should just toss it in the wastebasket in the corner of the post office lobby. No, that wouldn't be right. Besides getting in trouble with Dad, I would probably be breaking a federal law. I would have to bring it home.

I had stopped at the post office to pick up our mail on my way home from school. With a few spins of the dial on the combination lock of our post office box, I opened the door and pulled out the contents. There was always a lot of mail: letters from relatives, Dad and Mother's magazines, mailings for the church, and special things such as envelopes for me from stamp companies. That's when I found the big, fat envelope.

Our family had left Milwaukee and moved to the Village around Thanksgiving in 1941 when Dad accepted a call to become pastor of Emanuel Lutheran Church. At that time our family consisted of Dad and Mother, my brother Phil, and me. Phil was in fifth grade, and I was in kindergarten.

A lot of things had happened since we moved here. We had hardly settled into our new home, the big, white parsonage next to the church, when the news came that the Japanese had attacked Pearl Harbor. The U.S. was suddenly at war. Then, in the middle of the War, our family expanded when my sister Helene was born.

How quickly the years had flown by! Phil had finished high school and was now in college, though at home for summer and for breaks. Helene was already in the third grade. I was in high school.

I thought about the envelope as I walked home, I was pretty certain it was a call. Did that mean we might be moving?

If you're in a preacher's family, calls are a constant topic of conversation. I guess I better explain about calls since most people reading this are not members of preacher families.

A call is basically a job offer from a new congregation. At this time in the Lutheran church, pastors did not apply for a new position. Often pastors would let the district president know they were interested in moving. When a vacancy occurred in a congregation, the district president would suggest a number of pastors for the congregation to consider. Members of the congregation could also suggest names to be considered. The congregation members would then vote on who they would like to have as their new pastor. The pastor selected would then receive a letter of call, approved by the congregation and signed by the district president.

Sometimes the pastor would be aware that his (all pastors at this time were men) name had been proposed at a congregation, so when a call came, he was not surprised. Other times a call would be totally unexpected. I remember Dad had received several calls this way. Each time he had considered the call and then told the congregation he was not interested in moving.

I knew that Dad periodically talked about the possibility of moving to a new congregation. It would usually come up in a roundabout way when he would say something like, "I sure don't want to be like old Pastor Duberstein who has been up there in Blue Lake for 35 years." Or, "My father often said that a pastor shouldn't stay in one place too long." (Many years later I found out that the reason my grandfather never stayed too long was that quite often the congregation asked him to leave.)

Perhaps Dad had mentioned to the district president that he would be open to a call. Maybe someone from another congregation had heard him preach and suggested his name to a vacant congregation. It was hard to figure out.

No one was around when I came home. I put the mail on the kitchen table and went up to my room to change clothes.

I sat on the edge of my bed, looked around the room and started thinking back to all the years we had lived in the Village. What would it be like to move, I wondered. I vaguely remembered when we had moved from Milwaukee, but I had been only five years old at the time, so I didn't remember a whole lot. If we were to move now, things would certainly be different.

Instead of worrying about what might happen, I would just get busy with writing more about the things that had happened in the Village, from my last years in junior high to now. After I wrote a second batch of stories, Mother had gotten mad again, just like she had been after the first batch about Christmas had been written. She felt that I shouldn't talk about what went on in our house, and after all, what would the members think when they read it? And what would they say about her?

For Mother, members were constantly on her mind. Members, of course, meant parishioners of Emanuel Lutheran. Now I always thought the members were nice folks. I know Mother did too, but still she worried. What would they think of her new dress? What would they think if she always wore an old dress? What would they think if her children always knew all the answers in Sunday School? And what would they think if her children *didn't* know all the answers? And what would the members think if the lawn wasn't nicely mowed for Sunday morning? And what if ... for Mother the list of worries was endless. You can see why Mother would worry about what members might say about things I wrote in a book.

Other people had been after me to write more stories. Helene thought I should write more about her. Phil thought I should leave him out entirely. Dad didn't say much. If he encouraged me, Mother would get mad at him. If he didn't encourage me, I would think he wasn't interested. And I knew he was interested because he kept giving copies of my stories to his preacher friends.

So I decided that I better get going on the new stories just in case Dad decided to take the call that came in the mail. Besides, a lot of things had happened, and I remembered some other stories which I thought should be told, so I decided to write all those down. I just wouldn't show Mother until it was all done. After all, I remembered my Uncle Carl saying one time that it was always easier to ask forgiveness than it was to get permission. I don't remember what he was talking about, but it sounded like good advice to me.

OK, a lot of what I write never happened. I make some of it up. Oh, sure, some of it actually happened. Some of it could have happened and maybe even should have happened. And some of the people are real or kind of real. Some are just plain made up.

So if you think someone in the book reminds you of your old Aunt Mildred, go ahead and think it. Just remember — I probably never knew your Aunt Mildred or any of your other aunts for that matter.

All I ask, if you have any complaints, is that you tell me. For heaven's sake, don't tell Mother about it. I'll have enough trouble the way it is. I'll get busy writing this book and not worry about what is in that fat envelope I brought home from the post office.

I'd just have to wait and see.

Chapter 29

The Missing Library Books

I was going through the shelves of the Village's library, looking for books I hadn't read. The library was about my favorite place in town. One of the first things Mother did after we moved to the Village was to take Phil and me to the library to get library cards.

"You know, you're about my best customer," Mrs. Frank, the librarian, told me on more than one occasion. Probably right, I thought. I went to the library practically every week. During the summer I went more often.

I thought back to the summer after I had finished second grade. The library had a rule that kids could only check out one book at a time. By that summer I was reading all the time. I would walk to the library, check out a book and then as I was walking home, I would begin reading it. Since these were short kid's books, I would often finish the book by the time I got home.

Then I would walk back to the library, return the book and check out another one. One day I got tired of this after my third trip and said to Mrs. Frank, "How come I can only check out one book at a time? I'm getting tired of all this walking back and forth."

Mrs. Frank thought for a moment.

"That's been the rule for a long time, even before I started here. I think it must have been started when there weren't many children's books, so that no one could check out a lot of books and not leave any for the other children. But that was a long time ago. I guess there's no reason why you can't check out more than one book."

So from that time on, I could check out as many books as I wished. So could the other kids in the Village. And I did check out books. First the kid's books, then the so-called young adult books, and pretty soon I was reading everything.

The library did not have a large collection. There were a lot of westerns, mysteries, quite a few romances and a number of classics. The library itself wasn't all that big. It was housed on the first floor of the Village Hall. At the back of the building was the garage for the fire truck. In the front of the upstairs was the room where the Village board of trustees would hold its monthly meetings. At the back of the second floor was the G.A.R. room where organizations could hold their meetings and events. The Boy Scout troop held its meetings there.

"Why is it called the G.A.R. room?" I asked Dad.

"G.A.R. stands for the Grand Army of the Republic. It was an organization for veterans of the Civil War. It was like the American Legion is now for veterans of World War I and World War II."

He went on to say when he was growing up, there were still quite a few Civil War veterans around, and there was a big G.A.R. hall in the city where he lived.

"There aren't any Civil War veterans around anymore. It's been almost ninety years since the Civil War ended. I think there are still a couple of members of the Daughters of the G.A. R. in the Village; although I don't know if they meet regularly or not," Dad explained.

When we were at Scout meetings I had noticed there was a display on one of the walls that had a lot of medals and old pictures on it.

Finally, on the roof of the building was a cupola housing a bell and a siren. In the early days, when a fire was reported, the bell would be rung to summon the volunteer firemen. It had been replaced with an electric siren.

Now when there was a fire, it was reported to the telephone company (which was located next to the Village hall). The operator on duty would sound the siren, which was the signal for the volunteer firemen to come to the Village hall, put on their helmets and slickers, get on the fire truck, and speed to the fire. One fireman would stay behind to tell late arrivals where the fire was, and they would drive there by car.

Anyway, getting back to the library. I had been reading whatever looked interesting. I decided I would start reading on a more organized basis. For me this meant I would go from shelf to shelf, checking out three books and, when I had finished those, I would check out the next three books on the shelf. Sometimes I would get bored with the contents of a particular shelf and move to the next one.

I had gone through most of the shelves, which is why I was now looking for books I might have missed. I went back to the corner of the room where there were a lot of old books. As I was paging through a large *History of Fond du Lac County,* I noticed there was a door next to the shelf. I had not paid any attention to it before.

I finally found some books I had not read previously, and as I was checking them out, I asked Mrs. Frank, "Where does that door go?" pointing to the door in back. "I never noticed it before."

"There was a bookcase in front of it, but I was told that doors in a public building couldn't be blocked, so we moved the bookcase. But a lot of good that did since the door is locked and no one seems to have a key for it," Mrs. Frank explained.

"Can't they change the lock so there would be a key?" I asked.

"That's what I said, but the Village board didn't want to spend the money to bring in a locksmith to get it done," she answered, shaking her head. "Getting the Village board to spend any money on the library is really a tough job."

I nodded sympathetically, picked up my books and walked home.

Several weeks later when I was at the library, I was back searching for books I hadn't read. There were usually other people in the library, often older women, so I didn't pay any attention to the woman who was standing at the desk talking with Mrs. Frank. I was debating about checking out *The History of Fond du Lac County* when the woman at the desk started raising her voice. That was out of the ordinary since most people in the library always talked in hushed voices.

I listened.

"I don't care if it's a popular book. I think it's disgusting to have a book like that in this library, the way that Scarlet O'Hara woman carries on," she said. "And you've got a lot of other books here which God-fearing people shouldn't read. And what if young people read them?" she said looking at me.

"I'm sorry you feel that way, Myrtle, but I doubt if others feel the same way you do," Mrs. Frank replied in her most soothing voice.

"I think it's terrible," the woman said, slamming down the book on Mrs. Frank's desk. She picked up her bag and marched out of the door, calling over her shoulder, "This isn't the last you'll hear from me."

I had seen the woman before. She usually dressed in black and always carried a cloth shopping bag. However, I didn't know who she was.

I decided to read the history and brought it to the desk to be checked out.

"She sure sounded mad," I said. "Who is she?"

"Oh, that's Myrtle Wilson. She's always mad about something. Today she was upset that we had *Gone with the Wind* in the library. She thought there was too much immoral behavior in it. I think her main objection is that it is sympathetic to the South. But if she isn't upset about the books in the library, she's irritated with the Village board for not maintaining the Civil War memorial the way she thinks it should be done. She'll be up in the G.A.R. hall working on it and then will come down here to complain to me about what needs to be done."

"How come she's so interested?" I asked.

"Her father was one of the last Civil War veterans in the Village, and Myrtle is one of the last members of the Daughters of the G.A.R., so she is determined to keep his memory and the memory of the G.A.R. alive," Mrs. Frank said. "She always seems to be upstairs in the G.A.R. room. Sometimes when I close the library in the evening, she'll be up there. She must have a key."

At supper that night, I told what had happened in the library that day.

"Why," said Mother, "I read *Gone with the Wind*. I thought it was a good story."

"I read it too. I thought it was an interesting Civil War story," I agreed.

"Some people!" Mother said. "They always seem to find something to complain about."

"I'm glad she's not a Lutheran. She would probably come to me with all her problems," Dad laughed.

"Yeah, like Mrs. Schwartzbauer," Phil said.

We all smiled. Mrs. Schwartzbauer was a member who lived on the other end of town. She had a deathly fear of window peepers, so she kept her windows tightly covered. As a result, she often lost track of time and would periodically call Dad to talk to him about something she had heard a radio evangelist say on one of those late-night programs.

"Like the time she called you late one night and Walt answered the phone," Phil laughed.

The Village had a small telephone company. Most people shared a telephone line with one or more other households. We were fortunate that we had only a two-party line which we shared with the Schillers who lived across the street. Walt Schiller owned the Chevrolet garage in the Village. Now and then he would get a late-night call from the sheriff, telling him there had been an auto accident and he needed to come with his tow truck.

Our phone number was 56-3 which meant when the phone rang three times it was for us. The Schillers' number was 56-2, so two rings meant it was for them.

Late one night the phone rang. We were all asleep upstairs. The phone was downstairs. Dad was a sound sleeper, so he didn't hear it ring. Mother heard it, but she couldn't tell if there were two or three rings. Finally she realized it was three rings, so she woke Dad up, and he sleepily went downstairs to answer the phone.

About the same time Walt had also heard the phone ring in his house and didn't quite know if it was two or three rings, so he decided he had better answer it in case his tow truck was needed.

As Dad later recounted things, the conversation went something like this. Dad answered first.

"Pastor Kurtz? This is Mrs. Schwartzbauer."

About this time Walt picked up the phone just as she finished identifying herself.

"Where are you?" Walt asked, figuring it was someone who needed a tow.

"Why, I'm right in my house. Why are you asking?" Mrs. Schwartzbauer answered.

Dad wasn't quite awake and couldn't figure out who else was talking. "Who is this?" he asked.

"It's Mrs. Schwartzbauer. I just told you," she answered.

"Do you need a tow truck?" Walt asked.

"Why would I need a tow truck? I don't have a car," she told him indignantly.

"Then why did you call me?" Walt asked.

"I didn't call you—I called the pastor," she answered.

"Walt?" Dad was starting to wake up and began figuring out what was going on.

"Yes," Walt replied.

"I think this call is for me. It's Mrs. Schwartzbauer, and she doesn't need a tow truck," he told Walt.

"Well, I wish she had said that right away. Now I can go back to bed," Walt said, hanging up the phone.

"Why in the world did that man think I needed a tow truck?" Mrs. Schwartzbauer asked.

Dad decided there was no need to explain.

"Mrs. Schwartzbauer," Dad went on, "it's two o'clock in the morning. If you have something you want to discuss with me, please call during the day. Now why don't you turn off your radio and go to bed."

Mrs. Schwartzbauer agreed.

Dad went back to bed and assured Mother that everything was OK—no one had died.

Well, back to the library. I finished reading *The History of Fond du Lac County*. It was one of the dullest books I had ever read.

A few weeks later when I was in the library, Mrs. Frank was standing at one of the shelves, going through the books.

"What are you doing?" I asked her.

"I'm taking our annual inventory, and it's not going very well," she answered. "I can't account for a lot of books."

Since there was no one else in the library, I offered to help her.

"Maybe they just got put on the wrong shelf," I suggested.

"No, we don't have that many books to begin with, so it's easy to keep track of them," she answered. "But if you want to help me, we can compare the shelves with the shelf list I keep."

We went through the books, shelf by shelf, and Mrs. Frank made a list of all the books which were missing.

"Now let's see which ones are checked out," she said, going back to her desk and taking out the card file of the books which had been checked out. She then proceeded to make a list of the missing books.

"There are seventeen books missing," she announced. She began writing a list of the missing books. I continued to look through the shelves as she wrote.

"Look at this," she said, handing the list to me.

I read through the list. "The only one I recognize is *Gone with the Wind*," I said. "I haven't read the rest of these."

"You probably wouldn't be interested," Mrs. Frank said. "They're all romantic novels."

We looked at each other.

"Myrtle Wilson," we said in unison.

"If we thought someone was taking them, she would be my prime suspect," Mrs. Frank said. "She has been in the library reading magazines, but she hasn't checked out any books. I keep an eye on her when she's here."

"Well, maybe the books will turn up," I said, trying to reassure Mrs. Frank.

"I certainly hope so. With the small budget the Village board gives the library, we can't afford to replace these books."

Next week when I went to the library, I asked Mrs. Frank if any of the books had turned up.

"No," she answered, "and I think three more are missing. I thought of calling Leo Flannery, but I'm a little bit embarrassed to do that."

Leo Flannery was the deputy sheriff who lived in the Village. On the rare occasions when there was a suspected crime, he would be called in to investigate.

A few days later I was in the post office to pick up our mail. I thought I would check with the postmaster, Mr. Ruggle, to see if there were any new commemorative stamps in. I was a stamp collector, and Mr. Ruggle would always save the corner block from the sheet of the newest commemorative stamp for me. As I went to the window, I stood behind a woman who was having a discussion with the postmaster.

I couldn't see her face, but I recognized her voice—it was Myrtle Wilson. I looked down and saw she had placed her bag on the floor. I glanced at it and gulped. There were books in it. I tried to get closer to see if I could read any of the titles, but at that moment, she finished her business, turned around and walked out.

Later that day when the library was open, I went in and waited until the library was empty. I told Mrs. Frank what I had seen.

"Well, she hasn't checked out any books. Let me figure out if any are missing. It will take me a while, but I'll let you know," she told me. I stopped in a few days later and Mrs. Frank told me that three more books were missing.

It had to be Myrtle Wilson, we agreed. But thinking she was guilty and proving it was another matter.

"Do you think we should go to Leo Flannery?" I asked Mrs. Frank.

"I hate to do that unless we have some evidence," she answered.

One of my favorite authors at that time was Erle Stanley Gardner. I devoured his Perry Mason novels about the lawyer who always solved the crime when he represented the accused defendant. However, of the dozens of mysteries I had read, there was none called *The Case of the Missing Library Books.*

What would Perry Mason do, I wondered? He would certainly figure out who was the guilty perpetrator and would come up with a way to catch the criminal. I thought about different things I could do. Maybe I could sneak into her house and look for the books. No, that could get me in trouble. Or I could get some of my friends and we could stake out her house and follow her. But we would get noticed and someone would call our parents to ask why we were following Mrs. Wilson around. She would probably end up calling Leo Flannery and complain about us. No, that wouldn't work.

If only I could hire a private investigator like Perry did. There were a couple of problems with this. For one thing, I didn't have any money to hire a private investigator. And more importantly, there wasn't a private investigator in the Village.

The more I thought about it, the more I concluded that Myrtle must be sneaking into the library. I knew that Wes Carley, the Village maintenance man, cleaned the library, since Mrs. Frank was always complaining that he didn't do a very good job.

"Sometimes the wastebaskets don't get emptied for two weeks," she told me one time.

Maybe he left the door open, and she would sneak in. Or maybe Wes was stealing the books. No, that didn't make sense. I doubt if Wes ever read a book. And if he wanted a book, he would check it out just like everyone else—everyone but Myrtle, that is.

It suddenly came to me. The door. Not the front door, but the door without the key. Maybe somehow Myrtle got into the library that way.

But no one had a key. Maybe she knew how to pick locks, like I read about in some of the mysteries. Probably not, but still ...

Now you may not believe this, but a few Christmases ago, I had gotten a junior detective kit from my Aunt Ilma. It was kind of neat at the time. It had an ink pad for taking fingerprints and some dusting powder to check for fingerprints at the crime scene. I hadn't played with it for a long time since I had outgrown it, but it was still in my bedroom closet. I figured if I could dust for fingerprints, maybe I could dust for footprints.

I went to the library and when no one else was there, I told Mrs. Frank my theory and my idea.

"Do you think I could spread some of the dusting powder on the floor by the door?" I asked Mrs. Frank.

"Well, the way Wes cleans things, it could be there for a month without being disturbed," she answered. "Why not? What can we lose?"

On Saturday afternoon I came back to the library with my can of dusting powder. Mrs. Frank and I had decided that Saturday afternoon would be a good time to do it since the library was closed on Sunday and Monday.

"And when Wes does clean, he usually does it on Thursday, so we have four or five days," Mrs. Frank said.

So on Saturday I carefully dusted the area in front of the door. Tuesday after school I stopped in. Nothing was disturbed. The same results on Wednesday and Thursday.

"You won't believe this, but Wes actually swept the floor on Thursday, so the powder is all gone," Mrs. Frank told me.

"Let's try again on Saturday," I suggested.

"Might as well," Mrs. Frank agreed. "And as far as I can determine, no more books are missing."

On Saturday afternoon I again dusted the area. Nothing on Tuesday. Nothing on Wednesday, but then, on Thursday when I stopped in, Mrs. Frank was excited.

"Look," she said as she took me to the area by the old door. "See."

It was kind of dark in the shadowy area by the door, but I could see the powder had been disturbed. Looking carefully I could make out two sets of tracks which looked as though someone had entered and left.

"And," Mrs. Frank continued, "I'm quite certain that three more books are missing."

We stood there for a minute, thinking.

"I think you should talk to Leo Flannery," I suggested. "You could tell him our suspicions and see what he thinks."

"I'll do that," Mrs. Frank decided. "It won't hurt to let him know that library books are being stolen."

Our family left town for a few days since it was Memorial Day, and we always went to Mother's hometown for the holiday. Memorial Day was kind of a homecoming event there. It seemed that the town was filled with relatives we didn't know and with Mother's childhood friends who inevitably would pat me on the head and say something like, "Oh, so you're Minnie's boy."

Anyway we were gone, so I didn't know what Mrs. Frank had done about the missing books. We had hardly unloaded the car when I told Mother that I had to go to the library.

"For heaven's sake, we just got home," Mother said.

"I just remembered I have a book that's due today, and I don't want to have to pay a fine," I hastily explained.

I jumped on my bike and pedaled down to the library. Only Mrs. Frank was in the library when I walked in.

"You won't believe what happened," she told me.

"What did happen?" I wanted to know.

"I did call Leo. He came down to the library, and I told him the whole story—about the missing books, why we suspected Myrtle and then the footprints."

She said Leo listened, asked some questions, and then suggested that he and I go to Myrtle's house and talk with her.

"You should have heard Leo. He was really something. There he was wearing his uniform with his revolver on his belt. We drove to Myrtle's house in Leo's squad car.

"We went to the door. When Myrtle answered, Leo began to talk to her."

"'Myrtle, Mrs. Frank tells me that there are quite a few books missing from the library. We have reason to believe that you know something about this. Now I can't enter your house to look for them unless you give me permission. I will tell you, if you don't give me permission, I can go to the judge in Fond du Lac to get a search warrant to check your house for unauthorized possession of Village property.

"'Now, if I get the search warrant and I do find library books in your house, I will have to arrest you on suspicion of having stolen goods. And if you are arrested, it will be a matter of public record, which means it will likely be in the Fond du Lac newspaper. And since it's a rather unusual story, the Milwaukee newspapers will likely hear about it, and they will print stories. Everyone in the state will know about it. You wouldn't want that to happen, would you? Can you imagine what your father would have thought of you if he would have known you were taking books from the library like this?'"

Mrs. Frank continued, "Myrtle didn't know quite what to think. I thought at first she would deny everything, and I wondered if Leo really could get a search warrant. Myrtle just stood there, looking first at me and then at Leo. Leo crossed his arms and stood there, waiting. Finally he said, 'Well, Myrtle, I'm going to have to leave for Fond du Lac in a few minutes. What have you decided?'

"'I didn't really mean to do anything wrong. I just thought people shouldn't be reading those books. So I took them and brought them home. Come on in. You can have your old books,' said Myrtle as she started to sob.

"So we went in and there were the library books, all stacked up on the floor of her living room," said Mrs. Frank.

"'Take them. Just get them out of here,' Myrtle said.

"I looked at Leo and he nodded, so I began carrying the books out to the squad car. When I finished, Leo was still talking to Myrtle.

"'No, I'm not going to arrest you. But I am warning you. If you take any books out of the library without checking them out, I will arrest you,' he said.

"Leo looked at me, 'Do you think you have all the books?'

"'I guess so,' I answered, 'but I do have a question for Myrtle. How did you get into the library through the old back door?' Myrtle looked pleased.

"'I have a key,' she said triumphantly.

"'I thought there wasn't a key,' I told her.

"'I got the key from my father. He had keys to every door in the Village Hall from the days when he had been commander of the G.A.R. And I just kept the keys. So there,' she said.

"'In that case, Myrtle, I think you better hand over those keys, so you won't be tempted to try this again,' Leo told her.

"'Oh, all right,' Myrtle said. She went to the desk and brought out a key ring with several old-fashioned keys on it.

"'Here,' she said, handing the keys to Leo.

"'Thank you, Myrtle. And thank you for cooperating. I'm happy I didn't have to arrest you,' Leo said as we walked out of the house.

"And," said Mrs. Frank to me, "thank you for helping to solve this mystery."

Chapter 30

The Great Village Milk Conflict

I pulled my jacket collar up around my neck. It was cold walking home. Maybe I should have listened to Mother and worn my cap. Mother had this belief that if you wore a cap you would keep your entire body warm.

"I remember from my high school science class that heat rises," Mother explained. "Now if you wear a cap, when your body heat rises, it means that the heat will rise to your cap but stay in your body and you won't get cold. If you go without a cap, the heat will just rise and escape through your head and you'll be cold all over."

We kids, well, at least my brother Phil and I, resisted wearing caps. Some of it was we didn't like Mother telling us what to do. Another reason was the head-ware we had were old-fashioned stocking hats and if we wore them, we thought the other kids would make fun of us. So shivering was the price we paid for trying to be fashionable. Helene had a cute little cap she wore, so she never had an argument with Mother.

It was the middle of January as I walked home from school. Our house was eight blocks from the school and we walked it four times a day: to school in the morning, home for lunch, back to school, and then home at the end of the school day. And if there happened to be a school activity in the evening— a basketball game or a concert—it was another round-trip walk.

I was on my way home for lunch. When I got to the downtown area— the block-long business section of the Village—I stopped at the post office to pick up the mail. I knew Dad wouldn't have been there because he was already gone. He had left on the 7:30 a.m. train for a church meeting in Milwaukee.

"I'll be home on the 8:00 p.m. train," he had told us. There were four passenger trains each day. In the morning, the 7:30 a.m. train stopped on its way to Milwaukee. At 9:30 a.m. the train from Milwaukee would arrive. Then in the afternoon, the 5:00 p.m. train would head for Milwaukee, and at 8:00 p.m. the train would arrive from Milwaukee.

Life in the Village tended to be regulated by the trains. We'd usually be up by the time the 7:30 a.m. train came through. The arrival of the 9:30 a.m. train, with most of the day's mail, was a signal for many housewives in the Village to walk downtown to pick up the mail and do the shopping for the day. People didn't have much room to store a lot of food (due to small refrigerators, or even ice boxes), so women shopped every day ... well, every day but Sunday when the stores were closed.

One thing they didn't buy at the store was milk.

Milk was delivered every day—even Sundays—by Fred Rechlein, who ran the dairy. His farm sat at the edge of the Village, and his cows supplied the milk for the Village. The Village stores did sell milk, which people would buy now and then if they happened to run out of their delivered milk.

Like most people, we had a standing order with Fred—three quarts of milk each day. Milk was delivered in quart bottles. When they were empty, we would wash the bottles and place them in the milk box next to the side door. When Fred would come around in the morning, he would pick up the empty bottles and leave three quarts of milk. If we needed to change the order—say we had company coming and needed more milk—we would leave a note in one of the empty bottles telling Fred about the change. At the end of the month, Fred would leave the bill and the next day we would leave a check for him.

As I approached the side door, I noticed that the milk was still in the milk box AND it had frozen. The milk had expanded two inches about the necks of the bottle. I had to laugh: the bottles looked comical with the milk caps sitting on top of the frozen milk looking like little freshman students wearing beanies. Then I remembered that Mother had kept Helene home from school that day because my sister had a cold. In her anxiety over Helene's health, Mother had forgotten to bring in the milk bottles.

As I brought in the bottles, I thought back to last year when the whole Village was talking about milk. Now that I brought up the subject, I guess I better explain why milk of all things had become a controversial subject in town.

It had all started because of decreasing ice sales. All right, more explanation. As I mentioned, some people in the Village did not have refrigerators. They had ice boxes. These were old-fashioned devices which people had used before electric refrigerators came into use. They required blocks of ice to keep food cold.

Mr. Vandenicht had the ice business in the Village. He would deliver ice to people who had ice boxes. Summer was an especially good time for business since almost all of the summer cottages at the nearby lake had ice boxes plus, of course, ice melted much faster in summer. But Walt Vandenicht could see that the ice business was not a growth industry. More and more people were buying refrigerators, even the cottage owners. He knew he needed to get a new line of business.

He decided he would go into the dairy business. He had a refrigerated truck for delivery and he could easily convert his ice storage room so it could store dairy products. Since his business was in town, he knew he couldn't have a herd of dairy cows, so he made arrangements with one of the big dairy companies in Milwaukee to sell its products.

In September it came as a big surprise to most everyone in town when the *Village Times* carried a quarter page ad announcing that the Vandenicht Ice Company was now the Vandenicht Dairy and Ice Company, and that Walt Vandenicht would begin offering home delivery of a complete line of dairy products including milk, chocolate milk, dairy orange drink, and a whole lot more, "all delivered to your door in our refrigerated delivery truck," the ad concluded.

By far the most surprised person was Fred Rechlein. His grandfather had started the milk business more than 50 years earlier from his farm at the edge of the Village. Fred had taken over the farm and milk business when his father had retired twenty years earlier. Everyone in the Village had always bought their milk from him.

After Walt's announcement appeared, Fred talked things over with his wife and they decided they would run an ad in the Village paper, the first time they had ever advertised. Mrs. Rechlein wrote the ad which appeared the following week.

"You know your milk is fresh when it's from the Rechlein Dairy," the ad said. "The milk you get comes from our cows right here in the Village. It doesn't come from a factory in Milwaukee. Who knows where they get their milk?"

Sure enough, the next week Walt ran another ad pointing out that, "All the products we deliver come from a dairy where there is a state inspector on duty every day to ensure that everything you buy from us was produced under strict sanitary conditions. We are authorized to state that the company will refund your money if not completely satisfied."

Mrs. Rechlein decided to respond with a different tact—a poem. Mrs. Rechlein was widely known for her poetry, at least among members of Emanuel Lutheran. Whenever there was a major social event at church, Mrs.

Rechlein would produce a poem. Her fame extended beyond Emanuel since she even had poems published in *The Wisconsin Dairyman's Wife Magazine*. Now when the family's livelihood was threatened, she was ready with a counterattack. The next issue of the *Village Times* had this ad:

Now maybe our cows haven't gained fame
But we love them and call them by name
It's true we don't have Elsie the Borden Cow
But the ones we have we do love and how

You know your milk's pure
And you can be sure
That when the bottle says Rechlein
You know the product is cleaner than clean.

The entire Village was getting interested in this public feud. Probably the most interested was Mr. Henley, the owner of the paper. This was starting to be a nice financial windfall for him, since neither business had ever previously advertised.

People in the Village began taking sides. Since Walt and his family were members of the Dutch Reformed Church, he started gaining business from the Hollanders. This was helped when the pastor of the Reformed Church publicly complimented Mr. Vandenicht for not profaning the Sabbath by delivering on Sunday.

Most of the other folks in town liked having Sunday delivery, so they stuck with Fred. Up until this time, both dairies charged the same price for milk: twelve cents a quart. Then Walt passed out a flyer announcing that he would begin charging ten cents a quart.

Our family discussed this at the supper table.

"The guys at the station bet that the Milwaukee dairy was giving Walt a break on the price, hoping he could drive Fred out of business," Phil reported.

"And if that happens, you can bet the price will go up again—probably higher than it is now," Mother said.

Of course, there was no discussion about our changing. The Rechleins were members of Emanuel, and even if Fred only came to evening services, they were good members.

"Are you going to be like Rev. DeBrodt at the Reformed Church and tell our members to stick with Fred?" Phil asked Dad.

"No," Dad replied, "but if any of our members ask, I will certainly tell them we are staying with Fred."

Then word got around that while Walt had lowered the price on regular milk, he had increased the prices on his other products. Some of the customers who had switched returned to Rechlein's.

It was hard to know who was winning what some in the Village were calling the "Big Milk War". When someone would ask either Fred or Walt how business was going, each had the same reply: "Well, it could be better." It seemed there was an uneasy truce in place.

Then, the week before Christmas, readers of the *Village Times* were amazed when they read a small ad announcing that:

"As of January 1, the Vandenicht Dairy and Ice Company will no longer be selling milk. We will continue delivering our line of other fine dairy products for the convenience of our customers."

What had happened, everyone wondered?

Later we found out when Mrs. Rechlein stopped in with a Christmas gift for our family.

"Fred was really surprised when he got a phone call from Walt who asked if he could stop over. When he came he told Fred that he was tired of losing money on milk sales and said he was going to stick to selling his other products such as cottage cheese, chocolate milk, dairy orange and things like that. He said, 'I can deliver these three days a week, so that will be less work and less expense for me.'"

So just in time for Christmas, "The Big Milk War" came to an end.

At supper that night, when Dad reported the conversation with Mrs. Rechlein, he ended by saying, "And so, there is peace on earth, goodwill to men."

"And also to the cows," Helene added.

Chapter 31

I Buy a War Bomb

"Do you remember anything about the War?" Helene asked. We were sitting in the living room. I was taking care of my sister while Mother and Dad were at church for the Ladies Aid meeting. We both had run out of books to read, and there was nothing on the radio to listen to, so Helene thought it would be a good time to hear some stories from me.

"What makes you ask that?" I said to her.

"My teacher said her husband served in World War II, so I got to wondering about it," she answered. "Since you were around, I thought you might remember some things."

"Actually, I do remember a lot of things. I'll tell you some of the stories."

"Oh, good—I like stories," Helene said, as she curled up on the couch and waited for me to begin.

"You have to remember that I was only five years old when the War started. We had just moved to the Village from Milwaukee about two weeks before Pearl Harbor."

"What was Pearl Harbor?" Helene asked.

"Here's what I remember. It was Sunday afternoon. Phil was in the living room, listening to a football game on the radio. The Chicago Bears were playing, and Phil was hoping they would lose because then the Green Bay Packers would be the champions. I can't remember what I was doing— probably playing with some toys.

"Suddenly Phil called out that the Japanese had bombed Pearl Harbor. Mother and Dad came running to the living room, asking what Phil was yelling about.

"I didn't know what to think. I knew what a pearl was, and I knew what a harbor was, but it didn't make any sense to me that someone would bomb a harbor filled with pearls. You have to remember—I was only five.

"It didn't take long for me to find out that this was serious business, that it meant war. All of a sudden, everything changed. I don't remember exactly when things happened. I know that a lot of Mother's family got drafted to serve in the military."

"What does 'drafted' mean?" Helene asked.

"It means that the government said they had to go into the Army or Navy or some other type of service. Uncle Carl, Uncle John, and our cousin Luther were all drafted. I worried that Dad might get drafted. My friend Stevie Hull's dad, who was the doctor in the Village left to go into the Army. I figure if a doctor got drafted, a minister could go too. However, I found out later that ministers didn't get drafted. They could volunteer to be chaplains.

"I remember Mother mentioning that she was glad we had moved from Milwaukee."

"Why was that?" Helene asked.

"Well, Milwaukee had a lot of factories that made all sorts of war things—bombs and tanks and trucks and all kinds of stuff. I think she figured that Milwaukee would be a target for Japanese bombers."

"I guess the Village was a safe place," Helene observed.

"It probably was, but I can remember hearing stories about what could happen. People said the Shaler Company in Waupun was only ten miles away, and it made the rivets which were used for building airplanes and ships and things like that. And Ripon was only ten miles away in the other direction, and the Speed Queen factory there was doing all sorts of secret work. People said the Germans or Japanese might send rockets to attack these factories, and if one of the rockets would go astray it might hit the Village."

Helene pondered this for a moment and then asked, "But there was never any bombing around here, was there?"

"No, but we did have air raid drills. Dad was even an air raid warden."

"A what?"

"An air raid warden. You see, after the Japanese had bombed Pearl Harbor, a lot of people were afraid there would be more bombing, maybe here in the United States. Even the government didn't know if there might be bombing on the mainland. That's why they decided to get people prepared by having air raid drills. And to conduct drills, there had to be people in charge of the drills. That's where Dad got involved."

"How come Daddy was an air raid warden?" Helene wondered.

"I can't remember for sure. I suppose maybe the mayor or someone asked him to do it. A lot of the men in town were in the Army or working in defense plants, so Dad was available to do this. Maybe he volunteered to do it so he could do his part in the War effort. We'll have to ask him about it sometime," I answered.

"Anyway, there were air raid drills all over the country. The government wanted people to be aware that in case of an air attack, they would know how to turn off all the lights so enemy planes wouldn't be able to see any targets. So we practiced doing this. At a certain time, people would be alerted there was going to be a drill. The fire whistle would blow and everyone was supposed to turn out their lights and pull down their shades. It was the air raid warden's job to walk around the Village to see that everyone had turned off their lights.

"I remember how excited I was when Dad said there was going to be an air raid drill the next week and that he was going to be an air raid warden. I was really impressed when he showed us the white helmet he had been given with the words 'Air Raid Warden' on it."

"He had a helmet like that?" Helene exclaimed. "What happened to it?"

"I don't remember. I suppose he gave it back after they stopped having air raid drills.

"I remember that there was going to be an air raid drill the next Tuesday. There was a big story about it in the Village paper, and it was announced at school and in all the churches, so everyone was supposed to know about it.

"Tuesday evening came. The fire siren sounded. We turned out all our lights and pulled down the shades. Dad had a little flashlight which he had been given with instructions to use it only to avoid stumbling or running into things. Dad had half the town to patrol. I think maybe the Methodist minister had the other half, but I don't remember for sure.

"Phil and I peeked out the little windows by the front door where there were no shades. Phil said he was looking to see if there were any bombers in the sky, but I think he said that just to scare me. I couldn't see anything since it was pitch black outside. I remember Mother worrying about Dad tripping and falling, saying that she hoped he remembered to use his flashlight.

"After a while the fire siren blew again as a signal that the drill was over. As I peeked out the window I could see lights coming back on. Then Mother told us it was past our bedtimes, and we had to go to bed.

"The next day Dad told us about the drill. I remember Dad telling a story we kids thought was pretty funny. Almost everyone in town had their lights turned off. All the businesses were dark, the streetlights were out, and Dad used his little flashlight very carefully. As he went to the other end of town, he saw there was a light on in Mrs. Schoenbaum's house. She was a member of our congregation. Dad knew she didn't pay attention to a lot of things, so he went up to her door and knocked. 'Who's there?' she asked, without opening the door.

"'It's Pastor Kurtz,' Dad answered, 'You need to turn off your lights. There's an air raid drill going on.'

"'A what?' she asked. Dad explained that the Village was practicing what to do in case there was ever a threat of enemy bombing. Mrs. Schoenbaum didn't hear real well. She opened her door and asked Dad, 'They're going to drop bombs on us? Here?' Dad explained that no, there were no bombs, but this was a practice so everyone would know what to do in case there was an attack.

"'That's why they blew the siren. Didn't you hear it?'

"'I did, but since my house wasn't burning, I didn't pay any attention to it,' she answered. 'Was there a fire?'

"Dad explained there was not a fire, but the siren had been blown to announce the air raid.

"'Then why did you come? Did the church have the air raid drill?' she wanted to know.

"Dad patiently explained that the church did not conduct the air raid drill and that he was volunteering to be an air raid warden to be sure everyone turned out their lights.

"'Now, Mrs. Schoenbaum,' Dad said firmly, 'you have to listen to me and turn out your lights right away.'

"Since Mrs. Schoenbaum was a good German lady and when the pastor talked to her in this manner, she could respond in only one way: she turned off her lights immediately."

"Were there more air raid drills?" Helene asked.

"There might have been, but I can't remember. Maybe I was in bed if they happened."

"What else did you do?" Helene asked.

"I remember one fall, Phil picked milkweeds."

"What are they?" That was Helene—always asking questions.

"They're a weed that grows wild along the roads in the country. In the fall, they have little pods filled with a kind of silk. They used this to make life preservers for sailors and pilots who might crash in the ocean. I remember Phil's class at school went out every afternoon in the fall and picked them. I don't remember what they did with them afterward.

"But I remember we had scrap drives. We saved all sorts of things: newspapers, magazines, tin cans, even stuff like bacon grease. Bill, the junk dealer in the Village, collected all this stuff and hauled it over to Oshkosh."

I started laughing again.

"What's funny?" Helene wanted to know.

"I just thought of something else. One time there was a big scrap drive in the Village. People were asked to find old scrap metal and have it ready on Saturday when some of the men in the Village would come around and pick it up.

"Phil and I looked around. Since we had just moved here, we didn't have any old stuff sitting around. We found a couple of pieces of iron pipe in the upstairs of the barn, but it wasn't much. Phil and I looked around some more. 'I wonder what's in the back of the church?' Phil said. There was kind of a crawl space under the church. It had a dirt floor and it was all dark and musty.

"'Let's look,' I said.

"We crawled in. It was a little hard to see, but we did notice a pile of something along one wall.

"'Let's check it out,' Phil said.

"We crawled over to the pile. Phil picked up one of the pieces. 'This is iron,' he exclaimed. We took two pieces back outside so we could see them better. They were slender pieces of iron, about a foot long with a loop at one end. Phil studied them for a few minutes.

"'I think these are old window weights. Probably when they put in the stained-glass windows, they took out the old glass windows and someone saved the window weights. They'll make good scrap iron.'

"Now it didn't occur to us that we probably had no right to take them for the scrap drive. I remember Phil saying that they've been sitting here for thirty or forty years, so now, they'll do some good in helping to win the War.

"We hauled them to the street in front of the parsonage and waited for the truck to come. We had a good stack of scrap piled up. We felt good that we had found the weights.

"Finally the truck arrived. Bill was driving. Walt and a couple of other volunteer firemen were helping.

"'Quite a pile you have here,' Walt said. We beamed. 'Now you've got a choice,' Walt said. 'You can just donate this or we will pay you scrap iron price for it.'

"I looked at Phil. This was a whole new story.

"'I'd say this would be about four dollars' worth if you want to sell it,' Walt said.

"Phil quickly nodded. 'Yes,' he decided, 'we'll sell it.'

"Walt and the other men loaded it on the truck. Bill took four dollar bills out of his billfold and handed them to Phil. The men got on the truck and drove away.

"Phil looked at the money for a minute and then handed me two dollars.

"'Do you suppose we should have just donated it for the War effort?' I asked Phil.

"'No, we can use some of the money to buy War Stamps.'

"That sounded like a good idea to me."

As I finished that story I started to laugh.

"I just thought of another thing. When I was in first grade, I remember coming home all excited. 'We can start buying War Bonds in school,' I told Mother and Dad. Only I thought the teacher said we could buy War Bombs. I was only six years old. I knew what a bomb was, but I had never heard of a bond, so I just thought the teacher had said War Bomb.

"Anyway, I explained that you could bring in either ten cents or 25 cents a week. You would then get a little stamp which you would paste in a savings book. When you got to $18.75, you could get a War Bond and then in ten years the government would give you 25 dollars back. I couldn't quite figure this out, but I thought the government would just be happy that you had bought a bomb.

"Anyway, I brought in a dime each week; although it seemed to take forever to fill up the little book. One day our teacher announced that Alice Flannery had reached $18.75 and next week she would receive her War Bond. Alice had been buying 25 cent stamps, which is why she filled up the book. Since she was the first one in school to get a War Bond, there would be an assembly for all the students, and she would be presented with the bond at the assembly.

"I was really excited because I wanted to see that War Bomb. I didn't know what they would do with it in school, probably just show it. It sounded dangerous to have it there, but I figured the principal or the janitor would take care of it so we would be safe.

"Well, the next week came and, boy, was I disappointed. There was no bomb. All Alice got was a piece of paper. When I came home and told about it, I remember Phil laughing at me. 'Boy, are you dumb. You don't even know the difference between a bomb and a bond,' he said.

"'Don't make fun of him,' Mother said. 'Remember, you had to go to the dictionary to find out what a bond was.'

"That made me feel a little better. Anyway, I kept bringing in ten cents each week. I did get a War Bond; although the War was just about over before I finally got mine."

Just then we heard the door open and Mother and Dad were home.

"I'll tell you some more stories sometime," I told Helene.

"Promise?" she said.

"Yes, I promise."

Chapter 32

Laundry Tags, Yes; Checkbook, No

It was spring in the Village. The snow was finally gone, and it was warm enough so that I could put away my winter coat, wear my spring jacket, and ride my bike to school.

At the supper table, there would be frequent conversations about Phil's coming graduation from high school.

"I saw Mr. Rolfs in the post office this morning," Dad said at supper. Mr. Rolfs was the school principal. I quickly made a mental inventory of my recent behavior at school to see if Mr. Rolfs might have mentioned something to Dad. There was nothing I could think of, so I relaxed as Dad went on. "Yes, he said that it looks as though you will be the valedictorian if you get two more A's this semester," Dad continued, looking at Phil.

"I didn't think I was that close," Phil answered.

"That would be better than I did," Mother said. "I was just salutatorian of my high school class."

I thought of responding the way we frequently did when Mother brought up the fact she had finished second in her high school graduating class. I think it was Phil who originally answered, "Sure, but there were only two in your class." Mother would get indignant at this statement. "That isn't one bit true—there were five."

No, I thought, this is not the time to mention the size of her graduating class.

"Yes," Dad said, "it would be very nice to see you receive that honor, so I hope you'll work on getting two A's this semester. It will look good on your record when you apply to college."

We suddenly got quiet at the table. It was beginning to hit us that Phil would soon be leaving home to attend college this fall.

I wasn't all that upset about it. After all, that's what people did when they graduated from high school ... at least some of them. Besides, I could think of a lot worse things than having Phil leave home. While he was my favorite brother, it was only by default.

Most of the graduates from the Village high school did not go to college. Some would stay at home and work on their dads' farms. Some of the boys would join the Army or Air Force. A couple of the girls would go to secretarial school and get jobs in Fond du Lac or Oshkosh. Other girls would get married soon after graduating. Maybe three or four would go on to college, most likely to the nearby Oshkosh State Teachers College. One or two of the smarter ones would enroll at the University of Wisconsin at Madison, some 65 miles away.

There had not been much discussion about where Phil would go to college. Nor had there been any discussion that he would go to college—it was just assumed that he would go. As long as I could remember, Phil and I had started savings accounts for college. Mother talked about it quite often.

Of course, what I remembered the most was the time she had gotten upset at my behavior. (I don't recall exactly what I had done. I doubt if I had been all that bad.) Anyway I could still hear Mother saying to me, "Now if you keep behaving that way, you're going to make me old and grey. Then when you bring your friends home from college, you'll be so ashamed of how old your mother looks."

Somehow this type of threat was not particularly conducive to encouraging good behavior on my part, especially when she started saying that when I was seven or eight years old. However, it did emphasize that we children would go to college.

So the weeks passed. On occasion at supper Dad or Mother would ask Phil about his grades. He kept assuring them that he was doing OK.

"I sure hope so," said Mother, "but I don't see you bringing books home at night."

"I get all my work done in study hall," Phil answered. "Seniors will take their final tests early, so the faculty can determine class ranking."

"Well, you should start thinking about a topic for a speech if you do make valedictorian," Dad told Phil.

"Oh," Phil answered, "I had forgotten about that. Maybe I should try not to get those two A's."

"You'll do nothing of the kind," Mother said sharply. "Besides, if you're valedictorian, you are probably eligible for a college scholarship."

"What's a 'scholarship'? Is it a kind of boat?" Helene asked.

The rest of the family tried not to laugh.

"A scholarship is some money the college gives to good students. It helps pay college expenses," Dad explained to her.

"Then why do they call it a 'ship'?"

"I don't really know. I guess it's just what it's called," Dad answered.

The seniors took their final exams. A few days later Phil was smiling when he came home. Without saying anything he handed his report card to Mother.

Mother looked at it and then smiled.

"All A's," she said. "What a great job! Dad will be so pleased to see this when he gets home.

"Now," she said, "we've got to get busy on your speech."

One would have thought that Mother would have turned this duty over to Dad, since he prepared a speech every week—a sermon after all was a speech.

But no, Mother decided she would be the one who would help Phil prepare and deliver the valedictory. Dad explained that was what the speech was called.

"It's from the Latin," he told us. "The root word is *vale* which is Latin for 'farewell'. It means that the speaker is saying farewell to school, and the person making the valedictory is therefore called the valedictorian."

Dad sure knows a lot of stuff, I thought. However, Dad was perfectly willing to let Mother help Phil with his speech.

"I did get a first place in the declaiming contest," Mother pointed out.

"What is a 'declaiming contest'?" Helene needs to know the answers, I thought.

"It was when I was at the county normal. Our school competed with the other normal schools in forensics, and I took first place in the Original Declamation category. My talk was titled, 'Now That Women Have the Vote'. I still remember most of it."

Phil changed the subject. "I don't think that would be a good topic for me."

Mother agreed. "After supper, let's work on your speech," she said.

And so for the next weeks, every time Phil wasn't at school, working, or with Margie (his girlfriend), Mother would corner Phil and make him work on his speech. If Dad wasn't using his study, Mother would take Phil there, close the door, and work with him. I couldn't hear them; although one day I heard Phil say, "Well, maybe you should give the speech," and he stormed out of the study.

But he was soon back working on the speech.

One night at supper, Dad announced that Mr. Rolfs had asked him to give the baccalaureate sermon.

"What is that?" That was Helene again.

"It's like a church service for graduates," Dad answered. "Most schools have it."

The baccalaureate service was held a week before graduation. There were six congregations in town, but the Catholic, Congregational, and Evangelical United Brethren were small and were served by clergy from neighboring cities. The three resident pastors—Lutheran, Methodist, and Reformed—took turns giving the baccalaureate sermon.

"It's really not my turn, but since Phil is graduating this year, I think Mr. Rolfs decided to ask me, just like two years ago Rev. VandeMan preached because his daughter was graduating."

The baccalaureate service was held in the high school gym. Dad spoke, the high school girls' chorus sang, the graduates in their red robes (the Village high school colors were red and white) were on the stage, and the audience sat on hard folding chairs.

And then came graduation.

"Are you sure you have your speech memorized?" Mother asked anxiously the day before the program.

"I'm OK," Phil answered. "Jerry will have a copy of the speech, and he'll be sitting right behind me. If I get stuck, I'll put my hand behind me and he'll give me the words."

I don't remember much about his speech. I think most of it was taken from a recent article in Life magazine about what people could expect in the coming years.

I thought it was a little farfetched when Phil said that it wouldn't be too long before people would have television sets in their homes just like they had radios now. Since there was only one set in the Village, this didn't seem likely.

But Phil did fine. He didn't get stuck once, so Jerry never had to come to the rescue.

"Now we have a new graduate," Mother said at the supper table the next night. "And a valedictorian, too."

"Did you get a scholarship?" Helene remembered the earlier discussion.

"He's got to get busy and apply to college if he wants to get a scholarship," Dad pointed out. "You have to decide pretty soon. September will be here before you know it. After supper, let's sit down and talk about it."

Phil nodded.

"And," said Dad, turning to me, "you might want to be there too. It won't be long before you'll be thinking of college."

So after the dishes were done, we all gathered around the kitchen table. Mother wasn't going to let this discussion take place without her insights, and Helene decided she better be there too because she might miss something.

"The first thing you have to decide is where you're going to go," Dad started.

"Well," Phil answered, "there's Oshkosh State Teachers College. It's close by, and it's not real expensive. I could come home weekends and probably work at the station."

"But do you want to be a teacher?" Dad asked.

"I don't really know what I want to do," Phil answered. "A couple of guys from here go to Madison, and they like it."

"The university is a good school," Dad agreed, "but it's awfully big. What are there? 25,000 students?"

"What about St. Olaf?" Mother put in. Mother's brother Carl had graduated from St. Olaf, and Mother, like many Norwegians, thought that St. Olaf was the ultimate in colleges.

Phil made no response; although I knew he was thinking that St. Olaf was the last place he would attend.

"Ripon College is close by," I put in. Our class had recently attended a play there, and I thought it was a neat place. "It's only ten miles away."

"But it's awfully expensive," Mother said. "Why, it even cost more than St. Olaf."

"What about Wartburg?" Dad asked. Wartburg was where Dad had gone and where Grandpa Kurtz had gone and where a whole bunch of other relatives had attended. "It's really a growing school, and it is our church college."

"I've been thinking about that," Phil answered. "Gordy is going to be a junior there, and he says he likes it."

Gordy was a member of the congregation who was planning to become a minister. Dad had recommended to him that he enroll at Wartburg.

"But it's so far away," said Mother. "You'll hardly ever get home."

Hmm, I thought, that would be a definite advantage as far as I was concerned.

"Let me think about it," Phil said.

A few days later at supper, Phil announced, "Well, I've decided."

We all stopped eating.

"And?" Dad asked.

"I think I'll go to Wartburg," he answered.

"That's a good choice," Dad said. "Now you've got to get your application in."

The next few weeks were a blur to me. Every time Phil was home, he was talking to Mother or to Dad, or it might be more accurate to say that Mother and Dad were constantly talking to Phil.

One day when I brought the mail home from the post office, there was a small package for Mother.

"What's that?" I asked as I handed it to her. Mother rarely got packages addressed to her.

"When Phil comes home from work, I'll show you," Mother responded.

After supper, Mother told us to wait before we started clearing the table. She went upstairs and returned in a few minutes, carrying the package I had brought home.

"Look what I got for you," she told Phil as she handed him the package.

"What is it?" Phil asked.

"Open it and find out," Mother told him.

"I'll help," Helene said. Phil handed her the package. Mother had already opened it, so it was only a moment before Helene pulled out a long roll of cloth tags.

"What is this?" she said, holding up a long, colored strand.

Mother took it from Helene.

"See," she said, "name tags."

I looked and saw that Phil's name was printed time after time—a whole roll of "Philip Kurtz" name tags.

I guess the rest of us looked pretty puzzled, because Mother hastened to explain.

"They're for Phil's clothes when he goes away to college. That way they won't get mixed up."

"Mixed up with what?" Phil said.

"Why, when your clothes go to the laundry," Mother informed him.

"But you bought me a laundry case so I could send my laundry home," Phil answered.

This stopped Mother, but only momentarily.

"There may be times when you won't be able to send your laundry home or it might just get mixed up with your roommate's clothes. I read in my *Modern Homemaking* magazine that college students should have all their clothes marked, so I sent for these name tags."

Phil picked up the roll of tags and looked at it. "Well, with the amount of clothes I have, this should last me for a dozen years of college."

As a matter of fact, it did last Phil through college and seminary (but that's another story). Not only that, in later years when I went to college and then when Helene went to college, there were plenty of tags remaining, so

Mother clipped off "Philip" from the tags and used the remaining "Kurtz" tags on our clothing.

Soon Phil received word that he had been accepted at Wartburg College. A bit later he was notified that he would receive a $175 honor scholarship, payable the second semester.

"A hundred and seventy-five dollars," said Dad, "that will pay tuition for your whole second semester."

The entire summer seemed to center around getting Phil ready for college. There were several shopping trips to Fond du Lac. The person most excited about all the preparations was Mother. She was going to see that Phil was all set.

One evening after supper I was sitting in the living room, reading the newspaper. Helene was playing outside. Mother, Dad, and Phil were sitting at the kitchen table discussing Phil's finances. I wasn't paying any attention until suddenly I heard a loud cry from Mother: "MOST CERTAINLY NOT!"

Good grief, I thought, what brought that on? Had she decided that Phil shouldn't go to college?

I went through the dining room and stood by the side of the door to the kitchen to hear what was going on.

"He is not going to have a checking account," I heard Mother declare with a degree of vehemence I rarely heard from her. "Not after what John did."

Then I remembered. We would periodically hear Mother tell about her brother John. Mother had four brothers. Three of them were solid citizens: hard working, gainfully employed, and honest to a fault. John had none of these characteristics. I won't go into detail now, but I do remember Mother telling us about John's problems with money in college.

John attended a small Norwegian college in Iowa. He didn't have trouble with grades. He was smart and did enough to get by. When he went off to college, Grandpa set up a checking account for him at the bank in the town where Grandpa and Grandma lived.

John viewed the checking account as a money machine. When he wanted money, he would write a check, regardless of whether there was money in the account or not. When the check would bounce, the banker would call Grandpa, and Grandpa would make good on the check. John would then get a stern letter, and he would promise not to do it again.

And the process kept repeating and repeating. Grandpa was ready to close the account, but Grandma wouldn't let him, Mother told us. She said that in Grandma's eyes, John could do no wrong.

"And because John squandered so much money, it's the main reason I never got to go to a regular college," Mother pointed out.

Mother won her argument. Phil would not have a checking account. Nor would I, nor would Helene. It wasn't until I was in graduate school that I finally got a checking account ... and even then Mother worried.

Pretty soon it was August. I didn't spend a lot of time thinking about Phil's departure for college. When I did think about Phil leaving, I thought it was a good idea. Phil and I really didn't get along all that well. Mother wouldn't even let us sit next to each other at the dinner table so that we wouldn't start fighting about something. For as long as I could remember, I had always been the younger brother. Now that he was going away, I was looking forward to being the older brother at home. And I won't pick on Helene the way he always picked on me, I promised myself.

I did notice that Mother was much quieter around the house. No longer was she offering her usual helpful advice.

"Just think," she said wistfully to me one day, "in only two weeks, Phil will be leaving for college."

I thought of all sorts of things to say in response like, "Right, and won't that be nice!" or, "I can hardly wait," or, "When Grandpa Kurtz comes this fall, I won't even have to share my bedroom with Phil."

No, for once I kept quiet, just nodding agreement. Maybe Mother was sad—I certainly wasn't.

Right after our table prayer one evening at supper a few days later, Mother announced, "I think it would nice if we all went to Wartburg when Phil starts college."

Phil looked up. "Gordy told me that I could get a ride with him and the guys from Ripon. That way you wouldn't have to make the drive."

There were a number of students from the area attending Wartburg. Phil had gotten to know some of them earlier when he had gone to Bible camp.

"Would they have enough room?" Dad asked.

Before Phil could answer, Mother cut in, "No, I think we all should go. That way we can see where you're going to be living," she said to Phil.

Because Phil had applied late, he had not gotten a room in one of the dormitories. This meant he would be living off campus, and Mother was all worried about that.

Yeah, I thought, what if his clothes get all mixed up and some of them might not even be labeled?

"Yes, I think it would be nice if we all went. You know, my good friend from college and seminary lives in a town near Waverly. I think we can stay there," Dad said.

So that settled the matter. We would all go.

So right after church on Sunday, we packed up Dad's Chevrolet and left for Iowa. It was a quiet trip. Helene and I were basically bored. Phil was driving, and Dad was concentrating on the map. He had concluded there was no direct route from the Village to Waverly, Iowa. When I glanced at Mother, I could tell she was looking pretty sad. I even saw a tear or two.

I was a little surprised—not that she was sad, because she had been moping about the house for the past couple of weeks. Surprised because she was not giving Phil all sorts of last-minute words of advice. But then, I thought, maybe she had just run out of advice. After all, she had been going pretty much non-stop all summer as far as advice was concerned.

I would like to tell you all about what happened when Phil started college, but truthfully I don't remember. All I was thinking about was getting home and starting school. After all, I would no longer be Phil's little brother as I had been for all these years. Let Mother mope and be sad about Phil away at college. I would now be the important guy at home.

Chapter 33

When Dad Was Called Father

It was a rainy afternoon. I was in my room reading when Helene came in.

"I'm bored," she announced. "There's nothing to do. I can't go outside and play. I'm tired of playing by myself."

"How would it be if I told you a story?" I asked.

Helene brightened up. "I like stories," she said. She climbed up on the bed and lay on her stomach with her hands under her chin. "What kind of a story?"

"Well, you had said you wanted to hear more about the War, so I thought I would tell you about when Dad was an interpreter."

"A what?"

"An interpreter. I better explain a bunch of things. During the War, there was a real shortage of people to work in the fields and in the canning factory. A lot of the men were in the Army or were working in defense plants. But the country needed the peas and corn the canning factory produced. So the government decided that prisoners of war could help in this work."

"What are 'prisoners of war'?" Helene wondered.

"During the War, many German soldiers were captured. They were brought to the United States where they were held in prison camps. Under the rules, they could do things like work in fields or in canning factories. So a lot of the prisoners were brought to this area to work harvesting peas and corn, and helping to can the vegetables. The problem was that none of the prisoners spoke English," I explained.

"Since Dad spoke German very well, he was hired to be an interpreter. The boss would tell Dad what the men had to do, and then Dad would explain it to the prisoners in German. If the prisoners had questions, they would ask Dad, he would ask the boss who would answer, and then Dad explained it in German," I said.

"Wasn't Dad afraid of these prisoners?" Helene wanted to know.

"No, for one thing, there were guards around. But most of the prisoners were young guys who were just glad to be doing something other than sitting around in prison. I remember Dad said that they got paid, except they didn't get paid in real money. They got something called 'scrip', which they could use to buy candy or pop or other things from the prison canteen. I remember Dad telling that there was one guy who the men were kinda scared of. Dad asked why and was told that this man was a member of the Nazi party, and it was his job to see that the prisoners didn't cooperate with the Americans. Dad said none of the men liked him very much.

"Dad got to be friends with the prisoners. He helped some of them write letters to their families."

"They could send letters to Germany during the War?" Helene asked.

"Yes, the way Dad told it was that the letters first went to our government where they were read to see that they weren't sending back any military secrets. Then the government sent the letters to the Red Cross and from there they were sent to Germany. Dad said if our American boys were being held prisoners, their families here would appreciate getting letters from their sons.

"Another thing Dad did was to hold church services. Most of the prisoners were Lutherans, and they appreciated having a service in German. Of course, Dad said it was sort of strange holding a service at the prison camp with an armed guard standing in back.

"Some people criticized Dad for doing this, but he explained that Jesus told us to love our enemies even though we were at war with Germany."

"Then what happened?" Helene asked.

"Well, really, not much else. Once the harvest season was over, the prisoners were sent somewhere else, so Dad's work as an interpreter was ended. Then by the time of the next harvest, the War with Germany was over, so the prisoners were being sent back to Germany," I explained.

"What else happened during the War?" Helene wanted to know.

"The War changed a lot of things. For one thing, there was rationing."

"What was that?"

"Because of the War, a lot of food had to go to feeding the armed forces. Gasoline had to be used for the War. And a lot of the factories were making things for the War effort. This meant there were a lot of shortages. In order to make things fair so everyone would have enough, the government put a limit on what people could buy. Each family got rationing stamps which meant you could buy only so much meat, butter, canned goods, sugar, gasoline, tires ... all sorts of things.

"When you went to the grocery store, you not only had to have money to pay for things, you had to have enough rationing stamps or little red or blue tokens for each rationed item. It wasn't real bad for us. We hardly ever bought canned goods because Dad raised most of our vegetables in our garden. The farmers in the congregation would bring us meat. Dad was a pastor, so he got a special rationing stamp for gasoline. About the only bad thing was sugar rationing. I remember how glad I was when you were born. That meant that we got two pounds more of sugar each month. Since you were born in the summer, it meant we could have Kool-Aid more often."

Helene looked a little disappointed.

"But I was real happy to have a new little sister, even if we hadn't gotten more sugar," I assured her.

Helene looked relieved.

"And because of the War, there were hardly any candy bars," I said.

"Were they rationed?" Helene asked.

"No, they were just scarce. Chocolate had to come from across the ocean, so there were very few ships available to bring it. Besides, it was very dangerous for ships crossing the ocean since many of them got sunk by the Germans and Japanese. Every so often though, word would get around that one of the grocery stores had gotten a box of Hershey bars. We kids would hear about it and would immediately go the store, clutching a nickel so we could buy a Hershey bar. We hoped we would get there before they were all gone."

"Were there any other candy bars?"

"The only candy bars which the stores always had were Baby Ruth and Butterfingers. We kids figured they weren't very good if the stores always had them," I answered.

"What else was rationed?"

"Gasoline and tires were rationed. They needed a lot of gas and oil for the War. You can imagine all the ships, airplanes, tanks, Jeeps, and everything. People with cars had to get gas rationing stamps. Most people could buy only a few gallons a week. Some people were considered necessary for the War effort, so they could buy more—people who worked in defense plants, farmers, doctors, and even ministers. Dad had what they called a 'C' stamp which meant he could get more gasoline," I explained. I started to laugh again.

"What's funny about that?" Helene asked.

"I just thought of one thing which happened to Dad during the War. When Dad would go to Fond du Lac to make hospital calls he would always wear his clerical collar so the people at the hospital would know that he was a minister. One time when he was there, he had a flat tire, so he took the tire to a shop in Fond du Lac. Now Fond du Lac has a lot of Catholic churches, so a lot of the businesses are owned by members of these churches. When they see a man in black suit, wearing a clerical collar, they automatically assume he must be a priest.

"When Dad took the car to the tire shop, the owner assumed he was a priest and immediately took care of him. Every time he spoke to Dad, he called him 'Father'. He even sold Dad a new inner tube which practically no garage had. Dad said he never got such good service," I said.

"Didn't Dad say anything?" Helene asked.

"Dad said he never had a chance. And all the man charged him for was the inner tube. He even gave Dad a discount."

"Dad should wear his collar more often," Helene decided.

Just as Helene was asking me for more stories, Mother called that it was time for supper,

"That's all the stories for now," I told Helene.

Chapter 34

I Learn a Lesson

We had just finished our devotions after supper when the phone rang.

"Do you want to get it?" Mother asked Dad. "It's probably for you anyway."

Dad walked over to the phone in the dining room and picked up the receiver.

"Sure," we heard him say as we began clearing the table. We saw Dad look at his wrist watch.

"Half hour from now? That will be fine. See you then." Dad hung up the phone.

"Who was that?" Mother asked.

"It was Alfred Rieber. He wanted to stop over and see me for a few minutes. Said it was nothing serious."

Alfred was a member of Emanuel and had a farm about a mile east of town where he lived with his wife.

A few minutes before 7:00 p.m., Dad went into his study, closed the door to the living room, and opened the front door of the study. He sat at his desk and waited for Alfred to arrive.

I was outside in our back yard, so I didn't pay any attention to Dad and his visitor. It was not unusual for members to stop by and talk with Dad.

I was surprised when I heard Dad calling me, asking me to come in.

"Alfred wants to talk to you," Dad said as we walked into the study.

I said hello to Alfred and stood there, waiting to see why he wanted to talk with me.

"Alfred was wondering if you wanted to do a little farm work," Dad said.

"Yes," Alfred went on. "It's just about threshing time. Each farmer in our ring has to provide two people. Most of the guys have sons to work with them. Since we don't have any children, I need to hire a boy to work during the harvest. I was wondering if you would be interested."

I didn't know quite what to say. First, I wondered why he had talked to Dad rather than to me. And I had some questions.

"Gee," I answered, "I don't know what to say. What would I do? Where would it be? When would it start?"

I paused and looked at Alfred.

"It wouldn't be hard work. My nephew worked there for the past couple of years, and he handled the grain spout. That's where the grain comes out of threshing machine into the wagon or truck. You just have to be there to see that it doesn't get plugged up or the grain gets spilled on the ground. My nephew is working in the canning factory this summer, which is why I need someone else."

That didn't sound too tough, I thought.

"Where would this be?" I asked.

"Here's how the threshing ring works. Ed Huber owns the threshing machine. There are about a dozen of us who work with him. He moves it from farm to farm. We're usually at a farm for a day and then move to the next farm."

I knew what a threshing machine was. I had seen one in action at my uncle's farm. The grain had been cut and gathered into bundles. After the grain was dried, the bundles would be taken to the threshing machine, which would separate the grain from the stalks. The grain would come out one spout, and the straw would be blown out of the large spout and stacked up.

"I think I could do that. What about getting there?"

"You could ride your bike to Alfred's and then ride with him to the farms," Dad suggested.

That would be an easy bike ride, I thought.

And so, that's how I got my job.

"I'll let you know when we're going to start," Alfred said as he got ready to leave.

About a week later I got a call from Alfred. "Be out at my house at eight tomorrow morning. We're going to start at Vandermuhl's. Be sure to wear a cap," he added before he hung up.

The next morning I was up early. I had breakfast and by 7:30 was pedaling my bike out to the Rieber farm.

Alfred was backing out the tractor from the machine shed when I got there. He waved to me and drove the tractor to an empty hay wagon. He hooked it to the tractor.

"Jump on," he said.

I did and we moved out of the yard. It was a short drive to the Vandermuhl's farm. When we pulled in, there were other farmers there. I recognized some of them since they were members of Dad's congregation. As Alfred parked the tractor and wagon, I noticed a tractor slowly coming down the road, pulling the threshing machine.

"Here comes Ed," one of the farmers called. "Now we can get started."

Bernie Vandermuhl called the tractor drivers together. "I've got four fields of grain—three oats and one of barley."

"You growing barley, Bernie?" one of the farmers asked. I saw it was Walt Schmidt, a member of our congregation. "I thought you Hollanders didn't approve of growing barley."

This is kinda strange, I thought. Why wouldn't a Hollander grow barley?

"I'm going to use it for cattle feed," Bernie answered.

"Yeah, sure," a couple of farmers chimed in. I looked over—they were all members of the Lutheran congregation.

Later I asked Alfred about this.

"Why were they teasing Mr. Vandermuhl about growing barley?" I asked.

Alfred chuckled. "Most of the farmers who grow barley sell it to the breweries for making beer. The Hollanders don't approve of drinking, so most of them don't grow barley. Since it's a pretty profitable crop, some of the Hollanders have started to plant barley, but they always claim they will be using it for cattle feed."

And so threshing started. The farmers with the tractors and wagons went out to the fields and began loading up the bundles of grain. Ed got the threshing machine hooked up to the tractor. I noticed there was a belt which connected the tractor to the threshing machine to provide the power.

Mr. Vandermuhl pulled a wagon up near the thresher. "You handling the grain spout?" he asked me.

"I guess so," I answered. No one had told me, but Alfred had mentioned it, so I assumed that would be my job.

"OK," Mr. Vandermuhl said. "Climb in the wagon and see that the spout doesn't get jammed up. If it does, yell at Ed. When the wagon starts getting full, let me know and I'll switch wagons."

The wagons started pulling up. Farmers pitched the bundles into the conveyor belt of the thresher. Grain began pouring out of the spout. At the other end of the thresher, straw was being blown out of a big pipe. One of the farmers stood with a pitchfork. I noticed he was gradually shaping the straw into a stack.

It was dusty and hot. I was glad I had a cap.

After about two hours, the thresher stopped.

"Break time," yelled Ed.

Several women came out of the house, carrying trays. They were piled high with pastries and breads. There was coffee for the men and milk for the boys.

After the break, Ed started the threshing machined and work resumed.

Then it was noon. The farmers had pulled their tractors into the yard, and Ed stopped the threshing machine.

I noticed everyone was lining up at the stock tank where a row of towels hung.

"Time to wash up," Alfred told me as we walked to the large tank of water. After washing up, I noticed the farmers reached into the tank and pulled out bottles of pop.

"They just have pop at the Hollanders," Alfred told me. "When the crew is at one of our German farmers, there'll be a case of beer in the tank as well as pop."

Pop was fine with me. I looked in the tank and saw the pop was from the Waupun Bottling Works. At that time, many small cities had their own pop factories, always called bottling works. The bottles were mainly fruit flavors—orange, cherry, strawberry, and lime, but there was also root beer.

There were tables set up under the trees. I noticed there were several boys working, farmers' sons. I knew one of them, Herbie who belonged to our church. I joined him and the other two boys as we picked out bottles of pop.

Herbie introduced me to the other two boys: Ted and Bob. They attended rural schools as did most farm kids. The countryside was dotted with one-room schools which had one teacher who taught all the students in grades one through eight. After eighth grade, the students would come into the Village to attend high school.

We picked out places where we set our pop bottles and then walked over to the food tables. Goodness, I thought—what a spread of food. There was fried chicken, roast beef, and pork chops. There was Jell-o salad, three-bean salad, and coleslaw. There were two or three kinds of vegetables, homemade bread, pickles, and relishes.

"This is more food than the church picnic," I said to Herbie as I filled my plate.

"The women always try to outdo each other. My mother is already starting to prepare things, and we won't be there for a week," Herbie said.

I noticed a lot of the men went back for second helpings before heading over to the dessert table, which was filled with three kinds of pie, two cakes, and a big plate of cookies.

I was kinda groggy after dinner as I climbed back into the grain wagon. I didn't think I would be hungry for supper.

About 4:00 p.m. the last load was going through the thresher.

"Quitting time," Alfred said as he walked over to where I was working.

Well, at least I was done for the day. I was glad I didn't have to go milk cows, which all the farmers would be doing. Wisconsin was a dairy state: "America's Dairyland" the car licenses proclaimed.

"Farmers never get a day off," I remember one of our members saying to Dad. "Those cows got to be milked morning and evening, every day of the year."

In addition to the dairy cows, most of the farmers had other sources of income. They raised peas and sweet corn for the Village canning factory. Almost all of them had a bunch of pigs, which they would sell to the packing houses in Milwaukee. Every farmer's wife had a flock of chickens. The eggs were sold to the grocery stores in the Village. The egg money was the wife's private income.

When we got back to Alfred's, I rode my bike home. I was tired and dirty. I took a quick bath and then had supper; although I didn't eat much.

I recounted what had happened during the day.

"Well," Dad remarked, "it won't be long and there won't be threshing crews anymore,"

"There won't?" asked Phil. "How come?"

"They now have combines. These machines cut the standing grain and thresh it in one operation. No more cutting the grain, putting it in bundles and bringing it to the threshing machine. One man can do it all," Dad explained.

That would sure be a change, as I thought about the day's activities—all the farmers working together, the big threshing machine, the meals. The meals, I thought.

"I bet the ones who will really appreciate the combine will be the farm wives. They really work hard putting on those meals."

"You're probably right," Dad agreed.

I went to bed early. The next morning it was out to Alfred's and off we went to a different farm.

As we were eating the noon dinner, Herbie asked me, "How much is Alfred paying you?"

I paused. First, I thought, it's none of your business. Then I realized I didn't know. In talking about all the details of what the job involved and getting back and forth to the farm, it had never occurred to me to ask how much I would get paid.

"You know, Herbie, I really don't know. I didn't ask Alfred," I finally admitted.

Herbie looked at me, wondering if I was just trying to evade the question. "You really don't know?" he persisted.

"I really don't," I answered.

"I'd never take a job without knowing what I was getting paid," Herbie emphatically stated.

"Yeah," I agreed, "I shoulda asked, I guess."

As I stood in the grain wagon, I thought about this. Maybe I better start keeping track of the hours I worked.

That night at supper as I recounted what had happened during the day, Helene asked, "How much are you getting paid?"

Again I had to answer, "I don't know. Alfred didn't tell me."

"You mean you didn't ask?" Phil said. "That was pretty dumb."

I nodded glumly.

"I'm sure Alfred will be fair," Dad said reassuringly.

"Don't be too certain," Phil retorted. "Those German farmers aren't the most generous people around."

"Especially when it comes to the pastor's salary," Mother put in.

"OK," Dad said, "that's enough. Let's have devotions."

The days went by. It seemed that the threshing ring alternated between the German and the Dutch farmers. I noticed when we were at one of the German farmers, as Alfred had said, there was a case of beer in the stock tank. I also observed that many of the Dutch farmers were quick to grab a bottle of beer.

I mentioned this to Alfred.

"Oh, yeah," he said. "Most of the Hollanders enjoy having a beer. They just don't like to buy it. You probably never noticed, but all the taverns in the Village have back doors. We Germans call them 'Dutch Doors' since the Hollanders use them so they won't be seen going into the taverns."

You sure learn a lot of interesting things working on a threshing crew, I thought.

I was keeping track of how many hours I worked each day.

One morning Alfred announced as we rode out to the farm where we would be threshing, "Well, today should be our last day—unless it rains or Schulteis (the farm where we were headed) has a lot more grain than he usually has."

It didn't rain, and Schulteis had his usual grain acreage. It was about 3:00 p.m. when we finished. As we rode back to Alfred's, I thought. Well, I guess I'll find out how much I made.

We pulled into the driveway. Alfred parked the tractor.

"Wait here," he said to me. He went into the house and soon came back, holding an envelope in his hand.

"Here you go. Thanks for all your help. You've been a good worker."

"Thanks," I said, taking the envelope. "It has been interesting learning about how a threshing ring works."

"See you on Sunday," Alfred said as I rode my bike out of the yard.

When I got home, I went in the house. Dad was there as I opened the envelope.

I looked at it.

"Well?" said Dad.

I kept looking at the envelope. Mother came in.

"So you got paid?" she asked.

I continued to stare at the envelope.

Helene came in and got right to the point. "How much did you make?"

"Ten dollars," I groused. "Ten lousy dollars for two and a half weeks of work. Why that is only (I mentally did some math), that's only about 15 cents an hour."

No one said anything at first. Then Dad came over, put his arm around my shoulder, and said, "I know you're disappointed. But it is still ten dollars which is more than you would have had just hanging around the house. And you learned a lot about farm life and how farmers work together."

I nodded. "And I learned a lot more—mainly that I will never take another job without know what the pay will be."

Chapter 35

Cousin Esther Is in Charge

We had just finished devotions after supper when Dad said, "Just stay here. I have some important news."

Dad got up from the table and went to the study. We kids looked at each other. What was he going to get?

He quickly returned and held out a letter. "I heard from Marie today. She says the family reunion is all set."

Dad had been talking about the family reunion for almost a year. There were nine children in Dad's family—two boys and seven girls. They lived all over the Midwest. Dad was a pastor, and four of his sisters were married to pastors. With five clergy, it meant that there were periodic moves. In addition, one of his sisters was married to a railroad mail clerk. "They move around more than preachers," Dad observed one time.

Anyway, the siblings had been discussing getting together. They had a hard time reaching agreement on where to have the reunion and how to handle all the arrangements. Since most of them didn't have much money, it was agreed that they couldn't go to a resort or a hotel. But apparently something had been worked out.

"Yes," Dad continued, "Martha has said she will host the reunion."

Martha was Dad's oldest sister and lived in Omaha. She was married to a businessman, and I knew they had a large house.

"Martha has things figured out so there will be a place for everyone to stay. We'll have it in August. That will be after the churches are done with their summer Bible schools and before school activities get started. Omaha is fairly central, so everyone can drive there."

"How long will we be gone?" Phil asked. Phil didn't want to be away from his girlfriend for too long, I thought.

Dad looked at the letter. "Marie says the reunion will be three days. I figure it will be a two-day drive each way, so we'll be gone for about a week," Dad answered.

"Are you sure Martha will have enough room?" Mother asked.

"Marie said Martha has it figured out, so I guess we'll have to take her word for it," Dad told her.

"We can always stay with Ernie and Melva," Mother added. Ernie was Dad's brother, who also lived in Omaha.

"True," Dad agreed.

"Who will all be there?" I wanted to know.

"All the aunts and uncles except maybe Dean," Dad answered. We knew Uncle Dean was a farmer who couldn't get away.

"Will Grandpa be there?" Helene asked.

"Of course," Dad answered.

"Does that mean he won't be coming to our house this summer?" Helene asked again.

At this thought, we three kids all brightened up. Grandpa's visits were not the high point of our summer. I suppose I better explain. Grandpa Kurtz was a retired pastor. When he retired—shortly after Grandma Kurtz died— he had no place to live. He had always lived in a parsonage provided by his congregation. Having helped his nine children through college, he had no money to buy a house of his own. The problem was solved by having him rotate among his children. This meant that once a year he would come and stay with us for five or six weeks.

"It always seems like five or six months," I can remember Phil saying. When Grandpa stayed with us, Phil had to give up his room and share my room. We always hoped he would visit in the summer so he could smoke his pipe outside.

"He probably won't," Dad said. "He usually likes to spend the summer in Duluth with Helen and Walter, so I'm thinking he will go to the reunion with them and then probably stay with Martha after the reunion."

We tried not to look too pleased. If we said anything, Mother would likely give us a lecture on how we should respect our grandfather even though we knew that his visits were always difficult for Mother.

I changed the subject. "Will all the cousins be there?" I asked.

"I imagine so," Dad answered.

That should be interesting, I thought. I hadn't met many of my cousins. I did know all about them, however, thanks to the family's Circle Letter. The family's rotating collection of letters always included much fare about all my cousins. Well, it had recently been skipping Uncle Ernie. Uncle Ernie always wrote interesting letters, but once again he hadn't been particularly conscientious about writing and Aunt Martha had cut him off again (and not even Dad, who was older than her, would gainsay her). So I really didn't know about any recent developments with those cousins, but regardless I could look forward to meeting more of the whole group.

"That should be fun. I'll get to know a lot of my cousins, but the ones I know will be there too. Esther and I should have a good time," I said.

Mother and Dad looked at each other.

"I hope it won't be TOO good of a time," Mother finally said.

"We haven't gotten in trouble for a long time," I protested.

"Oh, yeah," Phil put in, "how about last Christmas?"

He would have to bring that up, I thought. Cousin Esther and I always seemed to be getting blamed for things, going way back to when we were three and four years old.

"But we're older now. There's no need to worry," I answered.

"I certainly hope not. People still talk about when the fire department came," Mother said.

Since August seemed like a long way away, I didn't pay much attention to the reunion. School was still on. Then there would be Vacation Bible School. After that, we would go on our usual summer vacation at a lake cottage.

It's funny how fast summer goes by. You get out of school and think you have the whole summer to have fun. Suddenly it was August, and we were getting ready to go to Omaha for the reunion.

So we packed up our silver-grey Chevrolet (the name General Motors had given to the color was "Battleship Grey", but Mother didn't think it was appropriate for a preacher to be driving a car with a war-like name, so she always insisted the car was silver) and off we went. Since Omaha was quite a drive from eastern Wisconsin, we went as far as Mother's hometown in southwest Wisconsin where we stayed overnight with Mother's brother, Alfred.

We left early the next morning. Whenever we took a trip with Dad, speed was not his highest priority. He would always find interesting places to stop ... at least interesting for him. We would never drive by a historical marker or any place where there was a family connection.

"OK," said Dad, "when we get to Dubuque, we'll stop at the seminary. I don't think you kids have ever seen it." He was referring to Wartburg Seminary where he had studied to be a pastor.

No use complaining, I thought. It won't do any good.

"We can't stay too long if we want to get to Omaha tonight," Mother reminded him.

"It's not much out of the way," Dad assured her.

So we stopped to admire the big tower with a statue of Martin Luther in front of it. Fortunately, Dad did not linger, and we were soon on our way.

Phil was driving as we continued our journey along the narrow Iowa highways.

"Boy, they sure grow a lot of corn here," Phil said. "You don't see anything but cornfields."

"Yes," Dad answered, "their state song even says 'We are from Iowa, that's where the tall corn grows.'"

We made pretty good time with Phil driving. We're lucky, I thought, Iowa doesn't have nearly as many historical markers as Wisconsin.

It was late afternoon when we pulled into Omaha. Dad had good directions, and we drove right to Aunt Martha and Uncle Ed's home.

As we pulled into the driveway, the car was suddenly surrounded by a mob of people.

"It's Henry and Minnie, and Phil, Harold, and Helene," I heard someone call out.

I recognized some people, but most were relatives I didn't know. But they all must be uncles, aunts, and cousins, I thought. As I got out, I looked around for Esther. She was there. Good, I thought. I know someone anyway.

The next two days were a blur in my memory. I was busy trying to remember the names of all the aunts, uncles, and cousins. It got more confusing because some of Dad's cousins and their families stopped in as well.

Cousin Barbara, the second oldest cousin, was in college studying to be a kindergarten teacher. She had planned activities for all the younger cousins ... and there were a lot of them. I never did keep them all straight. Helene thought it was wonderful to have so many cousins to play with.

At noon on Saturday the phone rang when we were having lunch. It was for Barbara. She came back to the table and said, "I just got called in to work this afternoon. One of the clerks got sick." Barbara had a summer job at a store and had arranged to be off during the reunion. She looked at Esther. "You'll have to take over this afternoon."

"I will if Harold will help. You will, won't you?" she asked, looking at me.

Actually I didn't want to. All the older boy cousins were planning to go to the park and play basketball, which I thought would be more fun than babysitting a bunch of kids.

"What do we have to do?" I asked.

"It's simple. I'm going to set up the lawn sprinkler in the back yard, and the kids can play in that. It will be a good way to keep them cool ... and occupied," Barbara explained.

Well, there was no way I was going to say "No" to Esther. She always did tell me what to do.

"OK, I guess so," I answered.

After lunch, Barbara went off to her job, the boys went off to the park, the adults went and sat on the front law under shade trees, the kids put on their swimming suits, and we went out to the back yard.

I noticed one of the little girls was hanging back.

"What's the matter, Dottie?" Esther asked. "Don't you want to play in the sprinkler?"

"Yes," she responded, "but it's too dangerous."

"Dangerous?" I exclaimed. "What's dangerous about playing in the sprinkler?"

"Well, Daddy said you shouldn't go in the water for two hours after eating because it's filled with cramps."

Esther and I tried not to laugh.

"That's OK," Esther assured her. "That's just for swimming. It's fine to play in the sprinkler."

Dottie pondered this for a moment and, thus reassured, ran and joined the other cousins.

Esther turned on the sprinkler. We pulled up two lawn chairs and sat in the shade, watching the kids.

"This is easy enough," I said to Esther.

Just then Cousin Ernie came up. Ernie was one of the biggest of the younger kids.

"What's up, Ernie?" I asked.

"It's too crowded with just one sprinkler and all the kids. The little kids are hogging all the water. Can we get another sprinkler or something?"

Poor little Ernie, I thought.

I looked at Esther.

"Let's see what we can do," Esther said. "Go back and take turns."

We got up and walked to the back of the house.

"What's that?" Esther asked, pointing to a panel with a number of faucets and handles.

"Oh, that's Uncle Ed's new sprinkler system. He just had it installed and was showing it to the uncles last night. It's really neat. There are little sprinklers in the ground all around the lawn, and then they come up and spray the lawn so it stays nice and green all summer."

We looked at the panel.

"This says 'Back Lawn'. I wonder if that would work for another sprinkler. Let's try it and see," Esther said.

I reached up and turned on the valve marked "Back Lawn". Sure enough, slowly we could see the small sprinkler heads rise from the edge of the lawn and a gentle spray emerge.

"OK, kids," Esther called. "You have more sprinklers here. You can all cool off now."

Esther and I returned to our lawn chairs and watched the young cousins cavorting under the sprinklers.

"Oh, oh, here comes Ernie again," I warned Esther.

"What's up now, Ernie?" I asked. "I thought you would be happy with all the sprinklers."

"Well, there just isn't enough water coming out of the new sprinklers. Can't you do something about it?" he complained.

How much longer until Barbara gets back, I thought.

"We'll see what we can do, Ernie. Now go back with the other kids," Esther told him.

Esther and I looked at each other, shrugged, got up and went back to the control panel.

"There's one that says 'Main Valve'. I wonder what that will do?" I asked.

"Let's try it and see," Esther said.

I reached up and turned it on. We looked back and sure enough, it really increased the water pressure. We could see the kids jumping up and down, screaming with pleasure as the water gushed out.

What we didn't know was that the Main Valve was also connected to the sprinklers in the front lawn. The uncles and aunts were sitting in the shade on the front lawn, drinking iced tea and listening to Grandpa tell stories about the early days of the family in the United States. Not all the uncles were there. Uncle Ed was working at his radio and television business, and Uncle Dean wasn't there either—he was back at his farm.

Everyone was dressed up since there would be a family photograph taken later in the afternoon, followed by the reunion dinner.

Suddenly Grandpa's story was interrupted with screams from the aunts as water started cascading on them. They looked at the sky. Was this a sudden cloud burst?

Then they saw the sprinklers, everyone started heading for the house.

"It's Ed's new sprinkler system. Someone go in back and turn it off."

Several of the uncles immediately went running to the back of the house.

Esther and I were busy watching the kids playing and screaming in the water that we didn't hear the commotion in the front yard.

Just then the uncles came in and yelled, "Turn off the water."

We jumped up.

"What? Why?" Esther asked.

One of the uncles went to the control panel. "What did you turn on?"

Esther and I quickly joined him.

"This one," I answered as I reached and started turning it off.

We immediately heard a shout from Cousin Ernie.

"Hey, who turned off our water?"

Well, the aunts and uncles (and Grandpa) all got dried off. We shooed the kids into the house and told them they were done playing in the sprinkler for the day.

Esther and I looked at each other.

"I suppose we'll get blamed for this, too," Esther said.

I nodded in agreement. "But then, it will give everyone something to remember about the reunion."

Chapter 36

The Unexpected Visitor

I was sitting in the living room one afternoon, waiting for my friend Rich to deliver the *Milwaukee Journal*. Mother and Dad were at the Ladies Aid meeting in church. Phil was at his job and Helene was playing at a friend's house.

As I watched out the window, a car drove up in front of the parsonage. I didn't recognize the car, but then noticed it had Illinois license plates. That wasn't totally unusual since the Village was on a main route to a number of lakes and periodically fishermen from Illinois would see my sign advertising night crawlers for sale and would stop to make a purchase.

I saw a man get out of the car and walk toward the front door. He was wearing a suit and tie. He does not look like he is going fishing, I thought, as I went to the front door when he rang the bell.

"Is the pastor here?" the man asked in a heavy German accent.

"No, he isn't," I answered.

"Do you know when he will be back?" he asked.

"He's at a meeting at church now. He should be back in 30 or 40 minutes," I told him.

"I would like to see him. I will return," he announced, turned and went to his car.

About a half hour later, Dad came home. He was puzzled when I told him about the visitor.

"He wasn't a preacher, was he?" Dad asked. Some of the old-time preachers still had heavy German accents.

"No, he didn't look like a preacher," I said.

"Well, we'll just have to wait and see," Dad said, turning and walking into his study where he could keep watch for his unexpected guest.

I went to the kitchen and told Mother about the visitor.

"I wonder who that could be," she said.

It wasn't too long until the car returned. Dad went to the front door and waited as the man came up the steps to the front door. Dad opened the door. I was in the kitchen and couldn't hear what was being said. He and Dad went into the study, and Dad closed the door.

By this time, the newspaper had arrived, so I went to the living room with it and settled into the chair closest to the study. I heard them talking, but was disappointed because they were talking in German. Mother came into the living room and suggested I bring the paper into the kitchen and read it there.

Mother started getting supper ready. When the Ladies Aid met, we always had leftovers from the meeting. The typical Ladies Aid menu was sandwiches, salad, and dessert. Those in charge of refreshments always made a lot of extras, and they would send them home with Mother and Dad.

"No one wants to run out of food at the Ladies Aid meeting," Dad explained. "They know the other ladies would talk about them if that happened."

We kids loved Ladies Aid lunch. We rarely had cold cuts since they had to be purchased. Our regular meals were pretty much things that Dad grew in the garden or that farmers in the congregation gave us. So things like Oscar Mayer bologna or Armour boiled ham were real treats for us. And there was usually Jell-o with fruit cocktail and little marshmallows. Sometimes there would even be my favorite—whipped Jell-o. We always looked forward to the Ladies Aid lunch.

Helene had come home from her friend's house. "Whose car is that in front?" she asked.

"It's a man talking to Daddy," Mother answered. "We don't know who he is."

Phil had the same question when he came home from work. He got the same answer.

We sat in the kitchen speculating on the mystery visitor.

"Maybe it's a long-lost relative," I suggested.

While we were pondering this possibility, we heard the study door open. We were totally surprised when Dad and the stranger came into the kitchen.

"I want you to meet Gunther Schroeder. I invited him to have supper with us."

Dad introduced us and then brought up another chair for Gunther. Mother set a place for him at the table.

"We're not having a big meal. We hope this will be enough for you." Mother told the visitor.

"It will be good. Thank you for having me," Gunther replied.

We said our table prayer and started eating.

"Gunther was a prisoner of war who worked at the canning factory during the War," Dad explained. "I got to know him when I worked as a translator."

"The pastor was more than a translator. He explained a lot of things about America to us and even had church services for us at our camp in Waupun," Gunther told us. "We laughed at him a little bit because we thought his German was ... what did we call it?" he asked Dad.

"I remember you said my German sounded old-fashioned or quaint, I think you called it," Dad answered. "I suppose it was since I did not know a lot of modern words."

I remembered that Dad had grown up speaking German at home and that German was used regularly in his classes at the academy, college, and seminary. He used to joke that he took English as a foreign language at college. Despite this, I never thought Dad had any kind of a German accent.

"There were 30 or 40 POWs working here. There was a big prison camp at Waupun. They would be bussed to the canning factories here and in the other towns around here. I would meet the bus and be with the workers during the day, translating the orders from the foreman and explaining their duties," Dad said. "I especially remember Gunther because he was working to learn English. He was always asking me about English words and how to say things. I remember when the POWs left Waupun, but after that I really didn't think about them until Gunther came today. Gunther, why don't you tell them your story about why you came to see me?" Dad said to him.

Gunther nodded and pulled up his chair closer to the table. "You will have to excuse me if my English is not good. I will do my best," he began.

"When we left here, the War was over, and all of us wanted to get back to Germany and see how our families survived the War. But it took quite a while," he said.

"Yes," Dad interrupted, "there were more than 500,000 German prisoners in the U.S., so you can imagine how long it would take ships to get them all back to Germany."

"I was lucky because I got home by Christmas time. My father was a farmer in a small village in Bavaria, which did not suffer damage in the War. I went home and worked with my father on the farm. When I was at the prison camp in Waupun, I had gotten acquainted with a *Fraulein* there. The churches in town would serve us a meal on Sunday noon," Gunther said.

"I did not get a lot of chance to know her real well since the guards had orders not to let us ..." He paused and looked at Dad. "What is the word I want to use?"

"I think you want to say 'fraternize'," Dad suggested. "There were some people who were pretty critical of the churches for serving these meals. They felt it was aiding the enemy. It was mainly the Lutheran churches which did that, since the churches were originally German Lutheran."

"Yes," Gunther agreed. "Some of the people even spoke German to us, which we were surprised at. And on Sunday afternoons one of the pastors would have church services. I especially remember when you were there, Pastor."

Gunther continued. "Even though I did not get to know her well, I was quite ..." He paused, searching for a word. He turned to Dad and said something in German.

Dad thought for a moment and then replied, "I think the word you are looking for is 'smitten'."

"Schmitten?" he asked.

"Close enough," Dad told him.

"I was schmitten with her. I did get her name: Marlene Schwintendorf. When I got back to Germany, I often thought about her. After a year or so, I decided I would write to her. I did not know her street, so I sent it to her name in Waupun, Wisconsin, U.S.A., and hoped she would get it.

"She did get the letter and wrote back to me. I wrote to her again, and we sent letters back and forth. Then one day I get a letter from her telling me that she is going to get married, so I should not write any more. I was ... *enttauscht*." He turned to Dad.

"Disappointed," Dad translated.

"*Ja*," Gunther nodded. "So I tried to forget her. Shortly afterward the United States opened a military base near our home. I heard they were looking for Germans who knew English to work at the base. I got a job as a groundskeeper, and because I knew English, I soon became the head of the groundsmen. It paid quite well, and since I lived with my parents, I was able to save money. There were a lot of single women around since so many men had been killed in the War. I went out with some of them, but all the time I kept thinking of Marlene.

"Then about six months ago, I got a letter from her. She said her marriage had not worked out, wondered how I was doing and if I still remembered her. I wrote back to her right away and told her that I certainly remembered her.

"We wrote many letters to each other. I finally told her I would like to come to America to see her. I heard back right away, saying that, yes, she would like that very much. So I started making arrangements to come. It took a while since I had been a member of the German army, but the commander at the American base helped me with things. Before I left I went to the PX at the base and bought a diamond ring. I wanted to be ready if things worked out," he smiled. "So I fly to Chicago where I rented a car and drove here."

"Apparently things worked out," Dad said. "The reason Gunther came to see me was to ask if I would marry them."

Mother and we kids clapped.

"That will be wonderful," said Mother. "Will it be here?"

"Marlene and I are still making plans. Since this is her second marriage, she wants it ... *einfache*," he said to Dad.

"Simple or plain," Dad responded.

"*Ja*," Gunther nodded. "She has her friend to be one of the people at the wedding, and she hopes her brother will also be one, but he hasn't decided if he will do it. Marlene said he served in the War and some of his friends were killed by the Germans, so he doesn't know how he feels about his sister marrying a German. He says he will think about it."

"Why isn't she getting married in her own church?" Mother asked.

"Marlene belongs to one of those strict Lutheran churches who frown on divorce. She talked to the pastor there, and he was making things difficult for her. That's when Gunther suggested that he would talk with me," Dad explained.

Gunther looked at the kitchen clock. "I have stayed too long. I need to get back to Waupun and tell Marlene about things. *Danke schoen* for supper," he said to Mother and got up from the table.

We all said goodbye, and Dad walked with him to the car.

"Isn't this wonderful," Mother said as we were clearing the table. "I just love weddings."

A few days later the phone rang, and Mother answered it.

"Oh, hello, Gunther," I heard her say. "It's so good to hear from you. How is Marlene?"

Poor Gunther, I thought. Anyone who called rarely had a short conversation with Mother. Even if it was a wrong number, Mother could extend the conversation to make it sound as though she was talking to a long-lost cousin.

Finally I heard her say, "Yes, he's here. Let me get him."

Mother went to the study and got Dad.

Dad's conversation was much shorter than Mother's.

"Yes, 3:00 p.m. would be fine. I'll see you then." He said goodbye and hung up the phone.

"Gunther and Marlene are coming to see me at three," he told Mother and went back to his study before Mother could recount her conversation with Gunther.

"Tell Marlene if there's anything I can do to help, let me know," Mother called to Dad.

I was busy mowing Mrs. Bruins' lawn—one of the four lawns I mowed during the summer—when Gunther and Marlene came, so I didn't see them.

At supper that night, Dad reported that plans for the wedding were moving along.

"They're going to have a simple wedding," Dad said. "Just the bride and groom and two witnesses: Marlene's brother and her friend. I suppose Marlene's family will attend. I don't think they will have anyone else."

"I can be there to help," Mother offered.

She didn't want to miss anything, I thought.

"That would be nice. Maybe you could make a bouquet from the flowers in our garden," Dad said. He knew there was no way he could keep Mother away from the wedding.

Dad mentioned when the wedding would be, then paused and turned to me, "They didn't say anything about a photographer. You have your new camera. Why don't you be ready to take some pictures?"

Dad did not have to ask me twice. I had been saving my money from mowing lawns and shoveling sidewalks for the past year. I had finally saved up enough to buy the camera I had been dreaming about for a long time: an Argus C-3, 35-millimeter camera with a flash unit and a tripod. I felt like a real professional photographer.

"Will they pay for the film and flash bulbs?" I asked.

"We'll work things out," Dad answered.

A week later Gunther and Marlene visited with Dad again. Dad checked that everything was in order. He made sure they would have their marriage license.

"*Ja*," Gunther assured Dad, "we went to the courthouse in Fond du Lac and got that. I had to prove I was of legal age. I had a copy of my discharge from the German army with me, and they said that was OK."

"They didn't even ask me," Marlene complained. "I wonder—do I look old?"

Gunther immediately assured her that was not the case.

"And you have the two attendants?" Dad asked.

"Yes. My friend Bonnie and my brother Myron. So we should be all set," she answered.

"That's wonderful," Marlene exclaimed when Dad mentioned that Mother would arrange a bouquet. "I hadn't even thought of that."

"And I will pay him," Gunther said when Dad told him I would take photographs if they wanted me to do so.

The wedding was set for 3:00 on the coming Wednesday afternoon.

"That's a nice time," Dad told him. "The stained-glass windows always look so nice in the middle of the afternoon."

So Wednesday came. It was a bright day with a light breeze blowing.

"A perfect day for a wedding," said Mother as she picked flowers in the garden.

Since I would be on janitor duty, I had double-checked that the church was clean and everything was picked up inside. I also had bought a 36-exposure roll of film and two sleeves of flashbulbs. I was all set.

About 1:30 the phone rang. Mother was in church arranging the flowers. Dad answered.

"Is that right? Yes, two are needed. Let me see what I can do. I'll call you back. Don't worry. It will work out," Dad said reassuringly.

Mother had just come into the house and heard the last few words.

"What was that all about?" she asked as Dad stood by the phone in deep thought.

"That was Marlene. She was in hysterics. Her brother just told her that he wouldn't be a witness at the wedding. He said he just couldn't do it after having friends killed by the Germans in the War," Dad said. "Now what are we going to do?"

"Could I do it?" I asked.

Dad shook his head. "No, you have to be 18 to be a witness."

Dad stood there thinking.

"What about Phil?" Mother asked. "He was 18 last March."

"I'll go over to the station and see if he will do it," Dad said. Phil worked at the filling station, which was right back of the church.

"I'll go lay out his suit and white shirt," Mother said.

Dad was back in a few minutes.

"Phil wasn't too excited about doing it, but said he would," Dad reported. He also said Phil's boss, Augie, told him to go ahead and do it.

Dad immediately went to the phone and put in a long-distance phone call to Marlene. He told her everything would be fine and that his son Phil would be the other witness.

"I'll see you soon," Dad told her.

A few minutes later Phil came in.

"Get washed up," Mother told him. "I have your suit and shirt all laid out for you. I didn't know which of your two ties you wanted to wear." Phil disappeared upstairs.

"If everyone else is going to be at the wedding, I want to come too," Helene announced. "Will there be lunch?"

"Yes, you can come. Go get changed. You can sit with me," Mother told her.

And so Gunther and Marlene were married. Marlene's mother and father were there, and our family was there. I took pictures before and after the ceremony. I told Gunther and Marlene that I would get the pictures developed and would have them ready when they got back from their honeymoon.

"I will pay you then," Gunther assured me.

They left. I closed the church, and we all went back to the parsonage.

"That was a nice ceremony," Mother said.

"Well, look at this," said Dad as he opened the envelope Gunther had given him.

"How much did we get?" asked Helene. The rest of us laughed because that was what Mother usually asked. Dad held up a bill.

Mother looked at it and gasped "Fifty dollars! You never, ever got 50 dollars for a wedding!"

"That's right," Dad agreed, "but then I never had a groom who came almost 5,000 miles to get married either."

Chapter 37

The New Boy at School

"Anything new at school today?" Dad asked. This was Dad's question almost every evening. Usually the reply from the three of us would be, "No, not much," or we would report on normal happenings such as a test or the new storybook Helene's teacher was reading.

Tonight, however, was different. I had some news.

"There's a new boy in our room," I reported.

"Oh, is that so? Who is it?" Dad asked. Dad was always interested when a new family moved into town.

"They might be Lutheran," he would tell Mother. There wasn't much in the way of evangelism in the Village. When a new family moved into town, word quickly got around on their denominational preference.

Dad would report that, "The new dentist is Catholic," or when one of the Village's grocery stores changed hands, Dad might note, "I hear the new owner of the IGA is Methodist." If Dad didn't learn of a newcomer's religious preference and if they had a Lutheran-sounding name—either German or Scandinavian—he would call on them and invite them to come to Emanuel. So the news of a new arrival in the Village was of interest to Dad.

"His name is Peter, and he's staying with his grandmother. I don't know why or for how long," I answered.

"Who's his grandmother?" Mother asked.

"I think it's Mrs. Pierce," I answered.

Dad thought for a moment. "She lives on the other side of the school. I believe she's Methodist."

"How come he's staying with her?" Phil wondered.

"He didn't say. He just said he would be staying with his grandmother while his parents were on the road."

"I hope they don't get hit," Helene said.

"What do you mean 'hit'?" Mother asked

"Well, if they're on the road, they have to be careful. You always tell me I should look both ways when crossing the street," Helene answered.

We smiled.

"When he said they were on the road, it meant that they were traveling, not walking on the road. It's just an expression," Mother quickly explained.

"Where are they traveling?" Dad asked.

"He didn't say, and I didn't have a chance to ask him. He seems like a nice guy," I replied.

The conversation ended as Dad picked up the Bible and we began our evening devotions.

When we kids would occasionally complain about having devotions every night, especially if we had something planned for the evening, Dad would explain that it was something that we did. "When I was growing up, we had devotions both in the morning and after supper. They were a lot longer than ours. In the early years they were always in German." He didn't add, "So you're lucky that we only have them once a day and they're in English," but we figured that if we pressed the issue we would hear this comment from him.

Little by little I learned more about the new boy.

"His name is Peter Struck," I remarked one evening at supper.

A while later I had more to report. "Boy, Peter is really an athlete."

Phil got interested. Phil was the athlete in the family. He played football, basketball, and baseball at the Village high school. True, it was a small high school, and most of the boys went out for all three sports—the only ones offered at school.

"What does he play?" Phil wanted to know.

"I don't know if he plays any team sports, but you should see him on the playground. He can do somersaults and backflips, and walk on his hands, and I don't know what else. He's really good."

"Sounds like he's a gymnast," Dad observed.

"What's a 'gymnast'?" asked Helene.

"A gymnast is an athlete who does these types of exercises like somersaults and tumbling and doing tricks on a swing or rings. When I was in the academy and college, that was our main activity in physical education. I suppose it's because the Germans were the ones who developed this as a sport. They even have special clubs called the *Turner Verein*," Dad answered.

Dad had gone to Wartburg Academy and College when they were still quite German.

I got to know Peter better and found he was a great guy. I wanted to ask him about his parents, but decided I wouldn't in case there might be some reason why he didn't talk about them. I did find out that his family was Lutheran.

"But as long as I'm staying with my grandmother, she says I should go to the Methodist Sunday School," he told me one day. "Grandma is real nice, and I like staying with her."

The weeks went by and the novelty of a new boy in school wore off. Peter became just one of the regular guys.

One evening at supper when Dad asked his usual "What's new in school?" question, Phil mentioned that there was going to be a Lyceum program the next week.

During this time, the University of Wisconsin Extension Service sponsored an educational outreach for schools around the state called the Lyceum program. About four or five times during the school year various groups and individuals would appear at the school offering a wide variety of programs. Sometimes they would be science. Other times there might be a travelogue, a magic act, or a musical group. Everybody in school attended the program, from the kindergartners to high school seniors. The programs were held in the school gym.

We kids loved the Lyceum programs, mainly because it meant that we could get out of class for a couple of hours.

"Our teacher told us about it. It's going to be a *trapoline*," Helene said, proud that she knew what was going on.

"A what?" asked Mother.

"I think she means trampoline," Phil answered.

"Right, that's what I said," Helene agreed.

"What is a 'trampoline'?" Mother asked.

"It's like a round spring board or something," I answered. I had read about it, but couldn't remember exactly what it was.

"It's really not a board. It's kind of a tightly stretched canvas on a round metal frame. You can bounce up and down on it and do tricks like somersaults and back flips and stuff like that," Phil explained.

When I went to school the next day I noticed a poster on the bulletin board advertising the program: "MIKE AND AL SOAR TO NEW HEIGHTS ON THEIR EXTRA-LARGE TRAMPOLINE." The poster said that Mike and Al had been champion gymnasts at the University of Wisconsin and would be demonstrating their skills on their specially built trampoline.

Thursday afternoon we all poured into the gym. Usually the little kids sat on the floor in front of the stage. The grade school kids sat on the bleachers along the side of the gym floor, and the high school kids and teachers were on folding chairs. Today it was different. The little kids sat on the stage because there was a large round trampoline standing some three feet off the floor.

Mr. Rolfs, the principal, came to the front and announced that before the program got underway he wanted to remind all the students to be on their best behavior and pay attention to the program. Most of us didn't pay much attention to what he was saying because he always said the same thing at every program.

"Now, let's give a warm welcome to our visitors, Mike and Al."

We all applauded as two young men bounded out from the side, climbed up on the trampoline and began a series of jumps. They bounced up and down, did some somersaults and back flips and then took turns bouncing back and forth.

"They're pretty good," I whispered to Peter who was sitting next to me.

"Not bad," he agreed.

Mike and Al climbed off the trampoline and began talking to the audience about what they had done and what they were going to do next. They climbed back on the trampoline and each went through a series of maneuvers, going higher and higher with each jump. They did all sorts of acrobatics. In between times, they would get off the trampoline and talk about what they were doing and how much fun the trampoline was and also what good exercise it was.

After they had finished their routine, they stood by the trampoline, and announced, "Is there anyone in the audience who would like to try?"

No response. Not a person volunteered.

"Come on. It's fun," Mike called out.

"I think Peter should try it," I whispered to my friend Norm who was sitting on the other side.

"Let's see if we can get him to go up," Norm answered.

We began shouting, "Peter! Peter!"

The rest of our class joined in, and the shouting spread throughout the audience. Soon everyone was chanting, "Peter! Peter!"

Peter looked embarrassed and ducked his head down.

"Come on up, Peter," Mike called. "It sounds like the audience wants you."

Peter gave me a dirty look, slowly got to his feet, and walked toward the front. The audience applauded.

I could see Mike talking to Al. I didn't know what they were saying, but I guessed they probably thought Peter was the class clown or a goof off or something.

Peter walked to where Mike and Al were standing. They helped him up on the trampoline and explained how to do things. Al demonstrated a simple jump and told Peter to try it.

Peter looked tentative, tried a jump, and promptly fell on his backside.

"No problem," Al said. "Here, let me show you again."

He went through a couple of jumps as Peter watched intently.

"Ok, Peter, now you try it," Al told him.

Peter took a tentative jump, bouncing up and down, and then fell again.

Norm whispered to me, "I thought Peter would be really good at this."

"I think he's just pretending. Watch what happens," I answered.

Meanwhile on the stage, Al said to Peter "Here, let me show you again."

Al did a couple of jumps. "OK, Peter, now you try it."

"You mean like this?" ask Peter as he took a couple of jumps.

"That's it," said Al, "keep going."

Peter took another jump and then another. Soon he was bouncing up and down, up and down, and then he flipped over and did a somersault, then another one. Then he bounced higher and did a back flip.

"Like this?" he called to Al and Mike.

They didn't answer—they just stared at him. Peter kept bouncing and doing all sorts of jumps.

The gymnasium audience began laughing and then burst into thunderous applause. Mike and Al just stood at the side of the trampoline, their mouths open in amazement. Peter continued bouncing, doing double back flips, side flips, and all sort of actions I couldn't even name.

The crowd began chanting, "Peter! Peter!" and then began a rhythmic clapping. Mike and Al couldn't believe what they were seeing.

Finally Peter made an extra-high jump, did a double twirl and then a double back flip before landing on his feet in the middle of the trampoline. The audience members went crazy, leaping to their feet and wildly cheering. Peter came to the side of the trampoline, grabbed the iron ring on the side, and swung down to the floor.

Mike and Al came over to Peter, patted him on the back and shook his hand.

"You've done this before, haven't you?" I heard Al say to him.

Peter leaned over and whispered something to them, turned to the audience and waved, and then came back and sat with us.

"That's was fabulous, Peter. You were sensational," I told him.

Mr. Rolfs came to the front, thanked Al and Mike for their fine program, and added, "And that was quite a performance from Peter, wasn't it?"

The audience broke into applause again.

"Now, everyone leave quietly and return to your classrooms. We'll start with the kindergarten, then the grade school, and finally the high school."

Mr. Rolfs always asked us to leave quietly, but we rarely did, especially not today, not after what we had seen.

When we got back to our room, Mr. Franklin said, "Well, Peter, that was quite a show you put on. I have a question for you: What did you tell Al and Mike?"

Peter looked a little sheepish. "Well, I hadn't really planned to tell anyone, but the reason I know how to do gymnastics is that my parents are circus people. I've been doing acrobatics ever since I can remember. Normally my parents perform just during the summer, and my sister and I go with them as part of the show. They're acrobats and trapeze performers. This year they got a chance to perform with a circus that plays in the South. My sister got a contract too, so she's touring with them. I'm staying with my grandmother until they're done with the tour. So when you guys started yelling for me to go up on stage, I decided I might as well do it. So I did."

That evening when Dad asked if there was anything new at school today, we had quite a story to tell.

Chapter 38

Mr. West Coast Makes a Bet

"Can I go ... ?"

"May I go?" Mother interrupted.

Yes, I thought, there's Mother again, always insistent that we use correct grammar. I could just hear her, "Can I go? Certainly, because you are able to go. However, 'May I go' means that you have permission."

I quickly changed to, "May I go to the locker plant to watch television?"

"What are you going to watch?" Mother wanted to know.

"The Purdue-University of Washington football game," I answered.

"Why do you want to watch that?" asked Phil. "The game was last Saturday and Purdue pulled a big upset, beating Washington 35 to 28. You'll just be watching a film of the game."

"I know, but I've never seen a Big Ten football game, so I want to watch it."

Before I go further, I probably should explain why I wanted to go to the locker plant to watch television. On second thought, maybe I should first explain about a locker plant.

Locker plants tended to be located in small towns. A locker plant was a business where people could rent a locker (usually a large drawer) in which frozen food could be kept. When farmers would butcher a cow or a pig, the locker plant would cut up the meat, wrap it, fast freeze the packages, and place them in the farmer's locker.

We had a locker which we kept filled with the produce from Dad's garden and with the meat that members of the congregation gave us. It was always fun on a hot summer day to walk into the cold locker area and go to our locker. Of course, when you came outside again, it would seem twice as hot as when you went in.

Anyway, Mr. Brueggemann, who owned the locker plant, was a good businessman. He knew that there were now home freezers on the market, which meant that people wouldn't need to rent lockers. They could have a freezer right in their home. Knowing this, he began to sell home freezers and other appliances in the lobby area of the locker plant.

Selling things was nothing new for him. Mr. Brueggemann was a religious man, and he sold various religious items in the locker plant. Especially popular were plaster plaques with religious scenes and Bible verses on them. These were good sellers at Christmas time. Probably every Sunday School teacher in the Village, regardless of denomination, had at least a half dozen plaques inscribed with John 3:16, Psalm 23, or the Lord's Prayer.

Of course, all of this doesn't explain why I wanted to go to the locker plant to watch television.

Television was brand new. WTMJ in Milwaukee had just started broadcasting at the end of 1947. Many of the first TV sets were sold to taverns that thought it would be good business to have a set behind the bar. The tavern keepers figured it would attract customers and would also encourage them to linger longer, increasing the sales of beer and brandy, the two most popular drinks in Wisconsin taverns.

It was generally accepted science that television signals could only travel about 50 miles from the transmitter.

"It has to do with the curvature of the earth," the science teacher at the high school explained to his physics class. Phil was taking physics and reported this to us at the dinner table one evening.

However, Mr. Brueggemann was not in the physics class, so he wasn't aware that the TV signal would only travel 50 miles from Milwaukee. He thought that if he put up a television antenna on the roof of the locker plant and made it higher than the normal antenna, he could pick up the signal. So he bought a TV antenna and had J.B., the telephone maintenance man, install an extra-high pole for the antenna. Mr. Brueggemann tried to keep all of this quiet, since if it didn't work, he didn't want to become an object of derision in the Village. But it was hard to be inconspicuous with a 50-foot TV antenna sticking up on the roof. Soon everyone in the Village was talking about it.

It took a while for the TV set to arrive, since the appliance supplier was in Chicago. The TV set finally arrived, crated up in a railroad boxcar. Almost everything arrived by train. Regular truck delivery was just starting to take place.

The train depot was just across the street from the locker plant. Mr. Brueggemann got Wes Carley, the village maintenance man, who also picked up the mail from the trains, to haul the set across the street in his handcart.

Mr. Brueggemann had hoped to have all of this activity take place in the evening when the locker plant was closed, but no such luck. By the time Wes delivered the set to the locker plant, the whole town knew about it.

A crowd began gathering at the locker plant. No one had ever seen television. Quite a few people were skeptical that a picture would actually come through the air.

"I don't think that pictures come through the air. I bet there's a little projector in the back, sorta like a movie," Old Man French said to his friend Hans Mueller.

The crowd watched J.B., who had stopped over from the telephone company to help Mr. Brueggemann unpack the set.

"Let me see the instruction book," he said to Mr. Brueggemann, "We'll have to figure out how this thing works."

Mr. Brueggemann handed him the large printed manual. J.B. began to study it. The crowd continued to grow as J.B. concentrated on the instructions.

"Look, everyone," Mr. Brueggemann announced. "It's going to be a while before we get this thing hooked up. Why don't you come back tomorrow?"

No one moved. J.B. kept reading. More people arrived. In hushed whispers they were briefed on what was happening.

Finally J.B. closed the manual and motioned for Mr. Brueggemann to go with him to the locker plant office. They went in and closed the door.

The crowd waited, speculating on what they were discussing.

The two men emerged from the office.

"J.B. says it will take some additional wiring from the antenna," the owner announced. "He'll try to do it after supper tonight, so you all might as well go home now."

J.B. nodded and started to leave. The crowd slowly followed him out the door.

Throughout the afternoon there was a steady stream of visitors to the locker plant as people came in and stared at the television set sitting in the middle of the floor. The locker plant closed at 5:00 p.m. Mr. Brueggemann shooed the remaining spectators out of the showroom and locked the front door.

"I wonder what we got ourselves into," he said to his wife as he turned off the office light and prepared to leave for home.

After supper J.B. joined Mr. Brueggemann at the locker plant. Though the door was locked, the crowd gathered on the sidewalk and watched through the windows as J.B. strung the wires from the antenna to the showroom. They saw the two men move the television set to the corner but then were disappointed when the set was out of their range of vision. They could see J.B. studying the operating manual.

"I think I have it figured out," J.B. said. "I'll hook it up, and we'll see what happens."

He began stringing the wires down the wall to the set.

"OK, Emil," he said to Mr. Brueggemann. "Turn it on. I might have to go up to the roof and adjust the antenna."

Mr. Brueggemann found the power button and turned it on. The fifteen-inch tube slowly began to glow. A snowy image gradually emerged. J.B. and Mr. Brueggemann stared at the set.

"I'll go up on the roof and turn the antenna a little more toward Milwaukee," J.B. said.

As he climbed the ladder to the roof, the crowd in front noticed him and came near the ladder.

"What's happening, J.B.? Is that thing working?" someone called to him.

"We'll soon know," he answered. He began rotating the antenna, making a guess on the direction of the WTMJ transmitter.

"Check it out, Emil," he called to Mr. Brueggemann, who was standing in the doorway.

"It's a lot better," came the response.

The crowd surged toward the door. Mr. Brueggemann halted them.

"Look," he said, "we still have a lot of adjusting to do. Come back tomorrow, and I hope we will have it up and running. Remember, they don't begin broadcasting until noon."

So that's how television arrived in the Village. For quite a while it was the only set in town. A crowd would gather there every afternoon, except on Sunday when the locker plant was closed.

My friend Norm had told me about the football game, and we had made plans to watch it. Mother gave her OK, so on Saturday afternoon I walked the two blocks to the locker plant.

There were 30 or 40 people already gathered around the set when we got there. Most everyone knew that they would be watching a film of last week's game, but they were all interested in seeing an actual Big Ten football game.

Norm and I found a place at one side where we had a good view of the set.

Everyone was quiet as the announcer introduced the players for both teams. Those who had been sitting rose to their feet when the stadium announcer introduced the Purdue University band to play *The Star-Spangled Banner.*

The game began. We all watched, straining to see the action and listening to the play-by-play announcer. A few more people joined the crowd. Most were quiet with a few whispering to get details of the game.

The door opened, and a guy wearing a suit came over to the group.

"Hey, who's playing?" he asked loudly.

"Purdue and Washington," someone responded.

The stranger watched as Washington intercepted a pass.

"Those West Coast teams are sure better than the Big Ten," he announced.

"Who is this guy?" I whispered to Norm.

"He's some salesman. He stopped in to see Dad—wanted him to try a new advertising scheme," Norm answered. Norm's dad owned the Ford garage in the Village.

"What makes you think that?" asked Herb Fredricks. Herb had attended the University of Wisconsin, and he didn't take kindly to disparaging remarks about the Big Ten.

"Oh, I used to live on the West Coast. Those Pac-10 teams just have a lot more talent than the Big Ten. See," he interjected as Washington scored a touchdown.

"Wait and see," Herb answered.

The crowd continued to watch in silence.

"Look at that!" the salesman shouted as Washington scored again. "Purdue doesn't have a chance."

"Doesn't that guy know this is a film of last week's game?" I whispered to Norm.

"Guess not. Dad said he didn't think the guy was too smart. If he was smart, he wouldn't have tried to get Dad to offer trading stamps. Can you imagine? Trading stamps at a car dealer? " Norm shook his head.

The game continued. Washington scored again.

"See—what did I tell you? Purdue doesn't have a chance!" the guy yelled.

"Don't be too certain," Herb told him.

"Not a chance," came the response. "I'll bet anyone ten bucks that Washington will win by at least two touchdowns."

Herb pulled out his billfold, took out a ten-dollar bill and said, "OK, Mr. West Coast. Here's my ten bucks. Let's see your money."

The salesman dug into his pocket and pulled out two crumpled five dollar bills.

"Emil," Herb said, "you hold the money," taking it over to Mr. Brueggemann who was working behind the counter.

You could see Emil didn't really approve of people gambling in his locker plant, but he didn't say anything as he took the money.

Washington scored again.

"Easiest ten bucks I'm going to make," Mr. West Coast smirked at Herb.

"Just wait," Herb said. People watching the game smiled at each other, but said nothing.

Halftime came with Washington leading 21 to 7. The second half was completely different. Washington kicked off, and Purdue ran the ball back for a touchdown.

"Lucky," Mr. West Coast snorted, "just wait."

Purdue kicked off and Washington fumbled the return. Purdue recovered and three plays later tied the score.

Mr. West Coast got quiet. He pulled up a chair and stared intently at the screen.

He brightened up when, after an exchange of punts, Washington put on an eighty-yard drive for a touchdown, making the score 28 to 21. In the fourth quarter, Purdue scored twice, and the Boilermaker defense held Washington scoreless.

On the last play of the game, Washington tried a desperation pass only to have it intercepted.

"Pretty lucky," he grimaced at Herb. "Pretty lucky."

He turned and walked out the door.

"Hick town," someone heard him say on his way out.

The door closed, and the whole crowd burst into laughter.

Herb went over to collect his winnings.

"Ice cream for everyone," he announced pointing to the freezer in the corner.

"Herb sure pulled a good one on that guy," I said to Norm as I selected a Drumstick from the freezer.

"He deserved it. He was not only a loud mouth, he was pretty stupid," Norm answered.

I nodded in agreement.

Chapter 39

The Lonely Norwegian

We had just finished our table prayer at supper when Mother burst out, "I heard the most exciting news at conference today."

Today was conference day. It was the regular meeting of the Lutheran pastors from the area. Each month the pastors and their wives would meet at one of the congregations. The pastors would gather in the church and have a meeting. Usually one of the pastors would present a paper on some topic related to Scripture which would be followed by a discussion. Then, according to Dad, the remainder of time would be devoted to discussing church news.

"I call it ecclesiastical gossip," Dad told me one time when I asked what they did at conference. The pastors talked about who might get a call to a vacant parish, what pastors in the district were having problems, and any current news on how merger talks were going with the Norwegians.

The congregations in the conference belonged to the American Lutheran Church or ALC, one of a dozen or so national Lutheran bodies. The ALC was German in background. For years it had been discussing a possible merger with the Evangelical Lutheran Church or ELC, a church with a Norwegian background.

Since Dad had married into a strongly Norwegian family and had grown familiar with the Norwegian church, he was very much in favor of the merger. Some of the other ALC preachers were not all that enthusiastic about a merger with the Norwegians.

"I don't know about merging with those Norwegians," I remember hearing Pastor Hasselmeyer say when he was visiting at our house. "A lot of those Norwegian preachers think we ALC pastors are a bunch of sinners because we'll drink a glass of beer on occasion."

I remember Dad smiling. About the only time he had a glass of beer was when he visited his Norwegian brothers-in-law.

While the pastors were discussing church business, the wives (it would be twenty years before women would become pastors) would gather in the parsonage for a social visit. At noon, they would join their husbands for lunch in the church basement.

Hmm, what could Mother's news be? I wondered. As far as I had ever heard, the conversation among the pastors' wives usually consisted of news about their children and incidents in their congregations. "Exciting" was not exactly the adjective which I would use to describe news from the conference.

"Yes," Mother went on before anyone else could say anything. "Mrs. Schoenweis told me some very interesting news."

"Who is Mrs. Schoenweis?" I asked. I had not recalled a preacher by that name in the conference.

"Her husband is the new pastor at Westwood," Mother answered. "I really like her. She's Norwegian."

I could understand why Mother would like her. Mother was Norwegian. She had grown up in a solidly Norwegian family who were active members of the Norwegian Lutheran church. When she married Dad, she became a member of the American Lutheran Church, where virtually all the clergy and their wives were German. So finding a fellow Norwegian among the clergy wives would be exciting for Mother.

In the Village, Mother felt especially isolated. It was largely a German community. There was only one other Norwegian in town, Mr. Rolfs, the high school principal, and his wife was German!

When we moved to the Village, Mother immediately noticed that several of the business owners in town had Scandinavian names including Mr. Nelson, who owned one of the three grocery stores, and Mr. Jensen, who ran the feed mill. Mother was very disappointed when she learned that they were Danes.

"Worse yet, they aren't even Lutherans," she lamented to Dad. "They're all Methodists."

For Mother, it was little short of treason when a person with a Scandinavian name was not a Lutheran. So when Mother found a fellow Norwegian who was Lutheran as well, she felt immediately that she had discovered a life-long friend.

"Well," said Dad, "that is big news. I did not know that Mrs. Schoenweiss was Norwegian."

"Oh," said Mother, "that's not why I'm excited. The exciting news is what she told me."

We kids perked up our ears. What kind of news could Mother have heard from Mrs. Schoenweis?

"She told me that a new fish market had opened in Oshkosh."

We kids looked at each other. What in the world?

"And," Mother went on, "I really got excited when she told me that they sold lutefisk."

I was a little familiar with lutefisk. My Norwegian uncles would frequently tell jokes in which lutefisk was the punch line.

Dad had explained to me one time that lutefisk was a dish which Norwegians ate at Christmas time and that it was dried codfish which had been preserved in a lye solution.

"It sounds terrible," I said.

Dad assured me it wasn't all that bad. "In the Norwegian part of the state, a lot of the Lutheran churches hold annual lutefisk dinners. We used to have lutefisk at Grandpa and Grandma Olson's once in a while. I rather liked it." Grandpa and Grandma Olson were Mother's parents.

"What is 'luderfish'?" Helene asked.

"It's 'lute-a-fisk'," Mother explained to her. "It's a Norwegian cod fish, which we always had at Christmas time when I was growing up, but I haven't had it for years. Now that I know it's available, I thought we should have it at Christmas time this year."

Hmm, I thought, that would be a change, not just having lutefisk, but having something which we actually bought. All of our holiday meals featured gifts of meat or poultry that we received from members of the congregation.

"Are we going to have lefse too?" Phil wanted to know.

My ears perked up. Now lefse—that was a major Norwegian treat.

Lefse was a little hard to describe. It was almost like a tortilla, round, soft and baked on a griddle. But instead of being made with corn or wheat, it was made with mashed potatoes. It was usually served with butter and sugar and rolled up.

We kids loved it, but we seldom had it since Mother didn't make it. She claimed she knew how but didn't have the right equipment.

"You need a special kind of rolling pin. My mother always said that the best lefse was made on a wood-burning kitchen stove, and we don't have that either," she explained when questioned why she didn't make lefse.

"Well," Mother hesitated. She really didn't want to admit that she didn't know how to make lefse. "Maybe I can locate some. I'll see."

That was the end of the lutefisk conversation. We finished supper, had our devotions, and began doing the dishes.

"Do you think Mother is serious about having lutefisk?" I asked Phil.

"Hard to say. You know, she comes up with a lot of ideas. Some of them she just won't drop. You know, like nagging me to get an accordion or pestering you to buy that saw. But a lot of times she'll just forget about the subject, and we'll never hear about it again. It's just hard to figure her out."

"Have you ever had lutefisk?" I asked

"I think I can remember Grandma Olson making it one time, but I don't remember much about it."

"It would sure be nice if Mother learned how to make lefse and would just forget about lutefisk," I said as I let the water out of the sink and hung up the dish cloth.

"Yeah, I wonder if she knows anything about cooking lutefisk," Phil answered.

Now Mother was a good cook. She had to be since the parsonage family got a wide variety of donated food. We never knew what to expect, especially in the fall when many church members would go hunting.

We might receive some pheasants—a real treat. Or we might get a pair of squirrels—not quite as big of a treat. We always got venison, and Mother learned a dozen ways to prepare it.

But lutefisk? Now it would be interesting to see how Mother handled that.

At supper a few nights later Mother brought up the topic again.

"You know, I'm getting excited about having lutefisk. It's been years since we've had it. When was the last time, Henry?" she asked Dad.

Dad thought for a few moments and then replied, "It must have been while we were in Milwaukee and your parents were living with Uncle Carl in West Allis."

"Why," Mother answered, "that's at least ten years ago."

"What else do they serve with lutefisk?" Phil asked, hoping to find some small ray of hope.

"Well, there's lefse, of course. And boiled potatoes. I remember Mother always served it with rutabagas."

Good grief, I thought. This may be even worse than I had imagined. I tried to put the topic out of my mind.

Little more thought was given to lutefisk as the Christmas season approached. Christmas was a busy time for everyone, but for the parsonage family it was especially busy. Dad had to prepare for extra services. There was the children's program on Christmas Eve, which meant three Saturdays would be devoted to rehearsals. Every shut-in of the congregation would want to have private communion, which meant that Dad had to make a dozen or more house calls to deliver the sacrament to those who could not make it to church services. There were extra rehearsals for the junior and senior choirs. Since Dad directed both groups, this took more time.

We kids were busy with school activities as well as church duties. At home, Mother was baking and getting the house ready for the holidays. We set up the Christmas tree and decorated the outside of the parsonage.

We gave little thought to Mother's plan to have lutefisk during the Christmas season. When we did think about it, we fervently hoped Mother had forgotten the subject.

We knew that we would be well remembered by the congregation with gifts of meat, poultry, and baked goods. We also knew very well that not one member would come bearing a gift of lutefisk ... not in our Germanic congregation. Sauerbraten maybe, but not codfish preserved with lye.

We would be alone for Christmas this year. No visit from Uncle Walter, Aunt Helen, and Cousin Esther. No surprise arrival of Grandpa Kurtz. We were usually alone at Christmas. We could not travel anywhere since Dad had all the Christmas services.

We generally didn't have company since most of Dad's relatives were preachers and could not get away. Mother's relatives were either dairy farmers who rarely were able to take vacations, or they lived so far away they could not make the trip.

Christmas dinner this year was a beef roast, a gift from one of the members. Mother tried something new—Yorkshire pudding.

"I've never heard of that kind of pudding," Helene said. "Isn't pudding dessert?"

"Well, it's really not a pudding," Mother explained. "It's more like a bread or a biscuit. I read about it in one of my magazines."

We all agreed it was pretty good.

"It could have been lutefisk," I whispered to Phil.

But we heard nothing about a Norwegian dinner that day or the day after Christmas. We kids silently breathed a sigh of relief.

But then, the next morning at breakfast as we were gathered at the table, Mother, who had gotten up to have breakfast with us—something which seldom happened since she was usually a late sleeper—announced: "Tonight's the night."

"For what?" Phil asked, a bit of an edge creeping into his voice.

"Tonight we're going to have lutefisk. Henry, I know there is nothing on your schedule today, so I thought we could drive over to Oshkosh and do a little shopping," she said.

Dad gave a bit of a start. My guess was that on one of his rare free days he was looking forward to relaxing after his busy Christmas schedule. But unless the phone rang with an emergency in the congregation, Dad knew that he might just as well plan on a trip to Oshkosh, some 30 miles from the Village.

"Do I have to go?" Helene asked.

"No," Mother replied, "you can stay home with Phil and Harold."

"Good, I want to play with my Christmas toys," Helene answered.

Mother and Dad left. We kids passed the time quietly. Helene played with her new toys. Phil and I didn't even fight; we just read the books we had gotten as gifts.

"You know," I said to Phil, looking up from my book, "it's only going to be one meal."

"Maybe we could disconnect the stove or something," Phil suggested.

"No, that wouldn't work. Mother would probably just use the gas burner in the basement. Besides, we would probably electrocute ourselves trying to disconnect the stove."

Phil nodded agreement. "Just a thought; I'm getting desperate."

"Now if we just had lefse, we could fill up on that and just take a few bites of the other stuff," I countered.

"Yeah, but with our luck, Mother will come home with rutabagas and lutefisk, but no lefse," Phil answered.

We glumly went back to our reading.

It was mid-afternoon when Mother and Dad returned. Mother looked a little sad as she took off her coat.

"We had the worst luck," she announced.

"Oh, what happened?" Phil asked.

"They were all out of lutefisk at the market," Mother answered.

"They were?" Phil and I exclaimed, almost in unison, doing our best not to sound jubilant.

"Yes," Mother replied, "so we bought some shrimp instead."

Now that would be a real treat, I thought. Suddenly we were looking forward to the evening meal.

At the supper table that night we sat enjoying this unexpected delicacy.

"Yes," Mother reported. "The man at the market said that they sold out of lutefisk right away. Seems everybody at the Lutheran church in Winchester came down to buy it."

"Well," I said, dipping another shrimp into Mother's homemade sauce, "I think that having shrimp would be a good Christmas tradition."

Mother smiled and thought for a moment. "I'm glad you enjoyed the meal tonight," she paused, "but next year I'll try to get to Oshkosh earlier."

"And maybe I'll be at college," I heard Phil say under his breath.

Chapter 40

Helene Sings a Solo

"I had an interesting conversation with Vera Pretzlaff this afternoon," Dad remarked at the supper table one spring evening.

"Oh, where did you see her?" asked Mother.

"She was in Herb Schmuhl's grocery store when I was shopping," Dad answered.

What could be interesting about Mrs. Pretzlaff, I thought. She was a Sunday School teacher who had been teaching third and fourth graders as long as most people in the congregation could remember.

"She even was teaching back when the congregation still used German," I remember hearing one of the members tell Dad.

"Yes," Dad went on, "she told me that she wasn't going to direct the children's Christmas program anymore. She said it was time for someone else to do it. And next fall she said she wouldn't be teaching Sunday School anymore. 'I am eighty-five years old, after all,' she told me."

"That is interesting," Mother agreed. "It's too bad. She really seemed to enjoy it."

"Yes," Phil put in, "but it's always the same thing. I don't think a thing has changed in 50 years."

"Why should it?" Helene put in. "The Christmas story doesn't change."

We all smiled. My sister had a logical mind, I thought.

"I know," said Phil, "but every year it's the same songs, the same costumes, and the kids saying the same pieces."

"I'm glad she told me now," Dad went on, ignoring our comments. "It gives me time to find a replacement."

Since Christmas was a long way off, there was no more discussion on the matter, and the conversation turned to other topics.

I don't know how hard Dad worked at finding a replacement. You see, Dad was not a big fan of Christmas programs. "People come to be entertained," I can remember hearing him complain. Now Dad was not a grim person. He enjoyed entertainment. The congregation had a lot of activities which stressed fellowship and entertainment. But these were held in the church basement, or Fellowship Hall as Dad called it. In Dad's view, that's where these types of activities should be held. The sanctuary should be reserved for the serious business of worship. But he was practical and knew that the Christmas Eve children's pageant was cast in concrete on the church calendar not only at Emanuel but at every Lutheran congregation he knew.

Summer passed; school started. All the church activities resumed after the summer break.

"Do you have someone to direct the Christmas pageant?" Mother asked one evening at supper.

"I talked to a couple of the Sunday School teachers, but they turned me down," Dad answered. "I'm working on it."

Nothing happened. September was coming to an end.

"I don't know what I'm going to do," Dad said at supper one evening. "Here it is—almost October—and I haven't found anyone to direct the Christmas program. I have asked every Sunday School teacher and even Willard Monk." Willard was the Sunday School superintendent. He always seemed willing to do most anything Dad asked him.

"Willard said no?" Mother asked.

"Yes, I was surprised at that," Dad admitted, "but Willard said this was just something he wasn't comfortable doing. And he is so good about helping in so many things that I didn't want to push him to do it. I don't know who I'm going to get."

We all sat there silently, mentally thinking who Dad might ask.

Helene broke the silence. "I have an idea," she said. "I think Mommy should do it."

Hmm, I thought, that's not a bad idea. Mother really likes to run things.

Dad turned to Mother. "Well, what do you think?"

"I don't know," Mother answered. "You know I don't really like to be in charge."

Phil and I did our best to keep from laughing. We knew Mother relished running things even though she always denied it.

"And what will the members think?" Mother pondered. No matter what the issue might be, Mother always worried about the reaction of the members of Emanuel Lutheran. She never stopped worrying about potential congregational reactions. Now the truth was that most members were pretty tolerant of how the parsonage family lived. No one ever accused Mother of being a bad homemaker if we inadvertently left the catsup bottle on the kitchen table, or that she was a bad parent if one of the ribbons on Helene's pigtails came undone. But Mother always worried about even the most trivial item.

After thinking things over, Mother decided she wouldn't worry (too much anyway) about what the members would think, and she would direct the Christmas pageant.

"I'm going to change a few things," Mother announced at supper one evening. "Instead of *Come Hither, Ye Faithful* like they always use as a processional, I'm looking for something different. Henry," she said, turning to Dad, "didn't your aunt write a song that they used for a processional in your uncle's church?"

"Yes," Dad answered, "that was my Aunt Minnie Kurtz."

We kids looked at each other. There was another Minnie Kurtz besides Mother?

"Who was that?" Phil wanted to know.

"That was my mother's sister. She married my Uncle William, who was a pastor in Iowa. And yes, she did write a song, which the church used as a Christmas processional. I may have a copy of it. I'll look for it," Dad said.

A few days later, as we were finishing supper, Dad got up, went to the study and returned with a sheet of paper.

"Here it is—Aunt Minnie's Christmas song," he told Mother.

Mother read the words out loud:

OH, WHAT MERRY, MERRY VOICES

Verse I   Oh, what merry, merry voices
Fill the air at Christmas time.
All my heart this night rejoices,
Praising God in tuneful rhyme.

(Refrain) Glory to God in heaven,
Peace on earth good will to men,
For to you is born a Savior
This day in Bethlehem.

Verse II   See the candles brightly glisten,
But such joys are not enduring.

Like the lights they fade away.
Jesus came for us securing. (Refrain)

Verse III Gifts and joys that last for aye
On the verdant Christmas tree,
While the holy angels listen
To our song so full of glee. (Refrain)

"Well, that's very nice. Where is the music?" she asked.

"Well," Dad hesitated a bit, "I'm not certain if you'll like it."

"Why, I like most music. You're the one who always worries whether the music is appropriate," Mother pointed out.

"I was never certain how come Aunt Minnie came up with using this tune, but she did. Apparently the people in the Iowa church really liked it," Dad answered.

"For heaven's sake, what is the tune?" Mother demanded.

"It's the old Methodist revival hymn, *Shall We Gather at the River,*" Dad answered almost sheepishly.

I burst out laughing.

"What's so funny about that?" Mother wanted to know.

"I was just thinking of Uncle Alfred's old joke," I answered.

Phil started laughing too. "Yeah, his story about the revival preacher who was giving the temperance sermon about the evils of drink."

"Yes," I managed to respond through my laughter, "and he said that all the beer and wine and whiskey should be dumped into the river. And after he said, 'Amen,' the choir director announced that the anthem will be ..."

"*Shall We Gather at the River,*" Phil and I said in unison. After all, we had heard Uncle Alfred tell the story dozens of times.

Both of us howled with laughter. Helene looked perplexed, and Dad chuckled.

"That's why I was a little hesitant about the music," Dad smiled.

"Oh, for goodness sake," Mother said. "That's no reason not to use the music. I'm sure no one in the congregation has heard Uncle Alfred's story."

"I'd be glad to tell it," I volunteered.

"You'll do no such thing," she admonished me.

Mother got busy working on the Christmas program. At supper in the middle of November she made her announcement, "I'm all set with the Christmas program."

"That's great," said Dad. "What is it going to be?"

It was evident that Dad had not been consulted on the matter since he seemed a bit surprised at Mother's announcement.

"I'm calling it 'Christmas in Many Nations', and we'll have carols from a bunch of different countries: Germany of course, Denmark, England, America, and Norway. Maybe one or two others if I can find them. And," she said, turning to Helene "I want you to sing a solo."

"Oh, good," Helene responded. "I'll sing *Now is the Hour* like I did last summer." During the Village's big centennial celebration the summer before, Helene had won third prize in the talent contest singing *Now is the Hour*.

"No," Mother told her. "You're going to sing *Jeg Er Sa Glad*. It's a Norwegian carol, and I'm going to teach you to sing it in Norwegian."

It figures, I thought. Mother always tries to find ways to remind us that she's Norwegian and that we kids are half Norwegian.

"I suppose so," Helene agreed.

"And we'll have the little kids speak pieces, so their parents won't be upset. I'm going to see about different costumes for the Nativity scene," she went on.

"It sounds great," Dad said.

"I think everything is set for the Christmas pageant," she reported at dinner one evening. "I just hope I haven't forgotten anything."

"Are you sure you have the Baby Jesus?" Helene felt she had to remind Mother of the important details.

Mother assured her that Baby Jesus would be a definite part of the Christmas program.

"Henry," said Mother, "I think it would be nice to have a carol sung in German. I was thinking you could sing something. Maybe *Luther's Cradle Hymn*."

"I could sing something," Dad agreed, "but the so-called *Luther's Cradle Hymn* isn't German, and Luther didn't write it."

"Is that right? Why, it's listed as *Luther's Cradle Hymn* in the Sunday School hymnbook," Mother answered.

"No, Luther didn't write it. There's no German version. But Luther did write a Christmas hymn. It's *From Heaven on High*, or in German it's *Von Himmel Hoch*. I can certainly sing that," Dad said.

"That would be wonderful," Mother answered. "And you're sure Luther didn't write *Away in a Manger*?"

"I'm positive," Dad assured her.

Now the Christmas season was generally one of chaos in the parsonage. There were all the normal family activities: buying the Christmas tree and putting it up, decorating the outside of the house, Christmas shopping, sending out the family Christmas letter to relatives and friends, Christmas baking, school activities ... you get the picture.

For Dad it was always a busy time. There were extra services. The shut-ins of the congregation would have communion brought to them in their homes. There were extra choir rehearsals. There were special church bulletins to write and mimeograph.

This year, chaos was replaced with pure pandemonium. Mother was constantly worrying about details. Would Helene remember the Norwegian words to the carol? Were there any members of the congregation who might feel slighted if their ethnicity was not included in the program? Most everyone was German, but what if someone had a Polish grandmother or a Bohemian grandfather?

"And," Mother explained, "I'll be playing the piano when Helene sings *Jeg Er Sa Glad.*"

"You'll have enough to do that night. Why don't you just let Mrs. Buehler play for her since she'll be doing the other accompaniment?" Dad asked.

"Why," Mother responded indignantly, "she doesn't know how to play Norwegian music."

Dad decided it was no time to press the issue.

It was late afternoon, about a week before Christmas, when the phone rang. Dad answered. "It's Herb Schmuhl," he said, handing the phone to Mother.

"Oh no," I heard Mother say. "I didn't know I was supposed to do that. Can you get everything?"

That sounded sort of strange, I thought. Herb was a member of the congregation and owned a grocery store in the Village. I wondered why he was calling Mother.

After talking a bit more, Mother hung up the phone and turned to Dad. "I didn't know I was supposed to order the Christmas bags. Herb said Mrs. Pretzlaff always took care of it, so he was waiting to be told how much he should order. I told him to just go ahead and order what he had done last year. He thought he would be able to get everything," Mother explained.

Now this was pretty serious, I thought. The Christmas bags were as much a part of the Christmas pageant as *Silent Night* and the Three Wise Men. All children got bags whether they were in the program or just visiting. Every year they were the same: a brown paper bag with a big handful of peanuts, a big, red Delicious apple, and Christmas candy—the hard, colored variety and the large chocolate covered mints. As long as I could remember, the bags never changed.

"Thank goodness Herb reminded me," Mother sighed. "I hope there's nothing else I haven't done."

On three Saturday afternoons there were rehearsals. Mother was close to collapse after each one. There was one thing after another. The children hadn't memorized their pieces. The costumes weren't done. And then there were the three boys portraying the Wise Men. "They don't act like Wise Men," Mother exploded. "They act like the Three Stooges! How in the world did Mrs. Pretzlaff do this for 50 years?" Mother exclaimed one Saturday. "I think I've aged 50 years since we started rehearsing."

But by the final Saturday before Christmas, everything seemed to fall into place. The children knew their pieces, the Three Wise Men were no longer the Three Wise Guys, and Herb Schmuhl had delivered all the contents of the Christmas bags and the Sunday School teachers had filled them. And Helene was doing her part. In fact, the rest of the family was getting a little tired of hearing her belt out:

> *'Jeg der sa glad hver juleveld*
> *Ti da blev Jesus fodt;*
> *Da lyste stjer —nem som en sol*
> *Og engler sang sa sodt."*

"At least she's only singing one verse," Phil said to me after her third rendition, "and not all five verses."

Christmas Eve finally arrived. As usual, the church was packed, and the ushers had to put up folding chairs in the aisle. Everything went well. Some of the older members got misty-eyed when Dad sang *Von Himmel Hoch*, thinking back to their childhood when the whole program was in German, and the *Tannenbaum* was illuminated with real candles.

The Christmas program was over. The Sunday School students had gotten their bags of Christmas candy and nuts. And they all had heeded Dad's admonition not to eat peanuts in church and throw the shells on the floor.

As Mother was leaving the church, old Mrs. Schoenbeck stopped her. "*Ach*, Mrs. Kurtz," she said. "You have such a nice little girl."

Mother beamed.

"She looked so darling with her blonde pigtails."

Mother beamed again.

"And such a nice singing voice."

Mother was ready to cheer.

"But," Mrs. Schoenbeck went on.

Oh, dear, thought Mother.

"There's one thing you have to do."

Now what could that be, Mother wondered.

"You have to work on her German. I could hardly understand a word of it."

No use explaining, thought Mother.

"Thank you, Mrs. Schoenbeck," Mother said. "Merry Christmas."

Chapter 41

Dartball—More Than a Game

"You look a little discouraged," Mother said to Dad one evening at the supper table. "Is something wrong?"

We had just said our table prayer and were preparing to eat.

"I really like being a pastor," Dad replied, "but it can be discouraging at times."

"What's wrong, Daddy?" Helene asked.

"Oh, it's nothing real major, but it's just one of those things that I work and work at, and nothing happens, so I end up being frustrated," Dad answered.

"What does 'frustrated' mean?" The way Helene was going, she will have the vocabulary of a college graduate before she is ten, I thought.

"Oh, it means that you try to do something and you just can't get it to come out the way you want it to," Mother explained. "You remember when I was trying to teach you the Norwegian Christmas carol, and you were having a hard time getting the pronunciation right, and then you started getting mad. You were frustrated."

"Oh," Helene nodded. "I see. Are you having trouble talking Norwegian, Daddy?"

We all smiled.

"No, it's a different sort of frustration," Dad told her.

He put down his fork before continuing. "You know, it's been so gratifying to have the Huehnes in church. Mrs. Huehne and the children are there every Sunday."

You may remember that the Huehne kids had been troublemakers in town, and then how Dad got things straightened out with them. Now Mrs. Huehne and the children were active church members.

"I have been after Mr. Huehne to come to church. Every time I talk with him, he agrees that, yes, he probably should come and he'll think about it, but he never shows up. I know Mrs. Huehne has been after him, too."

"Yes," Mother observed, "there are frustrations in the ministry."

Dad picked up his fork and resumed eating. The conversation turned to other topics.

A few weeks later, Mother brought up the subject of Mr. Huehne.

"Are you planning to visit Mr. Huehne again?" she asked Dad at supper.

"No," Dad answered, "but I have been thinking about what I can do. It's obvious that just inviting him to Sunday services isn't working."

"Too bad he isn't a kid. You could invite him to Vacation Bible School," Phil joked.

Dad thought a moment. "You may have something there."

"But he's too old for Bible school," Helene said.

"No, not Bible school," Dad smiled. "But maybe I can try something else."

"What would that be?" Mother asked.

"Maybe we could try the Brotherhood," Dad told her.

Dad had recently organized a Lutheran Brotherhood at Emanuel. The Lutheran Brotherhood was a men's organization. There had been a women's organization at Emanuel almost as long as the congregation had been in existence. When it was first organized, everyone in the congregation spoke German, and the women's group was called the *Frau Verein*—the wives' group. When English replaced German, it became the Ladies Aid.

The Brotherhood was a social organization for the men of the church. Dad had been trying to get a Brotherhood organized for a long time without success. Finally when he suggested that they have a dartball team, the men got interested. But before I tell you about the Brotherhood, I better explain about dartball.

It may sound strange, but dartball is a form of baseball, only it's played with darts thrown at a big board. It's a game which is particularly popular with church groups, especially Lutherans. The game has a large board about four feet square. It is printed in a bunch of colors—green, orange, blue, white, sometimes more. There's a diagram of a baseball field on it, and all parts are labeled with baseball terms like strike, ball, foul, single, double, triple, homer, out, and all the others.

Like baseball, there are two teams. Teams have nine players or there can be a smaller number. Players stand in front of the board and take turns throwing darts. If the dart hits a space marked "single", the next player will attempt to get a hit and drive the "runner" home, just like regular baseball. If a player hits the strike area three times, he's out. Scores are kept just like baseball, and if the team is part of a league, players' batting averages are also kept. Unlike baseball, there is no defense—only offense by the team throwing the darts.

Lutherans especially like the game. As Dad explained it one time, "The reason Lutherans like the game is that it's cheap. You don't have to pay like you do in bowling. It's easy to understand since everyone knows baseball. It can be played in the church basement, and the only equipment you need is the board and darts."

Emanuel had a team and played teams from other Lutheran churches in the area. Every now and then the team might play the Methodist or Congregational team, but they were not league members.

We kids would sneak over to the church sometimes and play with the darts. We didn't play dartball. We played our own game. Cousin Esther had shown me one time that if you threw the darts so they would skid across the concrete basement floor you could make sparks fly. So our game was to see who could make the biggest sparks. Of course, we never told Dad about our game, not even when he mentioned one time that some of the Brotherhood members complained that their darts didn't seem sharp enough.

The Brotherhood met monthly. Their meetings were held in the church basement. They would have a devotion and a short Bible study, but the main event was dartball. This was basically practice for the regular league games. Members would divide into two teams and play a game or two. The meeting would conclude with refreshments.

The dartball league played twice a month. There were eight teams in the league. At the end of the season, there would be a tournament with the top four teams playing. The winner of the tournament would represent the league in the State Brotherhood Tournament held in one of the larger cities in the church district.

But, getting back to our suppertime conversation. "Yes," Dad went on, "if Mr. Huehne won't come to church, maybe we can get him to come to the Brotherhood meeting. It could be the first step. I'll talk to some of the men and see if one of them will invite him to come. It would probably work better if one of the Brotherhood members invites him."

At supper a couple of weeks later Mother asked Dad if anything had happened with Mr. Huehne. "I talked with Harry Kroebel about him. Harry hires him now and then to work around the lumberyard. Harry wasn't real enthusiastic about inviting him. Didn't think he would be interested but said he would give it a try," Dad answered.

"Well, since Harry gives him work, Mr. Huehne might say yes to keep on Harry's good side," Mother observed.

"Good point," Dad answered. "We'll see what happens."

At the supper table one evening, Dad announced, "Well, I certainly had a surprise last night."

"Did you get a raise?" Phil asked.

"No, it was a Brotherhood meeting, not the church council last night," Dad responded. "The surprise was that Mr. Huehne was at the Brotherhood meeting. Harry brought him."

"How did it go?" Mother asked.

"I think he had a good time. He was very interested in dartball. He had never played it before, but he got the hang of it right away. I think he'll be back. He asked when the next meeting would be," Dad said.

And Mr, Huehne was at the next meeting. And the next.

"He is really good at dartball," Dad reported. "Arne Gruemann said he wanted to step down from the team so Mr. Huehne could take his place. 'I only have been playing because the team needed a ninth man,' he told the members."

With Mr. Huehne playing, the Emanuel team began to win. It looked as though the team would qualify for the league tournament. Dad made note of this in the Sunday church bulletin:

> Our Brotherhood dartball team is having a great season. The last game is Monday night against the first-place Grace Lutheran team here at Emanuel. If they can take two out of three games, they will qualify for the league tournament for the first time. The men would really appreciate a cheering section, so plan to attend.

"Does this mean I can go and watch?" I asked Dad.

"Sure," Dad answered, "I'm going to be there."

There was a good-sized crowd in the church basement. There were wives of the players, some of the church council members, and even some spectators from Grace Lutheran.

Dad was right, I thought, as I watched Mr. Huehne. He got on base every time he threw. The team had moved him into the number four position—the cleanup spot, just like baseball. Twice in the first game he drove in runs by hitting the double square on the board.

There was a round of applause when the Emanuel team won the first game 12 to 5.

"One more win and we qualify," shouted Art Schuster, the team captain.

But it didn't happen in the second game. Emanuel's players had a string of bad luck. They would get runners on base and then throw into the double play square or hit the out square when the bases were loaded. There was no applause from the Emanuel side when its team lost the game 10 to 2.

Art pulled the team into a circle. "OK, men. We really need this. Just concentrate on getting singles and we'll get the runs we need," he told them.

The strategy seemed to work. The Emanuel players were deliberate as they walked up to the line and carefully aimed the darts. Several times they had all nine team members throw in an inning. They went into the seventh inning leading 9 to 2. Emanuel's team members were relaxing on their side of the basement as the Grace team came to bat. It took only four players to make Emanuel team members lean forward as they saw their lead narrow. "Two home runs with men on each time," I heard Art mutter.

Things got worse. They weren't even hitting the strike area; they just kept getting on base. Emanuel's lead evaporated. Finally, the inning ended with Grace leading 11 to 9.

Seventh inning for Emanuel, and there were three quick outs. Fortunately, Grace didn't score in the eighth. Emanuel managed to get runners on base in the eighth, but couldn't bring them home. Grace added a run in the top of the ninth, making it 12 to 9. Emanuel begin seeing their tournament hopes disappearing.

"We only need four runs to win," Art called encouragingly.

Emanuel did not get four runs. But it did get three to tie the score and force an extra-inning game. Grace threw first and scored two runs. Emanuel tied the score with two singles followed by a triple. The eleventh inning saw no scores. In the twelfth inning, Grace got three runs.

Art Schuster shook his head. The bottom of the batting order was coming up. "It doesn't look good," he confided to Reuben Matz.

But the bottom three throwers each got singles. The bases were loaded. Then the leadoff thrower and the second thrower both flew out. Mr. Huehne, who Art had switched to the third spot, was up next. His first dart flew straight to the center of the board—a grand slam home run.

We all stood and cheered—well, everyone but the Emanuel team. They just slumped in their chairs, emotionally drained. Emanuel was in the league tournament for the first time ever! "I never knew dartball could leave you so exhausted," Art told Dad later.

Emanuel was on a roll. The tournament was held at Peace Lutheran in Rosendale with Grace Lutheran of Ripon, First Lutheran of Beaver Dam, and Emanuel. Emanuel's first three-game series was with First Lutheran, and Emanuel won the series, taking the first two games. Grace had defeated Peace in a three-game series, making the championship a rematch with Grace. Emanuel was fully confident of victory, although it took three games for it to win.

"We're going to the state tournament," Art Schuster told his celebrating team. He paused for a moment. "Does anyone know where it is?" he finally asked.

"It's going to be at Zion Lutheran in Appleton," Dad informed him.

"I hope I can find it. I've never been to Appleton," Art confessed.

"I know where it is. I'll give you directions," Dad assured him.

The tournament would be held in three weeks, the weekend after Easter. The whole congregation was excited about the tournament. Members who had previously not even known the Brotherhood had a dartball team began discussing the team's prospects and making plans to attend the tournament.

Even the Ladies Aid got involved. "Our men don't even have team shirts," the president of the Ladies Aid said. She called an emergency meeting after church services. The Aid approved buying them shirts "on condition they get them before the tournament."

Art called the Badger Sports Shop in Fond du Lac. Yes, they could get shirts done if someone would come and set up the design. Art and Reuben made a special trip.

"They're going to be real nice," he told the team. "They'll be red with white trim since those are the colors of the Village high school."

The shirts arrived the week before the tournament. On the front pocket there was a dart with "Dartball Team" at the top and "Emanuel Lutheran Church" below. They really did look nice, everyone agreed, even the members of the Ladies Aid who privately had worried about "what the men might pick out."

It was the day after the shirts arrived when the phone rang while we were finishing supper. Dad answered and we could hear him say, "Sure, come right over."

"That was Art Schuster," Dad said as he returned to the table. "He really sounded upset. Said he had to see me right away."

It must have been urgent because Dad said we would skip devotions since Art said he was coming right over. Dad had hardly gotten to the study when we saw Art's car pull up in front. Dad met him at the study door.

I had to clear the table, so I couldn't sit in the chair near the study door and hear what was going on. By the time I finished with my kitchen work, I heard Art leaving.

Dad came into the kitchen. "I have to go visit Mr. Huehne right away," he announced.

"What's going on?" Mother wanted to know.

"Well, Art was filling out the entrance form for the state tournament. After listing the names, he noticed that at the bottom of the list there was a statement which said, 'I certify that all the above are members in good standing of our congregation.' I told Art that I remembered that the issue had come up a few years ago when some of the teams had members from other churches. The state Brotherhood had passed a rule that team members could only come from the congregation," Dad explained.

"And Mr. Huehne isn't a member," Mother said.

"Not yet," Dad said, putting on his hat and heading out of the house.

Later Dad told us about his visit. "I explained the situation to Mr. Huehne. I told him that the men really wanted him to be on the team. I also told him that I knew he had been thinking of joining the church. I know you were confirmed, I told him. However, I don't want you joining the church just so you can be on the dartball team. If you agree to join, I want you to be in church with your wife and children.

"Mr. Huehne thought about it for a while and then said, 'Well, Pastor, I guess maybe it is about time I came back to the church. My life has been a lot better since my wife and the children have been going to church, so I guess I should give it a try. And I enjoy playing dartball with the guys.'"

That's how Mr. Huehne became a church member.

The team had a special meeting the Wednesday before the tournament. Art went over the schedule. "There are twelve teams in the tournament. Eleven are conference champions plus the host congregation gets to enter a team. It's double elimination which means every team gets to play at least two series. Teams that win the first two series advance to the semifinals. Play starts on Friday night with each team playing three series. Teams that win two series and then lose a series then go into the consolation bracket."

"Sounds kinda complicated," Herman Schroeder complained.

"I'm a little confused too," Art admitted, "but they seem to have the whole system worked out. All we have to do is to keep winning, and then we won't worry about how it works."

On the Friday of the tournament, the men gathered at the church basement to get their darts. There were twelve men going to the tournament: nine regular team members, a scorekeeper, an official, and a substitute player. Each team had to provide one official who would join with another official to referee a game in which their teams were not participating. They would rule on things such as whether a player had stepped over the line while throwing and other questions. As they were getting ready to leave, Dad and I went over to wish them well. Dad suggested they have a short prayer before they left.

Dad always seemed to have the right words for prayers, I thought as I listened to him ask that they have a safe trip and that they represent Emanuel in a Christian manner.

Saturday morning was always busy for Dad. There were confirmation classes, always called "Saturday School". This was followed by practice for the Junior Choir, which Dad directed. When Dad came home from these activities, he surprised us by saying "Let's have a quick lunch and go to Appleton."

"Why, Henry, it's Saturday. You can't go," Mother told him. "You have to work on your sermon."

Now that was Mother's usual response any time Dad suggested we do something on Saturday. The whole family knew that Dad worked on his sermon all week, but Mother seemed to feel that if he didn't spend Saturday night in his study, he would likely have to walk into the pulpit on Sunday morning and tell the congregation, "There won't be a sermon this morning because I didn't spend Saturday evening in my study."

"My sermon is all set," Dad assured her. "Art called his wife last night and told her that they won the first two series, so they will be playing this afternoon."

We ate lunch and got in the car. It was only about an hour's drive to Appleton, and we quickly found the church. Dad parked the car and led us into the gymnasium. Zion operated a parochial school, which had a good-sized gym.

The Emanuel team was just getting ready to play, so we sat down to watch. Playing dartball was a lot more fun than watching it, I decided. It was hard to see where the darts landed since our seats were about 30 feet from the board.

While the other team was throwing, Art came over to us. "Thanks for coming," he told us. "I know the team appreciates it."

"Where do you stand in the tournament?" Dad asked.

"If we win this series, we'll qualify for the semifinals," he explained. "If we lose, we qualify for the consolation round. Either way, we'll have at least one more series after this."

Well, I won't go into a dart by dart description of the match. Emanuel lost.

"We lost to a good team," Art told us. "They were state champions last year. But we still get to play in the consolation round."

We waited to see the next series which Emanuel won, which meant they would play for the third-place spot. "I think we should go home," Mother told Dad. "Helene and I are getting kind of bored with this." Dad agreed. He went over to the team, wished them luck and said he would see them in church on Sunday.

It was late at night when the phone rang. Dad went down to answer it. Usually when the phone rang late at night, it was an emergency for Dad. When Dad came back upstairs, I poked my head out of my bedroom.

"Who was that?" I asked.

"It was Art, letting me know that the team won third place," Dad answered.

Good for them, I thought, as I went back to sleep.

The next day at church the whole team was there wearing their red dartball shirts.

Dad had the team come up to the front and announced to the congregation that Emanuel had won third place in the state dartball tournament. And probably for the first time in its seventy-five-year history, the congregation stood up and applauded.

And the next Sunday Mr. Huehne was in church with his family. And the next Sunday, and the next Sunday.

At Sunday dinner, Dad talked about this. "It's sure good to see him coming to church."

"Who would have thought that God would use dartball to get a new member," Mother observed.

Chapter 42

Why I Remembered the Wildcats

I could hardly wait for supper, I thought as I walked home from school. It wasn't that I was starving to death—I was always hungry it seemed—no, it was because I really had some BIG news to share with the family. Well, at least I thought it was big.

Suppertime came and after we said our table prayer and even before I filled my plate I burst out, "Do I have some news!"

"OK," said Dad as he helped himself to a slice of meatloaf, "what's the big news?"

Mother, Helene and Phil paused in eating, waiting for me to continue.

"This morning Mr. Franklin announced that we are going to have a grade school basketball team."

"Didn't they used to have one? You played, didn't you Phil?" Mother asked.

"Yes, we used to have a team—a pretty good one. But then Mr. Franklin dropped it. Maybe not being able to use the gym for practice or ..." Phil paused, trying to remember. "Oh yeah, I remember now. Mr. Franklin was taking a class at Oshkosh Teachers College, and he had to leave right after school to get there on time. Then after our class went to high school, there weren't enough boys in the seventh and eighth grade to have enough for a team and a second team."

"That was the year when we had only one boy in the confirmation class," Dad added.

I started eating, waiting for them to stop talking so I could continue.

"Go on," Mother said, "I want to hear about it."

I silently said, "Thanks, Mother," and then continued.

"Mr. Franklin says we need to have a team because this year there's going to be a tournament for all the schools in the county, and it would be a shame if the Village was the only school that didn't have a team."

"Are you going to play?" my sister asked me.

"I hadn't thought about it," I answered. Glasses, I thought, they always seemed to interfere with sports. I had worn glasses as long as I could remember, and they always were a major bother when sports were concerned. If I left them on, they often would get pushed around or hit with a ball, or would generally get in the way. If I took them off, there was the problem of what to do with them; plus I really couldn't see all that well. And, I had to admit, I wasn't much of an athlete, not like Phil.

I continued adding the details about the planned team.

"Mr. Franklin said we're going to call the team 'The Wildcats'."

"That's a great name," Phil said, "a lot better than the Village high school team."

I agreed, the Village high school teams were called the "Scarlet Tanagers". No one seemed to know where the name came from—the teams had always been called that. I remember looking up the scarlet tanager in the encyclopedia. It said the scarlet tanager was a shy little bird which tried to keep out of sight by hiding in the forest. Some name for a team, I thought— sounded like it was afraid of everything. "Wildcats" was a much better team name.

"Where did he get that name?" Phil wanted to know.

"Mr. Franklin went to summer school at Northwestern University. The Northwestern teams are called the 'Wildcats' and Mr. Franklin thought that was a great name. He even has a Northwestern sweatshirt with a big wildcat on it," I explained.

"When will this start?" Dad asked.

"I don't know; probably when basketball season starts," I answered, wondering why Dad was interested ... then I remembered. Phil played on the grade school team during World War II when gasoline was rationed. Most people had an "A" card which allowed them to buy three gallons of gas a week. Because Dad was a pastor and clergy were considered essential to the War effort, he got a "C" card, which meant he could buy eight gallons of gas a week. So, when Phil's team had an out-of-town game, Dad was always asked to drive some of the team to the game. Dad didn't mind that, but it did mean that he would have to be away from home another evening. Much of Dad's church work took place in the evening, and this meant Mother would be alone. Helene was just a baby, so it put added stress on her.

Dad didn't have to worry about that, I thought. World War II gas rationing was now a thing of the past.

We resumed eating and starting talking about other subjects.

But my sister's question bothered me. I was excited that there would be a team. I wanted to be a part of it. However, I knew I wasn't very good. When we would choose up teams for various games and sports, I was usually among the last ones selected, unless it was something like spelling bees or other competitions where brains were more important than brawn, then I was always among the first chosen.

I decided I would talk privately to Mr. Franklin and ask his advice. The next day at school, before class started, I asked Mr. Franklin if I could talk with him after school. He said sure.

That afternoon when the bell rang dismissing class, I stayed at my desk, appearing to be working as everyone left the classroom. After they were gone, Mr. Franklin closed the door and we sat at the table in front of the classroom.

"What's up?" he asked.

I explained my dilemma.

Mr. Franklin listened intently, not saying anything as I talked. When I finished, Mr. Franklin thought for a few minutes.

"I understand what you're saying," he began. "If you don't want to play because other players might be better than you, don't worry about it. The idea of having a team is to have fun, to enjoy the game and work to get better. Every team member will get a chance to play. Sure, we want our team to win, but I want to be certain that everyone has a good experience.

"But I also understand your reluctance. Here's something to think about. Getting a team up and going will take a lot of organizing. There are all sorts of things to be done. We need to get uniforms, schedule games, publicize the games, keep score ... all sorts of things. I've been wondering how I'm going to do everything.

"What would you think about being my administrative assistant? You're a good writer. It would be easy for you to prepare articles for the Village newspaper. You can learn to keep score—it's not that hard. You would go to all the games with the team and help during practice, like seeing that balls are inflated properly and returned to the storage cupboard after practice ... that sort of thing.

"Think you might be interested?"

Yes, I thought, I definitely would be interested.

"Let me think about it," I told him. "I'll let you know tomorrow."

"Good," said Mr. Franklin getting up. "We'll talk again."

At supper that night I told the family what Mr. Franklin had suggested.

"Are you sure you wouldn't rather play?" Phil asked.

"I thought about that," I replied, "but there are a lot of really good players, and I know I would spend most of my time just sitting on the bench."

"What kind of benches do they have?" Helene was always inquisitive.

"It's just the place where players sit when they're not playing. It's nothing special," I explained.

"You know," Dad said, "the important thing is to do what you're comfortable doing. One of the things Martin Luther taught was that each one of us is unique and has different talents. You have to make your own decision, but think about what talents you have and how best you can use them."

Dad was able to make a little sermon on most everything, I thought, and they always made sense.

"How did you leave things with Mr. Franklin?" Mother wanted to know.

"I said I would get back to him tomorrow," I answered, "but I think I know what I'm going to do."

No one said anything more and we continued eating.

The next day after school I told Mr. Franklin that I liked his idea and I was ready to get started. The next few weeks were a total blur. I don't think I had ever been so busy. We needed to get uniforms for the team and for the cheerleaders, but first we had to raise the money to buy them. We decided to have a bake sale. I talked with Mr. Schmuhl, who was a member of Dad's congregation, and he said we could hold it in his store. I wrote stories about our new team and then about having the bake sale. All this plus my schoolwork, taking care of our lawn and the lawns of three neighbors ... and studying for confirmation class.

I also wrote to Northwestern University, telling them about our team, how we were calling them the "Wildcats" and did they have some posters with pictures of the Northwestern Wildcat mascot. Boy, did I get results. I got a letter from the sports information director wishing success to our new team, and that he was sending us a bunch of Wildcat posters and other materials. A few days later when we were in class, Mr. Rolf's secretary came to our room with a big box. It was like Christmas when we opened it. There were a half dozen posters saying "Wildcat Basketball" with a picture of a ferocious feline. I immediately saw that we could paste our team's schedule over the Northwestern schedule, and we would have great-looking posters. There was a bunch of other Northwestern stuff, all with pictures of the Northwestern mascot on them, a Northwestern basketball press book, a team picture and a Northwestern pennant.

"That was sure nice of them. Let's write a thank you letter," Mr. Franklin suggested, "and we can all sign it." Which we did.

When I reported this at dinner, saying what we had received from Northwestern, Phil observed that Northwestern wasn't particularly good in sports, and they probably were just pleased that a school wanted to name their team the "Wildcats". I ignored his comment and continued talking about plans for the team.

The bake sale was a success, and we made enough money so we could buy uniforms and material for cheerleaders' dresses. One of the cheerleaders' mother was a good seamstress and had offered to make the dresses.

One day after school Mr. Franklin, Fred (the team captain) and I went to Fond du Lac to order the uniforms. The shirts were white with purple lettering and the shorts were purple.

"And you're sure you can match the Northwestern purple?" Mr. Franklin asked the owner. The store owner showed him the sales book which identified the color as "Northwestern University Purple".

On the way home, Fred commented that he thought we should have our own fight song, not the same as the high school's which was *Forward Village* sung to the tune of *On Wisconsin*.

"I think half the schools in the state use *On Wisconsin*," he said.

"Maybe more than half," Mr. Franklin laughed.

"I'll try writing one. I'll use the Northwestern song."

"What's that?" Fred asked.

"It's *Go U Northwestern*. I think I know where I can find the music for it," I answered. I remembered Mother had a book of college songs which she would play from every so often.

Mother found the book buried in the piano bench. I began working on some words and a few days later I showed the result to Mr. Franklin.

> *Fight on you Wildcats*
> *Fight on for our fame.*
> *We don't play with balls and bats*
> *'Cuz basketball's our game.*
> *Rah, rah, rah*
> *Our team will win one*
> *That's no mystery*
> *When the game is finally done*
> *The other team is history.*

Mr. Franklin was softly singing it and then said, "Hey that's great. You said you have the music for it?" I said yes, and he told me to bring it to school and we would practice singing it in class.

November came and basketball season began. Mr. Franklin had worked with the high school coach to schedule practice and games. All the other conference schools had grade school teams, so the Wildcats would play the first game to be followed by the high school junior varsity and then the varsity game—

"A triple header," Mr. Franklin explained.

We began the season with games against the two neighboring communities which did not have high schools, but had small grade schools. Both were easy victories for the Wildcats. We then began our regular season playing before the high school games with the first game at North Fond du Lac. North Fond du Lac was different than the other conference schools. The other schools were all farming communities. North Fond du Lac was an industrial town with a big service center for the Soo Line Railroad.

It was a tough game for the Wildcats. The other team was bigger and tougher and the result was a loss—22-17. Then the season got better. The Wildcats went on a five-game winning streak before they took a break for Christmas vacation. I kept busy writing a weekly news story for the *Village Times*, keeping score at games, compiling statistics—I had even started keeping a shot chart. On a diagram of the floor I would write the number of each player who attempted a shot and where on the floor he shot from and then circle the number if the shot was made. Mr. Franklin told me this was very helpful in coaching.

When school resumed after vacation, we extended our winning streak with victories over Oakfield and Rosendale and then lost a heart-breaker 31-30 to—wouldn't you know—North Fond du Lac again.

Then it was time for the county tournament. Mr. Franklin had explained that there were two divisions: the rural one-room schools and the larger grade schools from the small towns. City schools which had junior high schools played in a conference tournament.

The tournament was held in the Fond du Lac YMCA gymnasium, a much larger gym than we were used to playing in. One problem with the gym was it had been designed for exercising rather than spectator sports. As a result, spectators were crammed into the sidelines with additional seating on the upper-level track. While it was somewhat uncomfortable for the audience, it did give players the feeling that they were playing before a packed house. Attendance at our regular games was rather sparse—comprised of the members of our class who weren't players or cheerleaders, younger siblings of team members along with parents and grandparents.

It was a three day-tournament with games played in the afternoons and evenings. The first game wasn't much of a contest. The Wildcats easily beat Eden by twenty points. I felt quite grown-up sitting at the scorer's table keeping score and wearing a badge which said "Official". The next game was against Oakfield, who we had just barely beaten in our first meeting. It didn't help that Tom, our best player, got into foul trouble and had to sit out much of the game. But we pulled ahead in the final minutes and won by three points, putting us into the championship game.

Wouldn't you know—North Fond du Lac managed to beat Campbellsport with a last-second basket. That meant we would be facing North Fond du Lac for the third time.

There were two championship games on Saturday afternoon, the one-room rural schools and the larger grade schools. I didn't keep score for the tournament final. Mr. Wilson, the high school science teacher, the regular scorekeeper for the high school teams, kept the score. I got to be with the team in the locker room and sat with Mr. Franklin on the bench.

North Fond du Lac was as tough as ever. At halftime they were leading by seven points. Before the team took the floor for the second half, Mr. Franklin gave a pep talk.

"You're a great team. You have had a great season. I think you have more talent than North Fond du Lac. You can win if you play your best. It's been 50 years since the Village has won any kind of a championship. This is your chance to make history!"

As I watched from the bench I thought it was a whole different team playing the second half. The seven-point lead soon disappeared, and the Wildcats went ahead by two points. Then by four, then six. The North Fond du Lac players got frustrated and began fouling. We were close to perfect on free throw shooting. I thought of the practices where Mr. Franklin had every team member shoot 25 free throws. It certainly paid off.

The Wildcats ended up winning by 11 points.

On Monday there was a big celebration in the high school gym with all the students from kindergarten through the 12th grade attending.

But for me the highlight of the season came later that week. I had written a report of the tournament for the Village newspaper. On Thursday when the paper came out, there on the front page was a picture of the team with the trophy and my account of the tournament WITH MY BYLINE. In the coming years I would have countless bylines, but none equaled the thrill I experienced on seeing my very first one.

Chapter 43

A Final Word

I suppose I better tell you what happened when Dad opened that fat envelope from the district president. I was right. It was a call to a new congregation.

Dad decided he would accept the call, which meant we had to move. Now I know a lot of people move. Some move to a new house in the same town. Others move half-way across the country. Sometimes it's easy to move, but most times it's not much fun.

For us kids it was quite a change. Helene had never known any home but the big white parsonage. Me? I had only limited memories of living in Milwaukee. Phil was in college, but he would be losing his connections with his high school friends. For Dad it meant having to learn a whole new congregation. And for Mother, well, she would have a whole new set of members to worry about how they would view the pastor's family.

So one day the movers came and packed up everything in the moving van, and as the sun was setting we left the Village—the four of us sitting silently in the car, lost in our own thoughts, thinking of the memories our family had and wondering what life would be like in our new home.

Some of you have wondered what did happen to the family in the years since we left, so I will let you know the details:

Phil enrolled at Wartburg College out in Iowa. Somewhere between his sophomore and junior year, he decided he would enter the ministry. He graduated from Wartburg College and went to Wartburg Seminary where he studied to become a pastor. After four years, he was ordained and became the seventh-generation pastor in the family. He spent almost all of his ministry serving parishes in Wisconsin.

A couple of years after Phil graduated, I too went to Wartburg College where I took up journalism. A few years after I graduated, Helene enrolled at Wartburg. She studied to be a teacher.

Dad continued as a pastor in Wisconsin, serving several parishes. He and Mother retired in Green Bay, close enough that when we visited them we could walk to Lambeau Field. Mother enjoyed retirement because for the first time in her married life, she no longer had to worry about what the church members were thinking about her and her children.

It has been years and years since I lived in the Village. Yet, even today, when someone asks me where my home was, I always tell about growing up in the Village in eastern Wisconsin, living in the parsonage next to Emanuel Lutheran Church—proving, I suppose, that you can take the boy out of the Village, but you'll never take the Village out of the boy.

Author's Acknowledgements

When I was a senior at Platteville (Wisconsin) High School during the 1950's, I was fortunate that my English teacher was Ruth Shepherd (later Balliette). She had a major impact on my life as an author. One event which stands out in my memory was when she was stressing the need to constantly revise our writing. Somewhere in her teaching career she had acquired galley proofs of a book by Marie Sandoz, a major award-winning author of frontier life and Native Americans. I have no recollection of the book's title or content. What I do remember is that after viewing the galley proofs (filled with re-writes and revisions) I vowed that I would someday have a book published. I remained friends with Miss Shepherd for the remainder of her life, and I was pleased that I could give her copies of my first four books while she was still living. Fortunately I also was able to personally express my gratitude to her in numerous ways including establishing a scholarship in her honor.

Now as I finish my 11th published book, I have others to thank. First to my family, who over the years have listened—usually attentively—to my stories: Grace, Steve and Valerie, David, Beth, Emily and Joshua.

I need to add an additional word of thank you to David for his suggestion that we combine the three Village books into a trilogy, and then said, "Dad, you'll need to write some new stories for it."

As always, I have to express my thanks to the residents of Brandon, Wisconsin (also known as "the Village") and the members of Emanuel Lutheran Church in Brandon for providing me with life-long memories, many of which were the source of material for my books.

I would also like to add belated thanks to the publishers who made my books a reality: Payne Thomas of Charles C. Thomas Publishers; Wilbur Flachman, of The Publishing House; Leonard Flachman and Karen Walhof of Kirk House Publishers. Without them, I would have remained an unpublished author. Special thanks also to Shirley Flachman who created the delightful cover illustrations for the three original books (which also inspired the current cover).

There aren't enough words to fully thank my wife Grace for all her editing and critiquing of my manuscripts. Her editorial skills and grammatical knowledge improved each of the books. How blessed I have been.

Harold Kurtz

Editor's Notes

For my father's birthday in 2017, I surprised him by announcing that I would lead the effort to turn a series of letters he had written to his brother Phil over the previous three-plus years into a book. It would be titled the same as each of the nearly 50 letters he had written, very simply: *Dear Phil.*

The main impetus for that project had been straightforward, mainly that, in reading through the letters, they simply called out to be gathered together, to be read in their entirety as a whole work. So it proved. It became, as Harold said, "The book I never intended to write."

Similarly, when he was innocently writing Christmas stories for the after-dinner Yuletide entertainment, it was the heartfelt work of a family-man, storyteller, and amateur small-town historian. Once *Hardly a Silent Night* had come into being, the additional stories certainly became a little more intentional in terms of being for release in book-format, but they still retained the essential nature of the first Village stories, as well.

However, after *Hardly a Silent Night, Ring the Bell and Count the People*, and *The Missing Library Books*—as well as after *Dear Phil*—I looked at the three slim volumes of his Village stories and thought that, these too deserved to live together in a united whole. Though only roughly intended by Harold to be published in brief chronological sequencing, they worked far better as a collected whole than he anticipated. Throughout the early part of the process of bringing *Stories from the Village* to life, he expressed both delight and a little skepticism that his original three volumes of stories would actually work well together. Once he caught the vision, his excitement helped propel him to finish up four new Village stories to round out the whole collection.

The first task was to procure the original files. The earliest ones did not live on Harold's latest computer (or they lay buried there waiting for the right sort of archivist), but he had an idea where we might find them. He contacted Karen Walhof, formerly of Kirk House Publishers, who did indeed have everything. Many thanks to her for getting all of them to me.

In putting these works together, I have edited with a light hand as much as possible, but with a certain amount of scrubbing where the nature of the compilation called for it. When the three were separate, small books, Harold presented some items differently than he would have within a single book, and that took some unweaving to enact. It was not done to change the nature of the stories or Harold's inimitable "Village" style, but simply to smooth out the reader's experience. In a few places these remain, essential to the individual stories, but (hopefully) not a distraction to the whole.

Finally, I read the stories through and pushed Harold on a few issues in which the original rendering left me with questions as to his full meaning. These places, as well as an original *errata* or two that deserved fixing, equated to some minor changes throughout from the original books, but this is irrelevant to readers new to the Village, while to those who have experienced the Village in the past it will hopefully create an even more enjoyable second trip.

David Kurtz

ABOUT THE AUTHOR

Harold Kurtz was born in Milwaukee, Wisconsin, but spent most of his early life in Brandon, a village of 708 people in eastern Wisconsin. His father was the pastor of Emanuel Lutheran Church. Harold lived in the parsonage with his parents, Henry and Minnie, his brother Philip, and his sister, Helene. In 1952, the family moved to Platteville, Wisconsin, where he graduated from high school. He earned a bachelor of arts degree from Wartburg College, and went on to graduate school at the University of Wisconsin, Madison, and received a master's degree in journalism. After a short career as a journalist at the Appleton (Wis.) Post-Crescent, he spent the remainder of his career in institutional public relations and fundraising, working as director of public relations at Lutheran General Hospital, Park Ridge, Illinois; director of public relations at The Medical College of Wisconsin, Milwaukee; vice president of Children's Hospital of St. Paul; director of development at the University of Minnesota, Minneapolis; and executive director of the Lyngblomsten Foundation, St. Paul. In 1963, he and Grace Jahn, also a Wartburg College graduate, were married. Their family includes son Steven and his wife Valerie; son David and his wife Beth and their children, Emily and Joshua.

He and his wife Grace live in New Brighton, Minnesota.

ABOUT THE EDITOR

David Kurtz is a lifelong Midwesterner, currently residing in Coon Rapids, MN, along with his wife Beth, daughter Emily and son Joshua. He founded New Brevet Publications in 2018 in order to publish his first novel *War and Peace in Dodge*. He is also the author of *Memoirs of Jesus as told to David Kurtz*. Visit him at www.newbrevet.com or contact him via email at newbrevet@gmail.com.

New Brevet books are released on Amazon KDP.
Find them at www.amazon.com

Other books by Harold Kurtz:

Public Relations for Hospitals (1969)

Effective Use of Volunteers (with Margaret Burrows) (1971)

Toward A Creative Chaplaincy (with Lawrence Holst) (1973)

Public Relations and Fund Raising for Hospitals (1978)

Fly the Banner High: The History of Wartburg College Journalism 1906-1991 (1992)

Hardly a Silent Night (2004)

Ring the Bell and Count the People (2008)

E.A. Kurtz, The Reluctant Pastor (2011)

The Missing Library Books (2012)

Dear Phil: Letters to a Brother 2013-2017 (edited by David Kurtz) (2017)

Books by David Kurtz:

War and Peace in Dodge (2018)

Memoirs of Jesus as told to David Kurtz (2020)